P47-00

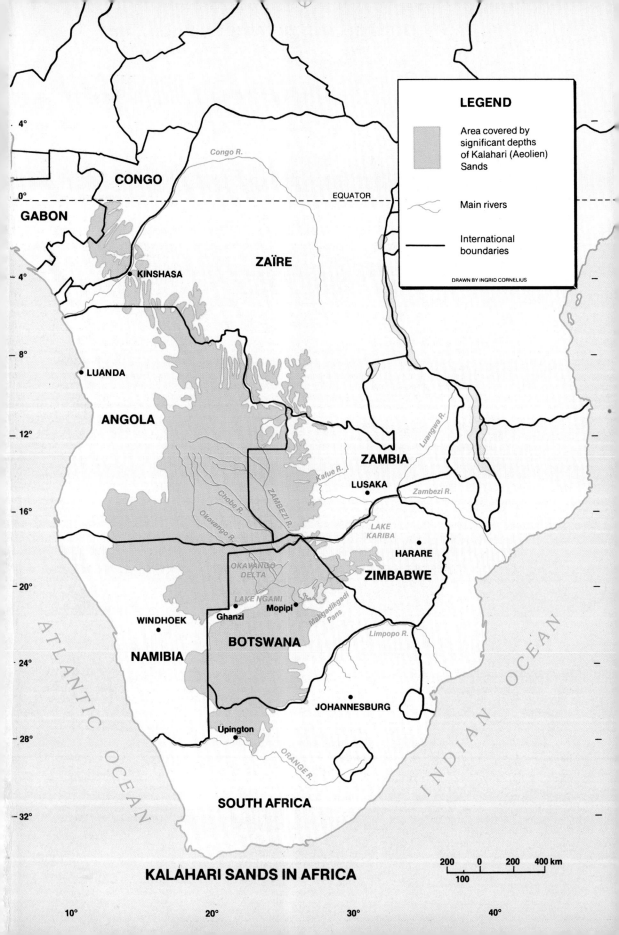

LEGEND

Area covered by
significant depths
of Kalahari (Aeolien)
Sands

Main rivers

International
boundaries

DRAWN BY INGRID CORNELIUS

EQUATOR

CONGO

GABON

ZAÏRE

KINSHASA

ANGOLA

LUANDA

ZAMBIA

LUSAKA

Kafue R.

Luangwa R.

Zambezi R.

Congo R.

Chobe R.

Okovango R.

ZAMBEZI R.

LAKE
KARIBA

HARARE

ZIMBABWE

OKAVANGO
DELTA

LAKE NGAMI

Mopipi

Makgadikgadi
Pans

Ghanzi

BOTSWANA

WINDHOEK

NAMIBIA

Limpopo R.

JOHANNESBURG

Upington

ORANGE R.

SOUTH AFRICA

ATLANTIC OCEAN

INDIAN OCEAN

KALAHARI SANDS IN AFRICA

200   0   200   400 km
100

4°
0°
4°
8°
12°
16°
20°
24°
28°
32°

10°   20°   30°   40°

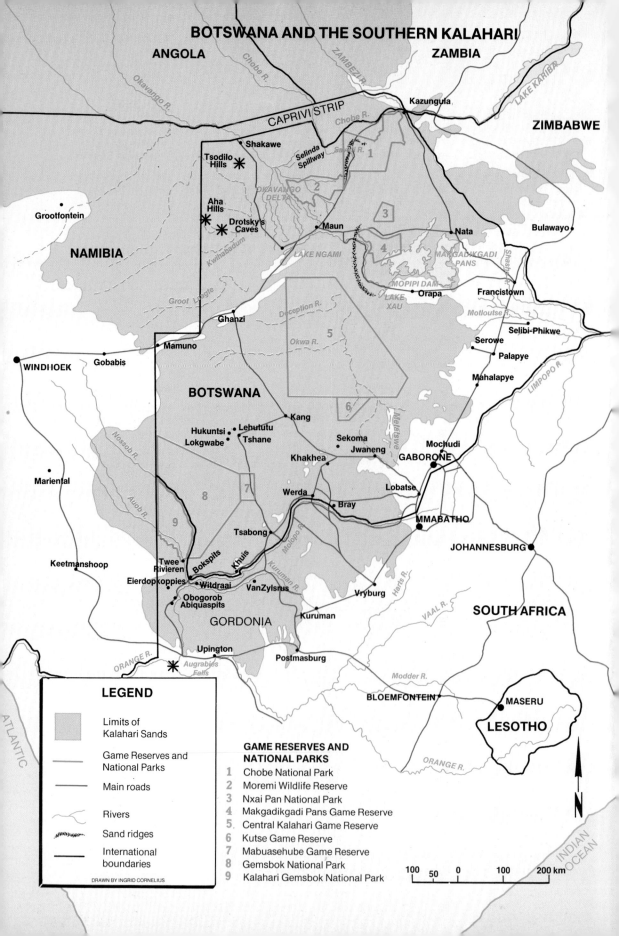

# KALAHARI

## Life's Variety in Dune and Delta

### Michael Main

SOUTHERN
BOOK PUBLISHERS

To Alec Campbell, who was the inspiration for this work and who, by being ever willing to share his knowledge and love of the Kalahari, ignited my interest.

ISBN 1 86812 001 5

First edition, first impression 1987
First edition, second impression 1988

Published by
Southern Book Publishers (Pty) Ltd
P O Box 548, Bergvlei, 2012
Johannesburg

Maps drawn by Ingrid Cornelius
Cover design by Graphicor (Pty) Ltd
Set in 9 on 11 pt Stymie
by Unifoto, Cape Town
Printed and bound by: CTP Book Printers, Cape
BD8594

# Preface

THE Kalahari excites me. Its vast open spaces, enormous, perpetually blue skies, incredible vistas and sense of timelessness somehow inspire me to a joy in life. For me, there is endless interest in the range of its unexpected differences: the deep caves, eroded once by massive volumes of flowing water, now set far into the driest part of sand dune country; the ancient lake, which once covered more than a third of northern Botswana, and the shores of which are still clearly visible today; the incredible adaptations of plants and animals. I take unconcealed delight in learning of large antelope that have evolved special cooling mechanisms for the blood that circulates to their brain, so that the rest of their body may soar to temperatures far beyond the limits of other living creatures. I am excited about spiders that fly, or mimic ants or use the sun to navigate, and by scorpions that fluoresce in the dark, young crocodiles whose sex is determined by temperature and leopards that hunt baboons during the night along the branches where they roost.

Part of the contradictions in this great area of arid sands is the swirl of green lushness that is the Okavango Delta. With its lagoons and islands, its herds of wild game and fascinating people, it is in utter contrast to the dryness all about it. Nearby is the Chobe River, dramatically distorted in its course by deep fault-lines that reach down from the East African Rift Valley. Not far from it is the Savuti channel, the flowing of which is switched on and off by tilting movements of the earth's crust. Lake Ngami, 'the disappearing lake', also lies in this region and, when it has water in it, sees some of the greatest concentrations of birds in Southern Africa.

But it is not only the natural history that attracts me. I am fascinated by new discoveries in archaeology, which show that the Kalahari has been home to man far longer than was first thought. Iron Age people lived in the arid wastes for a thousand years longer than was originally believed and they have done so cheek by jowl with Stone Age man, who gave up his stone tool-making crafts less than 200 years ago. He survives to this day in the form of the Bushman people, whose sad fate and dismal future give cause for much concern.

This work does not set out to be a definitive study of the Kalahari. It is a collection of information about life in and on the largest continuous area of sand in the world. It is by no means comprehensive and represents only those aspects which I find absorbing and would like to share with others. The book was born during two years of work in Botswana which sometimes required me to travel great distances across the Kalahari.

Like so many others, I was spurred to learn more about the things that I saw. I quickly realised that others were asking the same questions and, as I was, were finding the answers elusive. I decided to find out for myself and this work is the result of my own research. In many instances there are no answers at all and I have tried to indicate this, hoping that others might be moved to investigate areas where our ignorance is so great.

There are a great many people to whom I owe a considerable debt of thanks. For support, succour, friendship and encouragement, during the highs and the lows: Maurice Boaler for keeping the home fires in such impeccable order, Judy and Alec Campbell, John and Sylvia Cooke, John and Sandy Fowkes, who were loyal and supporting friends through it all, Ian and

Shona Lockhart, Heather Jones, Ian and Jean Marshall, who provided all the great love, care and concern of a second home, Jennifer Mason-Jones, Jessie Neil, John and Vanessa Pritchard, the staff of Gametrackers, Botswana (Pty) Ltd, all the staff at BPI (Pal), University of the Witwatersrand, for innumerable teas, ideas and good company, Hannes and Marlene Roets, Murray Russell, Wally Vise, Philip Welch whose concern, great generosity and untiring labours kept the various forms of transport in running condition, Elaine White, and, above all, Elizabeth Way, who will know why.

For reading the manuscript and offering endless ideas which have helped shape the final product, I am indebted to the following people: Gail Dixon, Ann Harben, Elizabeth Way, and Constance Zaaijman.

For technical assistance many people came to my help. The list is long and I apologise to any one whom I have unintentionally omitted. Those who were so generous with their time and their knowledge include: Ronald Auerbach, Ulrich Balke, John Begg, Carner Bentzon, Mr and Mrs Christo Botha, Dr Jeffrey Bowles, Dr Eddie Braddley, Chris Brown, David Buckley, Kingsley Butler, Alec Campbell, Harry Cantle, Dr Mike Cantrell, Dr Graham Child, Stewart Child, Dr John Condy, Professor John Cooke, Gert and Emily Cooper, Mary Cooper, W A de Klerk, Dr Jim R Denbow, Dr 'Co' J J de Vries, Dr Ansie Dippenaar, Joannie Dobbs, Ellen Drake, Mrs Anna Christina Drotsky and her daughter, Mrs Anna Christina Drotsky, 'Bob' R B Drummond, Dick Eaton, Jack Enbuske, Dr S Endrody-Younga, Christie Engelbrecht, Willie Engelbrecht, Ed and Jill Flattery, Pam Francis and the staff at the National Archives of Zimbabwe, Francis Gamble, Mike Griffin, Mike Gunn, Wulf Haacke, John Hardbattle, Dave Hardy, Professor Richard Hartland-Rowe, Dr H J Heinz, Alan Hill, Chris Hines, Bob Hitchcock, Professor Eric Holm, Professor Tom Huffman, John Irish, 'Jane' of Cas Camera, Professor Trevor Jenkins, Jimmy Kalafatis, Willie Katsch, Martin Thomas Kayes, Alan Kemp, Willie Knoesen, Dr James Kitching, Rian and Lorna Labuschagne, Paul Larkin, Mike Leech, Elias le Riche; the kindly and very understanding library staff at the University of the Witwatersrand and the Transvaal Museum; Dr L A Lister, Tim Liversedge, Dr Norman Lock, Charlie Luca, Stein Lundbye, Des McIntyre, Allistair McFarlane and Apple Computers of Botswana, Dr Judy Maguire, Stuart Mingham, Helen Moss, Dr Gerry Newlands, Professor L O Nicolaysen, Gus Nilsson, Lionel Palmer, Professor Mike Parr, Simon Paul, Mary-Louise Penrith, Willie Phillips, Barry Price, Professor Mike Raath, Andy Raffle, Dan Rawson, George Riggs, John J Seaman, A/Superintendent M Selerio, Harry Selby, Dr Paul Shaw, Peter Smith, Dr Reay Smithers, Mrs Gertie Stadler, Frank Taylor, Malcolm Thomas, Rob Toms, Dr Tony Trail, Malaki Tshweneagae, Klaas van der Westhuizen, Dr L Vari, Dr 'Balt' Verhagen, Theunis Vickerman, Petri and Zaan Viljoen, Sister Maria Vise, Dr Liz Voigt, Dr John Vogel, Jan Vossen, Richard White, Doug Williamson, Ursula Wilmot, Dr Roger Windsor and George Woodman.

For companionship along the road, Jeremy, Andrew and, of course, Gypsey.

In certain instances I have drawn on material published in scientific papers and journals. Without wishing to clutter the text too much, I have acknowledged these sources wherever possible and I am deeply grateful to those whose research I have used. The interpretations and conclusions that have been drawn are mostly my own and any errors of fact are my own responsibility.

# Contents

# Part 1
# And Thus Was It Shaped

# 1. Gondwanaland

THE Kalahari, one of the African continent's most evocative names, occupies much of central Southern Africa and, even today, there are places within it where man seldom ventures. It is called a desert, which it really is not, and beyond the fact of its existence, is relatively little known by the outside world. It is a place of mystery and has about it an aura of the unknown while in fact, although much still remains to be discovered, a great deal is known about the Kalahari.

Generally it is agreed today that the solid crust of our planet was formed some 4 600 million years ago. It may help to understand this immense span of time by imagining a movie camera, far out in space above the earth, taking one single frame every 10 000 years. When the film is played back at twenty-four frames a second, you would see fourteen and a half million years of the planet's history flash by every minute. To watch the whole movie, from the dawn of time to the present day, would take more than five hours. Man, as we know him, would appear at some time in the last nine seconds. The oldest known form of life, a single cell bacterium, found in South Africa's Eastern Transvaal, appeared 3 200 million years ago, but the oldest multicellular creatures are a mere 600 million years old.[1]

Throughout this vast amount of time the continents have not stood still. Being made of lighter material, they float upon the surface of the earth and are constantly in motion, separating, moving together and colliding, like gigantic rafts upon a sea of boiling rock. The process is not violent; it is slow, infinitesimally slow, driven by convection currents spawned at the very heart of our planet. It is inexorable, though, and, despite their mass, our continents are moved about like paper boats in the lightest breeze. Their surfaces are continually shaped and sculpted by the agents of erosion so that a dynamic, planet-wide system of change never ceases. How many times the continents have come together in groups and parted again we do not know, and may never be able to tell. What is more certain is that the land masses, mostly to be found in the southern hemisphere, cohered at least once to form a supercontinent and that this last occurred in relatively recent geological times. Today, that continent is called Gondwanaland.

About 225 million years ago Gondwanaland consisted of what today we know as New Zealand, Australia, India, Madagascar, Africa, South America and Antarctica. That time was near the beginning of an era known as the Mesozoic, an early portion of which is called the Triassic period. Throughout that vast continent during the Triassic there existed an almost limitless expanse of desert. It was a time of extreme aridity and winds were probably very strong. Despite the exceptionally dry conditions, life was abundant, and plants and animals flourished wherever there was water. Dinosaurs, in great numbers and diversity, roamed the land.

I once touched plants from this period of time. It was at a quarry site, somewhere not far south of Johannesburg. We were digging out the fine clays from the bed of a long-dead lake. The rocks were geologically young, fragile, and sedimentary. It was not difficult to ease large chunks from the cutting wall or to find a comfortable place to sit, rock supported between one's knees, chisel and hammer ready. The rock was firm but not hard, and gave easily along the lines of sediment. A few taps with the chisel and a crack appeared; followed round, gently tapping, the crack widened. Our excitement grew. In a moment the rock split and the magic began. It was winter and a warm, clear-sky, blue-sunny day. As the two halves of the stone separated, sunlight fell on the imprints of a mass of leaves, leaves which had been entombed for 220 million years. The staggering immensity of time passed, the complex of probabilities and risks that had brought them to this point, can only imbue one with a massive sense of man's insignificance. It was a salutary and rewarding experience.

Throughout the Triassic conditions remained largely unchanged. Erosion was king. The rocks were ground down by wind and rain and ice, while unimaginable quantities of sand-like sediment accumulated. This sand was to form the raw material of what today are called the Cave Sandstones. Anyone who has visited the Drakensberg Mountains in South Africa will have seen the great cliffs that stretch unending kilometres and which provided, in their numerous caves from which the name of this rock is derived, homes for some of South Africa's last Bushmen.

These Karoo sediments — as they are more generally referred to — also provided a resting place of a very different sort for countless numbers of fossilised dinosaurs and mammal-like reptiles. Their discovery is almost entirely due to the dedication of Dr James Kitching, from South Africa's University of the Witwatersrand. Dr Kitching's father was a road supervisor who spent much of his time in the central Karoo region. In the course of his work he frequently came across fossilised bones and made a significant collection of them in his garage. Although he knew little about them, he guessed at their importance and maintained an enduring interest in them. His collection eventually came to the notice of Dr Robert Broom, a well-known palaeontologist, who encouraged Kitching to continue with his fossil-hunting and, at the same time, fostered considerable enthusiasm for the hobby in Kitching's son.

Thanks to the generosity of Dr Bernard Price, a Palaeontological Institute was established at the university and, in 1942, James Kitching took up a position there, where he has worked ever since. Without

any extensive academic background this remarkable man set off on a methodical search of the Karoo strata for his beloved fossils. Forty-three years later Dr Kitching is considered an eminent authority on dinosaurs and mammal-like reptiles of this geological era. He has personally searched for and found 823 different fossil sites, discovered taxa never seen before, found, complete with embryo, some of the few dinosaur eggs in existence and perhaps has done more than any single individual to expand immeasurably our knowledge of South Africa's early faunal heritage. His skill in knowing where to look and what to look for is legendary. In the early 1970s he helped an American expedition in the Antarctic locate important fossils and in grateful acknowledgement they named Antarctica's Kitching Ridge after him.

The long period of erosion was not to last. About 210 million years ago began the most cataclysmic of events. The earth opened and a vast outpouring of basaltic lava commenced. The scale was not local but spread over huge areas. Cracks and fissures appeared from which the lava oozed forth. There was some volcanic eruption, as we would call it, but, for the most part, Gondwanaland was covered with a slow oozing of molten rock: the Stormberg Lavas. Age after age the devastation continued. Australia, Antarctica, India and South America all bear evidence of their close contiguity at this time. It is difficult to reconstruct events precisely, but estimates suggest that as much as 2 million km$^2$ were covered with lava, an area of 2 000 by 1 000 km in Southern Africa alone, of which 140 000 km$^2$ remains to this day. The depths of lava almost defy imagination. Whilst they varied greatly, in Natal for example solid lava extended for a depth of 9 km. At Mwenezi, in southern Zimbabwe, the depths extend to between 7 and 8 km. Vulcanicity, as this process is known, lasted for nearly 100 million years, coming to a halt about 130 million years ago. All this activity was not without significance for it heralded the birth of a new order of continents: Gondwanaland was breaking up and the Kalahari was soon to make its appearance in the new African continent.

The exact times and order in which the super-continent fractured are not known. However, it is unlikely that the sea penetrated modern coastlines much earlier than 167 million years ago. The latest research suggests a more recent date of 135 million years.[2] Antarctica, with Australia abutting its eastern side, moved away from the south-eastern side of Africa at about this time. Earlier, and from slightly further north, India and Madagascar had already separated, the former beginning the long journey that was to bring it into collision with Asia, the impact of which created the Himalayan Mountains. Interestingly, Madagascar is now thought to have originated not from the area of Mozambique, as was once believed, but from the vicinity of modern East Africa. South America, on the Atlantic side, began to move away between 129 and 127 million years ago.

Whenever it began, fragmentation was

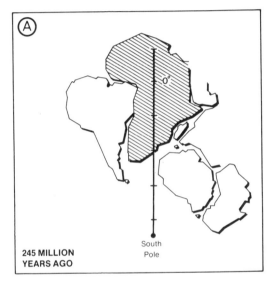

245 MILLION YEARS AGO — South Pole

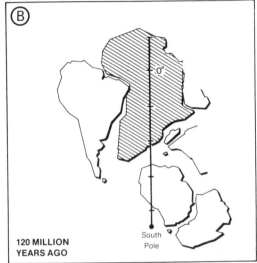

120 MILLION YEARS AGO — South Pole

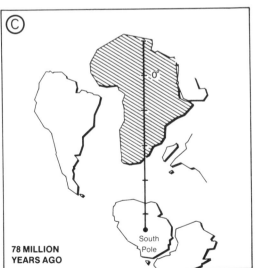

78 MILLION YEARS AGO — South Pole

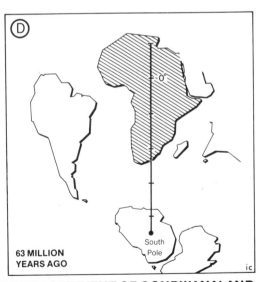

63 MILLION YEARS AGO — South Pole

**THE EMERGENCE OF AFRICA FROM THE SUPERCONTINENT OF GONDWANALAND**

During this time, Africa rotated anti-clockwise and moved south. Notice the migration of the Antarctic land mass towards the point of the South Pole. Australia remains very close to it: these two continents did not separate until between 10 and 5 million years ago.
**Source:** Adapted from R.V. Dingle, W.G. Siesser and A.R. Newton, *Mesozoic and Tertiary Geology of Southern Africa*, A.A. Balkema, Rotterdam, 1983, p 6.

progressive, inexorable, irrevocable but never hurried. By 100 million years the separation was almost complete and the outlines, much as we know them today, were clear. Although her nearest continental neighbours were closer than they are now, Africa at last stood alone, a new continent in its own right, entering upon a period of relative geological calm when, once more, erosion would set to work.

Although freed of her cumbersome neighbours, Africa was not released from the mechanism which drives the continents. At the time of separation Africa was further north than it is now and the orientation in relation to a north-south axis was significantly different. Africa has continued to move. Partly for this reason, climates changed dramatically in the ensuing epochs. Antarctic glaciation is also relatively young and only began some 33 million years ago. Even so, it did not reach its present levels until the mid or late Miocene period, about 10 to 13 million years ago, when Antarctica separated from Australia, thereby allowing, for the first time, complete circumpolar circulation of air. This resulted in a deterioration of Africa's climate and the establishment of the present climatic systems of our southern hemisphere.

The sequence of rocks in Southern Africa known as the Karoo Supergroup ended with the Stormberg Lavas. The end was not sudden; it occurred at different times in different places, but somewhere around 130 million years ago the energetic issue of lava was finally exhausted. Towards the end of the Cretaceous period, and some 85 million years ago, quiescence was established. Rain, running water, wind and ice began their work anew, wearing down mountains, filling valleys, depositing sediments in some areas, removing them from others, always with the same aim in view: the gradual reduction of the whole continent to a single, level plane. The period of time that followed the break-up of Gondwanaland was not entirely free of geological activity, however. Certainly the most dramatic of these events was the emergence of diamond-bearing kimberlite.

Africa is not the only continent in the world where diamonds are found but the biggest producers are established there and it is to the Cretaceous period that they owe their wealth. Diamonds are formed under conditions of immense pressure, deep beneath the earth's crust. Under certain circumstances the matrix in which they lie is subjected to such great pressure that it escapes by literally punching its way to the surface in a 'pipe' of molten material, which we call kimberlite. The power of this explosive force is phenomenal, capable of driving through great distances of semi-molten or solid rock from deep within the earth, sometimes, but not always, reaching the surface. Most of the kimberlite pipes known to us were formed during the Cretaceous period, and many of them occur in the Kalahari. Throughout this period and for some time afterwards, dykes, sills and intra-continental movements persisted but never again on the same scale as during the last stages of the Karoo lavas.

Generally, however, planation continued unabated. The southern part of Africa developed into an astonishingly level plane and the characteristically flat aspect, which is so much part of the sub-continent today, owes its origins to this period of time. It is from somewhere in this period that we can begin, realistically, to speak of the Kalahari.

During the Tertiary era, which followed the Cretaceous and extends from 65 to 2 million years ago, the area that was to be called the Kalahari began to acquire a familiar form. The climate became more arid and desert conditions spread. Much of the sub-continent was covered with sand, the end product of the now well-established erosion regime. During the Tertiary, river valleys became choked with gravel, sand and clay; new stream channels were cut and deposition of heavy sediment loads was concentrated on ephemeral, braided floodplains. The region that is today the Kalahari then formed the largest area of sedimentary deposits in that part of Africa and was thus a collection point for all the eroded sediments which accumulated to great depths. With the coming of more intense aridification, strong winds spread the sand widely. It was deposited in natural collection basins, covering the clays and gravels which had earlier blocked the valleys. It was not until as late as 15 to 10 million years ago that there was set in motion a chain of events that changed the Tertiary landscape.

Nearly 100 million years of erosion had taken place by the middle of the Miocene epoch, about 15 million years ago. Massive quantities of rock had been reduced to boulders, gravels and sands. The forces of nature, working with exquisite slowness, had reshaped and reformed the surface of the land. Towering heights were reduced or removed completely and the massive weight of the continent had been redistributed. Whether it was this or some other unknown mechanism we cannot say, but certainly, at about this time, much of Africa, like some immense resting giant, stirred gently in its sleep and the mantle of rock and earth that was its cover was rearranged.

Like sinews rippling beneath the skin, lines of tension were drawn across the land. In some parts new areas of uplift emerged; in others, gentle depressions were formed. The surface of the land was dimpled by these changes and, with infinite viscidity the southern margins of the continent were raised and tilted outward. In parts, so slow was this process that rivers already flowing across the margin were able to continue on their course, cutting down through the gently rising rock.[3] Today this can be seen in the great gorges of the Eastern Cape. Even more dramatic examples of this extraordinary phenomenon can be seen among some of the rivers in India, especially the Brahmaputra, Indus and Sutlej. Each of these rises on the north side of the Himalayas and breaks completely through the range in a series of breathtaking gorges to reach the southern side, flowing in much the same direction as they were before the mountains, which are relatively young and are still growing, came into existence.

The Rift Valley system of Eastern Africa may also have been formed at about this time. Great valleys spread across the face of the land, reaching out from the distant north, far down into the south, as if the very fabric of Africa was being torn at the seams. Southern Africa came to resemble something like an inverted saucer, with steep sides falling away and a shallow depression in its centre. Not all the rivers maintained their original courses; some changed drastically. The Molopo, which passes through the southern reaches of the Kalahari, is an example. In the central Transvaal there is a very old drainage area known as the Bushveld Basin or, as it is more commonly called today, the Springbok Flats. Renewed sinking of nearly 300 m has taken place. A study of the diamondiferous gravel in the Lichtenburg district shows that these were laid down by the headward continuation of the Molopo River which was brought to a halt by the lowering of the Springbok Flats.[4] In this way the Molopo lost its headwaters and diminished, accordingly, to a much smaller river. Further evidence of this can be seen in the several gorges along the now ephemeral Molopo's course, all far beyond the erosive power of the river as it is at present.

As the continent twisted and warped in response to these new and powerful forces, distinct and visible lines of distortion emerged. They appear as surface expressions of underlying points of weakness deep within the continental structure. Some emerge as areas of uplift and others as deep faults with downthrows of considerable depth. Two of these axes are of particular interest in the evolution of the Kalahari. The first is little studied and little known. It runs from south-east to north-west, bisects the southern half of Botswana and cuts through some of the most forbidding areas of the Kalahari. Named the Bakalahari Schwelle by the German explorer and geologist Passarge, it is almost impossible to distinguish with the naked eye. However, along its crest lie a myriad salt-pan features and it is certainly of sufficient magnitude to divide the rainwaters, such as they are, which now flow north and south of it. It lies directly across the route of what may have been a major southward flowing river.

The second feature is what is known as the Zimbabwe-Kalahari axis. Starting in Zimbabwe, perhaps as far north as Harare, this area of uplift passes through Bulawayo and on down the eastern side of the Kalahari, eventually petering out in the wastes of sand. More will be said of these features in later chapters. Suffice it to say here that their emergence had dramatic and far-reaching effects on the entire geomorphology of the Kalahari Basin.

Thus, then, was the Kalahari formed. From earliest imaginable times it may have been a low-lying area. During the Triassic period, between 250 and 213 million years ago, it was part of a staggeringly large desert that blanketed much, if not all, of Gondwanaland. Conditions were so extremely arid that desertification was widespread. Central in Southern Africa today, the Kalahari seems destined to remoteness from the sea. At the time of the supercontinent it was still further removed from this life-giving source of rain since the bulk of Australia and India to the east, and South America to the west, stood between it and the oceans.

During the next 100 million years, when the outpourings of Stormberg lava continued unabated, the Kalahari area, in common with so much of the supercontinent, received its share. Vast areas of the Karoo sediments, capped with the younger lavas, underlie much of the Kalahari. From Cretaceous times the basalts and sandstones were steadily eroded. In the process low-lying valleys were filled and the debris, instead of being carried away, accumulated, forming what today are called the Kalahari Beds. As arid times returned in the Tertiary period, which followed the Cretaceous and dates from 65 million years ago, so desert conditions once again prevailed. Strong winds redistributed abundant sands which collected in natural drainage basins so that vast areas were inundated. With the later return of more tropical conditions, the rivers once more set about their work. But not in the Kalahari. There the rivers did not return; they had been turned aside by the mid-Miocene warpings. Rainfall, although certainly copious at times, was never sufficient to

carry away the sands, as it did elsewhere. The drainage basin was blocked, sealed with its own debris. Instead of scouring it out, the rain soaked in and the heart of the Kalahari was formed.

Beyond the margins of the Kalahari, the wind-blown sands were, with the return of wetter climates, being carried away by fast-running waters. The climate was not everywhere favourable for this, however. Great changes had taken place. Africa's global location had altered, the Antarctic was becoming increasingly important as a weather generator and new cold currents were appearing. The climatic pattern of the world was never to be the same again. Thus, in places, the sand remained, leaving the wind-blown Kalahari sands as the largest continuous stretch of sand in the world. Today they begin north of the Orange River in South Africa, embrace the western two-thirds of Botswana, more than a third of Namibia, and stretch north through eastern Angola, western Zimbabwe and Zambia to Zaire.

## REFERENCES

1. **Barghoorn, E S.** 'The Oldest Fossils' In *Life, Origin and Evolution*. California: W H Freeman & Co, 1979, p 67
2. **Dingle, R V, Siesser, W G and Newton, A R.** *Mesozoic and Tertiary Geology of Southern Africa*. Rotterdam: A A Balkema, 1983
3. **King, L C.** *South African Scenery*. London: Oliver and Boyd Ltd, 1942, p 183
4. Ibid, p 186

In addition to the above, the following books are recommended as offering an interesting and general background to the geology of Southern Africa and the Kalahari:

**Flint, R F.** *Glacial and Quaternary Geology*. New York: John Wiley & Sons, Inc, 1971

**Du Toit, A L.** In *The Geology of South Africa*. Edited by Haughton, S H. London: Oliver and Boyd, 1954

**Mountain, E D.** *Geology of Southern Africa*. Cape Town: Books of Africa (Pty) Ltd, 1968

# 2. Of Rivers and Lakes

ONE fascination of the Kalahari is the abundant but tantalisingly inconclusive evidence that it was once very much wetter than it is today, and that the major drainage patterns we see now were vastly different in the past. A better understanding of the Kalahari can be reached by an awareness of how the present drainage lines came about and of their significance. The subject is vast and complex and it is not my intention here to describe it exhaustively; an examination of the rivers in and associated with Botswana's Kalahari allows us an ample glimpse of the extraordinary events that have taken place.

Today no significant rivers rise on Kalahari sand. Some rivers did once but nothing remains of them but broad, desolate valleys, empty of moisture. They are home to little more than the desultory whirlwinds that pick their way between the distant banks on columns of swirling dust. Some rivers flow great distances across the sands, leaving them before their life-blood is sucked from them; one river dies within it, a victim of the thirsty sand and searing sun. Through the southern Kalahari flows, from the east, the Molopo river (see map). Further south, and parallel to it, is the Kuruman, which joins, near the southernmost tip of Botswana, with the Auob and Nossob rivers, which begin far in the west and likewise make their way across the sands. All four rivers become one and turn due south to join the Orange River which drains the western side of South Africa.

The Orange is a perennial river but the four tributaries from the Kalahari are not. When their combined waters last reached the Orange is not known and today they flow for significant distances only in times of exceptional floods. The ridge of slightly higher land that extends from south-east

Botswana across to the north-west, known as the Bakalahari Schwelle, serves as a watershed dividing that part of the Kalahari into two large hydrological basins. From its northern side several major dry-river systems part the sands with wide and gently sloping valleys but, as the lower reaches of their gradients are approached, they fade into nothing and seem engulfed in the waste of sand. Among these are the Meratswe, Okwa, Deception and the Groot Laagte. Like the more southerly rivers, these four do not flow today. In the north-west, three major rivers are of great interest to us for they include two of the largest rivers in Southern Africa and their presence and their influence are a recurring theme in the story of the Kalahari.

Two of these rivers rise in the highlands of Angola and follow roughly parallel courses to the south-east, across hundreds of kilometres of Kalahari sand. The most southerly one is the Okavango. After entering Botswana this river spills out into a gigantic delta and incongruously creates a vast wetland of rivers, waterways, lagoons and shimmering, forested islands that float upon their own reflections. The second river has several names but it is perhaps best known as the Chobe. It touches Botswana a little to the north of the Okavango and, as it reaches the border, abruptly turns through a right angle and flows north-east to meet the third river, the Zambezi. The Zambezi rises in northern Zambia, flows westwards into Angola and turns south again to re-enter Zambia before curving gradually to the east and, after joining the Chobe, follows the north-east trend of the latter and plunges with it over the Victoria Falls.

The Zambezi is divided by geomorphologists into three sections. The Upper Zam-

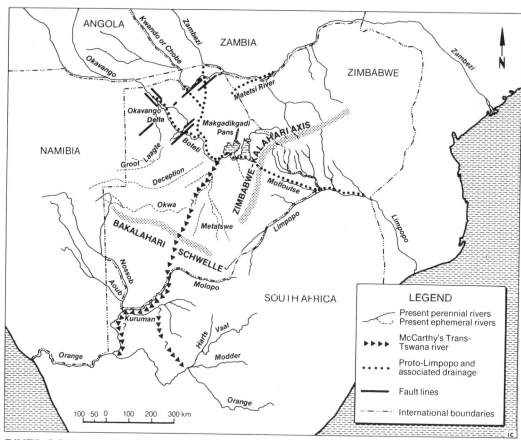

## RIVER COURSES: ANCIENT AND MODERN

bezi stretches from the source to the Falls; the Middle Zambezi extends from below the Falls, whilst the Lower Zambezi refers to that portion mostly within Mozambique and closest to the sea. A glance at the map will draw your attention to the extraordinary and unlikely change in direction of the Chobe and Zambezi rivers. It is now known that the reason for this is because of major fault-lines that lie deep beneath the surface sands and extend from the north-east to the south-west. They are, in fact, extensions of the East African Rift Valley system and continue further south to embrace the Okavango Delta and are responsible, too, for its existence. These fault-lines and the effects they have produced played a major part in the realignment of Botswana's ancient river systems. Flowing out of the Okavango is a relatively thin trickle of water, insignificant when compared to

the huge volumes that entered it, but considerable nevertheless. This is the Boteti River. The Boteti meanders eastwards, far into the Kalahari, finally sinking lifeless into the sand, close to the two enormous pan features which are together called the Makgadikgadi Pans.

To the east of Botswana, starting in the south and flowing north along the border, is the Limpopo River, which eventually turns east and flows down to the Indian Ocean. The Limpopo is the main drainage line for the eastern side of Botswana and into it flow all the rivers that exist on that side of the country. None of them is very long, for there is a ridge of higher land that extends down the eastern side of Botswana, on the eastern flank of which all these rivers start. To the west of the ridge, the Kalahari rolls endlessly across the heart of Southern Africa. The ridge is called the Zimbabwe-

Kalahari axis and forms the watershed from the centre of Zimbabwe, south-west through Bulawayo and southwards through Botswana to the eastern end of the Bakalahari Schwelle. It too has played an important part in the evolution of the Kalahari's rivers.

The Kalahari region has undergone incredible changes during its long history. How widespread and dramatic these changes have been is a fascinating illustration of the plasticity of our planet's surface and belies the feeling of solidarity and security we derive from touching solid rock. There has been a great deal of speculation as to the effect these changes may have had on the courses of the ancient rivers. Because the timespans involved are so enormous and we lack sufficiently accurate means of reading our distant past, theories are at best little more than good guesses. They are supported only by small pieces of hard evidence which, if not conclusive, at least are difficult to refute.

One such theory is that the Okavango, the Chobe and possibly the Upper Zambezi, all flowed together, running southwards through the centre of Botswana's Kalahari to join the Orange River. Today there is no known physical trace of this massive river and, although the theory has been debated for some time, it has only recently been seriously considered and now at least one university is devoting resources to researching it further. Perhaps evidence of such a valley will be found but at first glance it seems unlikely. Both the Bakalahari Schwelle and the Molopo River lie across the probable course of such a river. The former may well, however, be the result of geologically recent crustal warpings and the Molopo may possibly have been part of that south-flowing river. The valley of the Molopo is far too large for the present river. At Khuis, near the southern end of Botswana, it has cut a gorge 30 metres deep through nearly 10 km of hard quartzite. Where did all that water come from? We already know that the headwaters of the Molopo were much reduced by crustal movement and the sinking of the Springbok Flats, but is this sufficient to explain the reduction in volume? Or does the south-flowing river theory have some validity?

Further support for the theory comes from a recent discovery on the Orange River, some 30 km downstream from its junction with the Vaal River, at a point due south of Botswana's Kalahari. At this point the Orange has high banks, towards the top of which are terraces of alluvial gravels, deposited at a time when larger volumes of water passed through the valley and the valley itself was not as deep. The interesting fact is that included among the gravels is a rather unusual form of banded ironstone, which appears in considerable quantity. Moreover, on the north and opposite bank is an impressive valley of considerable size, which extends to the north-west, in the direction of the Kalahari.

Dr T S McCarthy, who conducted this research, believes that the unique gravels were brought down to the Orange by a once massive river in this valley that was at least equal in size to the then Orange, if not three or four times larger. He speculates that its catchment area may well have extended far into tropical Africa and proposes the name Trans-Tswana for this gigantic river. He has also found evidence to suggest that this river was abruptly truncated and ceased to flow – suggesting a demise attributable to tectonic factors.[1]

A second shred of evidence suggesting that the Trans-Tswana River may well have been a reality long ago is offered by ichthyologists, some of whom suggest that there was an invasion of northern fish species, via the Okavango, to the Orange River and that this could only have taken place by a direct link which, they consider, would have existed about 3 to 4 million years ago. There are several species of fish in the southern Cape which are directly related to certain northern species and the fact that present-day Okavango species are poorly represented in the Orange and the southern Cape is accounted for by assuming that the connection was broken a very long time ago. It is generally accepted, however, that all the southern Cape primary fish species owe their origins to this connection.[2]

Not all the evidence, such as it is, supports the idea of a trans-Kalahari river, however. Both the northern rivers, the Okavango and the Limpopo, as well as the southern rivers, the Molopo and the Orange, contain significant deposits of limestone. These have been examined for fossil shells. The northern rivers have revealed large numbers of species such as Ampullaria, Lanistes, Melania and Viviparus, but these have been found neither in the Molopo nor the Orange. Nor have specimens been found in any of the now dry central Kalahari rivers.[3] These would surely have been connected to a trans-Kalahari river and, one would expect, would have hosted some of these molluscs. Why do no examples of the northern species occur in the southern rivers if, as is claimed, they were once connected? Hopefully new research will shed light on this mystery in due course, although three or more million years ago is so far back in time that we may never have a definite answer. It is nevertheless intriguing to stand upon the Kalahari and to imagine this vast volume of water surging through the sands on its way to the western sea.

A second theory about ancient river systems has progressed beyond the level of mere speculation and in many quarters it is accepted without question. Although proof is not overwhelming, what there is is difficult to refute and as the event has happened comparatively recently, a great deal of the evidence is there for all to see. The hypothesis holds that the Okavango, the Chobe and, possibly, the Upper Zambezi rivers, once flowed together across the Kalahari and entered the Limpopo River, by way of which they reached the Indian Ocean. Once again the evidence is equivocal but it leads, on balance, to supporting the idea.

It is thought that the relic river exists, in part, in the form of the Boteti. Far too large for the present volume of water it now carries, it may once have accepted the Okavango and the Chobe and led them across the sands to the east. Today the Boteti, in times of exceptional floods, will reach the edge of the Makgadikgadi Pans, which are themselves the remains of a once vast lake. From Makgadikgadi to the Limpopo the old river course is not known, but there are several important clues. To look at the first, and strongest, evidence, we need to examine the Motloutse River and learn the

story and the significance of the diamonds that were discovered there.

The Motloutse River flows east to the Limpopo and rises on the ridge of higher land that follows Botswana's border. In total length it measures something under 300 km. For the size of river that it is today, the valley is considerable, suggesting a river of far greater volume in the past. The Motloutse was the site of Botswana's first diamond discovery. Three small stones were found in its sandy bed near the main road at a village called Foley. The prospecting company scoured the river and its headwaters to find the point of origin of these stones, but without success. As prospecting efforts were intensified in later years, new companies returned to the same area and took up the search again. They confirmed the original find, and added several more stones found about 80 km further west. Still the source eluded them and the focus of the search shifted to other areas of Botswana. These too proved barren. With renewed determination amounting almost to an obsession, the prospecting teams returned to the Motloutse and its handful of diamonds. Where had these stones come from? There had to be some explanation.

Dr Gavin Lamont recalled the work of an earlier and brilliant geologist, Dr Alex du Toit. Du Toit had been one of the first to postulate the idea that the Okavango and its attendant rivers had once flowed east across the Kalahari to the Limpopo. It was he who first suggested the emergence of the Zimbabwe-Kalahari axis of uplift as a mechanism by which this major river would have been severed. Suppose, reasoned Lamont, that the Motloutse was the eastern remains of this river. If that were so, then its original headwaters would not be where they are at present, but very much further to the west, beyond the low heights of the upwarp. The diamonds could have been carried from somewhere in that region. An extensive sampling programme was carried out on the western 'uphill' side of the ridge and, although kimberlitic material was found, its distribution was inconclusive. It looked as if the upwarp theory was wrong.

Reluctant to give up so easily, one last reconnaissance was carried out, this time very much further to the west, between the villages of Mopipi and Letlhakane, immediately to the south of Makgadikgadi. Almost at once abundant traces of garnets and ilmenites were found, sure evidence of kimberlite pipes in the close vicinity. Within six months these early discoveries led to the location of the world's second largest diamond pipe and the site of the future mine of Orapa.[4] The upwarp theory had withstood a severe test and there now appeared to be little doubt that rivers from the Kalahari did indeed flow to the Limpopo from further west than they currently do and that this flow was cut off by the emergence of the Zimbabwe-Kalahari uplift.

The Motloutse valley had been the route taken by these waters which had carried with them, millimetre by millimetre, a small but precious load of diamonds, for a distance of over 200 km. These stones had lain in the now dry bed of the river for possibly more than 50 million years, awaiting the arrival of diamond prospectors.

In the south-east corner of Sowa Pan there is an indistinct and remarkable feature that may have played a part in the story of the proto-Limpopo. Paradoxically, the feature is at first indistinct because of its enormous size. Professor John Cooke, from the University of Botswana, showed it to me when I shared a journey with him and his wife Sylvia. John is a tall, grey-haired and robust Lancastrian with a deep interest in the palaeo-geomorphology of the Kalahari and a generous willingness to share his knowledge. He is probably the foremost authority on the subject.

We were following a track beside one of Botswana's veterinary fences and had dropped off the higher land to the south of Sowa, onto the very edge of the pan surface itself. John stopped the Land Rover and we climbed onto the roof, looking in a south-easterly direction. At first I could not see what he was talking about but, with his patient help, suddenly realised that I was looking at a huge river valley. The floor was quite flat and appeared to be between 8 and 10 km in breadth. No river traced its way across it now. At either edge were low hills, perhaps no more than 50 m high. I

could have driven past the feature many times without recognising what it was without John's experienced eye to point it out to me. Today the valley rises gently towards the east and quickly loses its shape and form but its sheer size suggests that it might once have formed part of the proto-Limpopo. It may have been the route followed by the Boteti as it flowed east into what we now call the Motloutse River.

Less convincing, perhaps, but worthy of consideration is the evidence for an Okavango-Limpopo link that comes, once again, from fish distribution patterns. The tiger fish (*Hydrocynus vittatus*), a sleek and vicious predator renowned for its fighting ability when caught on a lure or hook, is found throughout the Okavango, Chobe and the Zambezi systems, including the Upper Zambezi above the Victoria Falls. As none of Southern Africa's fish has the ability to surmount a vertical rise of more than 1,5 m, how is it that the tiger fish is so prolific above the Falls?

Central tropical Africa is the source of origin of all the fish in Central and Southern Africa. Fish spread outwards from this focal point as avenues for migration became available to them. It is suggested that in the late Tertiary period, about 5 million years ago, there were two main drainage basins in Central Africa. The western one included the Cunene, Okavango, Chobe, Kafue and the Upper Zambezi rivers. (At that time the Upper Zambezi did not join the Middle Zambezi, but probably flowed into the Okavango.) The eastern drainage basin included the Middle and Lower Zambezi, and Lake Malawi and its associated rivers. The tiger fish evolved in the eastern systems.[5] Fish can move between one system and another through river captures, diversions and watershed exchanges. To explain the present tiger fish distribution, ichthyologists suggest a link between the Lower Zambezi and the Limpopo. Both today meander across the great sedimentary coastal plain of Mozambique and it is possible that they may once have shared a common delta. If this were so, tiger fish could have populated the Limpopo, as they do today, and via its waters have occupied the Okavango, Chobe and the Upper Zambezi. When the Upper and

Middle Zambezi sections linked up in the vicinity of the Victoria Falls both would already have been populated by tiger fish.[6] It is interesting to note that over eighty fish species occur in the Zambezi above the Victoria Falls and seventy in the Middle Zambezi, but only thirty are common to both.[7] This reinforces the idea that the fish populations evolved at a time when the two systems were separate. If they were, it seems that only via the Kalahari and either (or both, at different times) the Limpopo and the Orange, could the upper Zambezi have reached the sea.

The most overwhelming evidence in favour of a link between the north-western rivers and the Limpopo is that which strongly suggests the existence, in relatively recent times, of a vast lake that covered much of present-day Botswana. The supposition is that the proto-Limpopo, flowing eastwards across the Kalahari from the direction of the present Okavango, via the Boteti and Motloutse rivers into the Limpopo, was ponded by the rising ridge of the Zimbabwe-Kalahari axis. Its flow checked, it formed a massive inland sea that existed long enough to leave irrefutable evidence of its size, even though its genesis, history and subsequent demise leave a great deal of room for speculation.

Vanished mammoth lakes are not a new phenomenon in Africa. A now dry caldera, or crater, in south-eastern Sahara, near Tibetsi, shows that it contained a lake more than 350 m deep about 15 000 years ago. Lake Chad was once incredibly vast, covering an area of more than 300 000 km[2.8] Astronauts circling the earth and looking down on Botswana, plainly see the outlines of its super-lake and, once you know what to look for, the evidence is plain upon the ground. The most obvious fact is the existence of the two great pans – Ntwetwe and Sowa, which together are called the Makgadikgadi Pans. Irregularly shaped and each roughly 100 km long by more than 50 km wide, their surfaces are hard, grey clay, perfectly flat, without a ripple, a stone or blemish of any kind, and without the slightest trace of vegetation. There are many places where it is possible to stand upon the surface and see nothing about you but the peerless blue of the sky and the

unending grey of the pan. It is a strange and disorientating experience, not unlike what one would imagine it to be like on some distant and alien planet. Clearly, the Makgadikgadi Pans are the last remnants of the super-lake. The lowest and the deepest portion, they survive today to give us some important clues to past events.

Beyond the outer perimeters of the pans, and often distances of 100 km or more from them, are to be found a series of ancient shorelines. The shorelines of the super-lake are not everywhere visible and, even where they occur, it sometimes takes the eye of an expert to discern where once they were. Often there are long gaps in a single shoreline, perhaps because of a lack of human resources and time to trace them all, but more often because the terrain over which they pass has not been suitable to retain the impressions they leave. Despite this, many of the shores are very clear. Most frequently these occur where rocks abound and kilometres of rolled pebble beaches mark the place where waves once washed onto these now dry and dusty shores. Sometimes gently rising slopes are terraced by shorelines of different water levels. It is an amazing experience to sit and watch the drab, drear winter slope, bereft of greenness, waiting out the dry season, as the sun slowly moves across the sky. At just the right moment, when the sun is at a certain angle, the terraces, which have hitherto merged with the background, suddenly spring into sight. Outlined by shadow, they seem to stand proud of the slope and a clear impression of the awesome size of the long-gone lake is vividly experienced. The fact that shorelines are at so many different levels attests to two important facts: firstly, the level of the lake fluctuated considerably, and secondly, it remained at each level long enough to etch its existence clearly onto the earth.

Two of the most prominent shores, however, consist neither of terraced slopes nor pebble beaches, but of enormous sand ridges. The first and most southerly of these is the Gidikwe Ridge. It is more than 100 km from end to end and follows a gradual curve, roughly parallel to the Boteti River, a little to the west of it. It is not easily seen with the naked eye, although it is clear on aerial photographs and from outer space. It rises gently to a summit about 30 m above ground level, but does so over a distance of 4 to 8 km. The crest at its lowest level is 930 m above mean sea level; its highest point is 950 m but its average height is between 945 and 950 m.

The second sand ridge is the Magwi-khwe. Further north and more to the west, it half-circles the western side of the Mababe Depression. Also about 100 km long, it is about 180 m wide and stands some 20 m proud of the great flat plain to its east. It has a lee dune field to its west, made up of wind-blown lacustrine deposits from the floor of Mababe and in which can be found traces of older shoreline sand ridges. The average height of Magwikhwe is also about 945 m. Unlike Gidikwe, Magwikhwe rises more abruptly from the Mababe Depression. It is much more prominent and the summit is reached within 1,5 km of the gradient's beginning.[9] There is considerable argument as to the precise meaning of these two features. Some claim that they are off-shore barrier ridges,[10] while others maintain that they were on-shore beaches built up into high ridges by the prevailing winds which came from the north-east, sweeping over the vast reaches of the lake. Whichever explanation is correct, they mark the minimum western extent of the super-lake. Both have unpatterned dune fields in their lee, suggesting that at one time the waters extended through or under them some distance further to the west.

The shorelines exist throughout the range of levels from 912 m to 945 m. However, the most strongly marked are at 912, 920, 936, 940 and 945 m. The super-lake obviously fluctuated between these various levels but part of the problem in charting how it did so is that in some places the lower shorelines appear to be older and more eroded than the higher ones. In other words, the lake was first at a low level for a considerable period of time, then at a higher level before returning to the lower level again.

It seems that it was not a simple progression from very large to significantly smaller, culminating in its desiccated state today.[11] To estimate the size of the Kala-hari's super-lake, geomorphologists work on the area covered by the highest shore-line. The 945 m level is generally agreed to represent this but, unfortunately, its presence is not everywhere clearly delineated. Long stretches have to be 'roughed in' by some field-work and more guesswork since detailed contour maps are not available. Estimates of the lake's former size, therefore, vary. If the level is taken at 945 m, the lake would have included all of Makga-dikgadi, most of the Boteti valley, all of Lake Ngami, nearly one third of what is now the Okavango Delta and all of the Mababe Depression. It would have covered between 60 000 and 80 000 km$^2$.[12] The depth of the super-lake may have been considerable. Given that the highest shore-line was at 945 m and that the present surface level of Sowa Pan, the lowest point, is 890 m,[13] the lake must have been at least 55 m deep. However, the sedimentary deposits within the pan vary from 50 to 100 m[14] and so, depending on the periods when the lake was at a higher level, it may have been up to 100 m or more in depth.

There is less disagreement on how the super-lake came into being than there is on where its water supply came from and how and why it was reduced so drastically in volume. Dealing first with the source of its water supply, there are several problems which compound the difficulties in assessing this question. Firstly, the volume of water can be gauged only from the size of the super-lake and here there seems to be little agreement, with estimates varying from 34 000 to 80 000 km$^2$. Two of the foremost authorities' estimates are closer to the latter figure and 60 000 km$^2$ might be a conservative estimate. A further area of contention relating to this issue is the era when the lake was thought to be full. This is not known for certain, as we shall see. The era is relevant because the Kala-hari's climate has undergone marked changes, even within the last million years, the only period for which we have some limited idea of what might have taken place. Climate affects two factors: the rate at which water evaporates, and therefore the higher rate at which it needs to be delivered, and the rainfall patterns in the catchment areas. If the temperature is

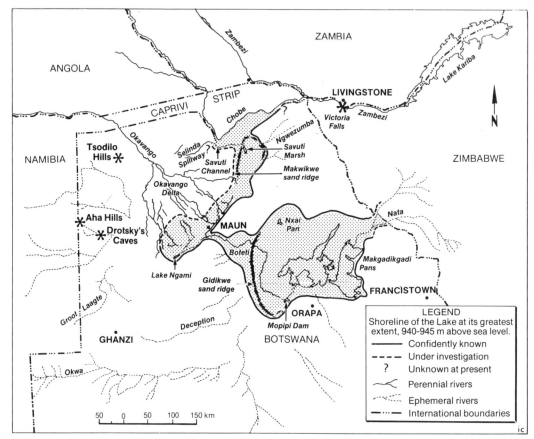

## THE KALAHARI'S GREAT LAKE

**Source**: Compiled with the assistance of Prof. J.H. Cooke and Dr Paul Shaw, University of Botswana, Gaborone, May 1986.

lower, even by a few degrees, everywhere within the region, water becomes more abundant because less of it evaporates. If it increases, the opposite occurs.

In looking for a water supply for a super-lake of 60 000 km², it is generally agreed that a volume of about 40 to 50 km³ would be needed to sustain it under present-day climatic conditions.[15] The outflow from the Okavango River as it is now, at 0,3 km³, would not be sufficient. Given existing rainfall and evaporation levels, the entire Okavango discharge could sustain a lake of only some 200 km². Even the massive influx of nearly 16 km³ before the heavy toll of evaporation takes place is only sufficient to maintain a lake of about 5 000 km². The nearby Chobe, a much smaller river, with an annual flow of 3 km³, could perhaps have maintained a lake in Mababe of 2 000 km². Clearly, a greater

volume of water would have been required, far beyond the combined capacity of the Okavango and the Chobe rivers. The Upper Zambezi seems to be the obvious and only choice. Its mean annual discharge today is approximately 40 km³ and, if it indeed flowed to the Limpopo, the Chobe and the Okavango must necessarily have flowed with it. The combined volumes would have met the maximum 50 km³ required to sustain the super-lake.[16]

At best, this is only an educated guess, for we cannot be sure of the effect of past climatic changes. Any of the three rivers involved may have been larger, the evaporation rate may have been lower or the rainfall higher. Despite these complications, it is the considered opinion of scientists that it is highly probable that all three rivers supplied water to the super-lake.

Assured of such an abundant supply of

water, why then did the lake disappear? The answer to this question is complex too because, once again, many factors are involved. The whole area of northern Botswana is tectonically unstable (see Chapters 7 and 8), particularly the north-western portion, where the Zambezi, Chobe and Okavango rivers run. It is an extension of the East African Rift Valley system and is still developing today. It is generally agreed that when the super-lake first formed, the Okavango Delta probably did not exist. It is thought that the widespread faulting followed rather than preceded the appearance of the lake, and it may even have been triggered by the incredible weight of accumulated water on an already weakened crustal zone.

Two forms of crustal movement have made an impact upon the existence of the super-lake. One form is sub-continental in scale and the other is more local. We have seen how in the late Tertiary period the southern part of Africa experienced uplift at the continental edges, forming, among other things, the great internal drainage basin of the Kalahari itself. This was not a single, continuous process, but may have occurred in a series of separate events. It consisted not only of tilting but also of warping. Among its manifestations was the emergence of the Zimbabwe-Kalahari axis, which possibly occurred too quickly for the proto-Limpopo to cut down through the slowly rising rock. It led instead to the ponding of that river and to the creation of the super-lake.

With uplift of the continental margins widespread tilting occurs and new erosion cycles are initiated. Work in nearby Zimbabwe by Dr L A Lister has shown that it is possible to identify these separate erosion cycles and the different angles of continental tilt that were established by the separate phases of uplift.[17] For example, she was able to show that uplift at the end of the Oligocene era, 25 million years ago, created a gradient of 1:250, sloping from east to west. In simple terms, if you can imagine the continent as a hinge, with the centre-line running from north to south, it is easy to see how, when the sides of the hinge are raised, the angle of slope towards the centre increases but the centre itself

remains at the same height. Located in the centre of the sub-continent, the Kalahari lies along the centre-line of the hinge. It is this hinge effect that can cause rivers to reverse their flow and is probably the fundamental reason accounting for the demise of Greater Lake Makgadikgadi.

Part of the problem in accounting for the size of the super-lake is that it could not exist at its fullest extent today. The shape and levels of north-western Botswana have so altered that such a feature would pour away into the Zambezi River and over the Victoria Falls which, at 879 m,[18] are 10 m below the lowest level in Sowa Pan today and 66 m below the highest level of the palaeo-lake. However, the shorelines are irrefutable proof that the lake did exist and that it did so over long periods of time. One is led to the inescapable conclusion, therefore, that land levels have changed and that tilting so altered the lake basin that its waters were able to find a new exit and that it was in this way drained dry. The prime cause of the demise of the super-lake, therefore, was tectonic activity, firstly by tilting the continent so that the rising waters found a new exit to the sea and, secondly, by altering the pattern of drainage of the rivers that created it and cutting off its supply.

The three right angle bends on the Chobe River are fault controlled. This means that the direction of that river is not the result of usual river course selection but that it has been changed because of fault-lines deep within the earth, held in that position today by those features. In all probability this same mechanism altered the course of the Upper Zambezi, deflecting it and the Chobe towards the north-east, to join, eventually, the Middle Zambezi and in the process initiate the Victoria Falls. With the removal of both these rivers, the super-lake would have been substantially reduced in size.

The fault-lines which so affected the Chobe also extended further to the south-west, creating a huge trough 300 m deep and as much as 150 km wide. This trough, the most southerly extent of the Rift Valley, trapped the Okavango River and probably absorbed its entire flow, isolating the palaeo-lake and leaving it to certain desiccation. In time the Okavango trough was filled with sand and debris and the Okavango River once more flowed across it. When this happened climatic features may have already reduced its flow and it assumed its present typical delta shape because of the low gradient over which it was now flowing. The sun carried away as much as 96 per cent of its waters and what was left could do little more than sustain Greater Lake Makgadikgadi at very low levels indeed. Eventually increasing aridity reduced even this small amount and today the lake bed is dry.

It is possible to try and piece all these events into some sort of chronological order but it would really only be guesswork, based on possibilities and probabilities, with only the flimsiest evidence to support it. Four to five million years ago Botswana's three north-western rivers may have flowed together and followed a course south, through the central Kalahari, to the Molopo and the Orange River beyond. Late Tertiary warpings of the earth's crust may have created the Bakalahari Schwelle, blocking the river's passage to the south, diverting it instead to the east and the Limpopo. The date of the emergence of the Zimbabwe-Kalahari axis is difficult to ascertain, estimates ranging from 2 to 5 million years ago. Current theories favour a more recent date, perhaps nearer 2 million years before the present. The super-lake formed, fed by three major rivers from the north-west as well as by a considerable influx from the north and north-east (present-day Zimbabwe). At some stage within the last million years local crustal movement began to reduce the lake's supply of water and to affect its size. Perhaps, at the same time, the continent tilted, tipping the lake back in the direction of its source. It found a new escape to the sea and, in time, was completely drained, although it lingered, at lower levels, until relatively recently.

When the lake was last full is uncertain. It seems likely that the 945 m level existed for long periods well before 50 000 years ago, the oldest date for which there is reliable information. After that date there is evidence of wide-ranging fluctuations in level. About 46 000 years ago the lake stood at low levels, but between 35 000 and 40 000 years before the present it stood at the 945 m level, although it never returned to that point again. Since reaching the highest level there is ample evidence to show that the fluctuations continued. We know that the lake was at the 920 m level on a number of occasions between 25 000 and 10 000 years ago.[19] It would not, of course, have reached its fullest extent at this shallow depth but it would certainly have been a considerable expanse of water and may have existed as three separate entities centred on Makgadikgadi, Ngami and Mababe. In the last 10 000 years the lake was at the 912 m shoreline on a number of occasions and even today, in years of especially heavy floods, sections of the pans are covered with a shallow layer of water.

Whilst the disappearance of Greater Lake Makgadikgadi is due primarily to tectonic factors, climatic changes also played a major role. This is especially true in more recent times when the supply from the Chobe and Zambezi rivers was absent and the lake had to depend more upon the Okavango and local rivers, influx from the latter source, particularly, being much more erratic and unreliable than from a major river. Its drainage basin is smaller, the volumes are lower and the river, usually within the Kalahari itself, is subject to the same extremes and changes of climate as the lake it feeds. It is this factor which explains the dramatic fluctuations in lake levels that have characterised the last 50 000 years. There is good evidence that the lowest levels of the lake, the Magkadikgadi Pans, held substantial quantities of permanent water as recently as 1 500 years ago. John Cooke's work suggests that rainfall may have been very much higher than present-day levels until as recently as 500 years ago. If this is indeed the case then the great pans, if not actually flooded, may have been a vast wetland, and the western side very much like the present-day Okavango Delta.

Assessing and describing palaeo-climates is a highly specialised science in which we lack real refinement. Moreover, the more distant in time the era we are trying to describe, the more difficult, and inaccurate, the assessment becomes. Certain major events are known from past eras but their combined effects are often difficult to understand. It is known, for example, that the Antarctic continent only appeared as a separate entity some 10 million years ago and that this event had a significant effect on weather patterns in the southern hemisphere. It allowed a complete circumpolar circulation of air, causing climatic deterioration which resulted in the present climatic regime in the hemisphere by about 8 million years ago.[20]

The cold Benguela current which flows northwards along Africa's west coast did not begin until about 3 million years ago and did not reach its present extent until 2 million years before now. Its emergence had a marked effect on the aridity of the Namib Desert and undoubtedly affected weather patterns in the Kalahari.[21] During the million years of Europe's Ice Age every part of the world was affected. On average, world temperatures were about 4 °C cooler, whilst in the northern hemisphere they were 8–12 °C cooler. At its maximum ice covered about 71 million km² as against the 25 million km² that it covers today. There were four major Ice Ages, during which time, as the earth's water was alternately absorbed and released from the ice, sea levels rose and fell. Sometimes the fall would be as great as 100 m below present levels.[22] The short-term effects upon climate of these fluctuations in the sea's level can be dramatic and widespread. Climatic sequences are thus very difficult to establish as there are often repeated and rapid changes in some areas and every kind of evidence has its own complications and margins for error.

There is little reliable climatic evidence for the Kalahari extending beyond 130 000 years ago. Since then, until about 40 000 years before the present, evidence suggests that the regional climate was semi-arid and that there existed a productive savannah ecosystem. Rainfall in the southern Kalahari might have been much higher than it is today and there is some evidence of a gradual decrease in overall temperatures. In the period from 40 000 to 25 000 years ago the Kalahari was very much wetter than it is now, with rainfall at about twice present levels, and temperatures were lower. It was during this time that the super-lake last stood at its former high level

and this would have been attributable as much to increased rainfall and river run-off as it was to lower evaporation rates. At 19 000 years ago Europe's last glacial activity reached its maximum extent, and in the Kalahari this was reflected by the driest period in 125 000 years. Temperatures were much lower and lake levels fell. In the next 9 000 years rainfall gradually increased again. The lake partially refilled and evidence from other pans and from caves shows a greater abundance of water. Regional variations in climate were great and within the Kalahari there are signs that there were considerable differences over relatively small distances. In the last 10 000 years there has been a trend to increasing temperatures and a more erratic distribution of rainfall, resulting in some fairly wet periods within this time as well as some unusually dry periods.[23] In these unpredictable circumstances the lake rose and fell but never regained its former massive size.

To me it is amazing and a source of endless fascination that the dry, hot, dusty Kalahari of today has been the scene of such remarkable events. It has borne upon its sands great rivers and vast lakes. It has heard the sound of crashing waves and witnessed wild storms, and it has seen rivers, swollen beyond their banks, coursing in untamed flood across its thirsty sands. Now, it is a thirstland, without rivers or lakes and the only sound in the distant bush is the soft sighing of the wind.

REFERENCES.

1.  McCarthy, T S. Evidence for the Former Existence of a Major, Southerly-flowing River in Griqualand West. In *Transactions of the Geological Society of Southern Africa*, No 86, 1983, pp 37–49
2.  Gaigher, I G and Pott, R McC. 'Distribution of Fishes in Southern Africa'. In *South African Journal of Science*, Vol 69, 1973, pp 25–7
3.  Rogers, A W. 'Surface Geology of the Kalahari'. In *Transactions of the Royal Society of South Africa*, Vol 24, Part I, p 59
4.  Orapa Mine Company Report. De Beer's Consolidated Mines, Public Relations Department
5.  Bell-Cross, G. 'The Distribution of Fishes in Central Africa'. In *Fisheries Res. Bulletin*, Zambia, Number 4, 1965–1966, pp 3–19

6.  Bond, G. 'Pleistocene Environments in South-
    ern Africa'. In *African Ecology and Human
    Evolution*. Edited by Howell, F C  and Bour-
    liere. London: Methuen & Co Ltd, 1963, **pp
    312-14**
7.  Bell-Cross, G. 'The Fishes'. In *Mosi-oa-Tunya:
    A handbook to the Victoria Falls Region*.
    Edited by Phillipson, D W. London: Longmans,
    1975, **pp 185-87**
8.  Flint, R F. *Glacial and Quaternary Geology*.
    New York: John Wiley & Sons, Inc, 1971,
    **p 457**
9.  Mallick, D I J. Habgood, F and Skinner, A C.
    'Geological Interpretation of Landsat Imagery
    and Air Photography of Botswana'. In *Over-
    seas Geological and Mineral Resources,* No 56,
    1981, **pp 1-35**
10. Grey, D R C and Cooke, H J. 'Some Problems
    in the Quaternary Evolution of the Land Forms
    in Northern Botswana'. In *Catena,* Vol 4, 1977,
    **pp 123-33**
11. Lancaster, N. *Quaternary Environments in the
    Arid Zone of Southern Africa*. Dept of Geo-
    graphy and Environmental Studies, University
    of the Witwatersrand. Occasional Paper, No 22,
    **pp 45-7**
12. Dingle, R V, Siesser, W G and Newton, A R.
    *Mesozoic and Tertiary Geology of Southern
    Africa*. Rotterdam: A A Balkema, 1983, **p 293**
13. Lancaster, N. Op cit, **p 45**
14. Cooke, H J. 'Landform Evolution in the Context
    of Climatic Change and Neo-tectonism in the

Middle Kalahari of North-central Botswana'.
In *Transactions of the Institute of British Geographers*. New Series, Vol 5, No 1, 1980, **p 85**
15. Van Zinderen-Bakker Sr. 'The Evolution of
    Late-Quaternary Palaeoclimates of Southern
    Africa. In *Palaeo-ecology of Africa,* Vol 9.
    Edited by Van Zinderen Bakker, E M. Cape
    Town: A A Balkema, 1976, **p 195**
16. Grove, A T. 'Landforms and Climatic Change
    in the Kalahari and Ngamiland'. In *The Geo-
    graphic Journal,* Vol 135, 1969, **p 210**
17. Lister, L A. *The Erosion Surface of Rhodesia*.
    Unpublished PhD. Thesis, University of Zim-
    babwe, 1976, **p 203**
18. Cooke, J. Personal communication. August
    1985
19. Cooke, H J. 'The Evidence from Northern Bo-
    tswana of Late Quaternary Climatic Change'.
    In *Proceedings of the International Symposium
    on Late Cenozoic Palaeoclimates of the South-
    ern Hemisphere*. Rotterdam. A A Balkema,
    1984, **pp 265, 278**
20. Dingle, R V, Siesser, W G, Newton, A R. Op cit,
    **p 8**
21. Lancaster, N. Op cit. **pp 16-17**
22. Inskeep, R R. *The Peopling of Southern Africa*.
    Cape Town: David Philip, 1978, **p 43**
23. Deacon, J, Lancaster, N and Scott, L. Summary
    of the evidence in the symposium on 'The Evi-
    dence for Late Quaternary Climatic Change
    in Southern Africa'. University of the Wit-
    watersrand, Johannesburg, South Africa, 1983

# Part 2
# Hidden Secrets of the Sands

# 3. Islands in a Forgotten Sea

AS we have seen, much of northern Botswana once lay deep beneath the still waters of a massive lake. Today the lake is long since gone and in its place, where the very deepest parts lay, are the grassland plains and the great pans of the Makgadikgadi.

Perhaps it is the bone-jarring surface of the gravel road from Nata to Maun that prevents one from appreciating the unique qualities of Makgadikgadi when crossing it, for it is like roller-skating on cobblestones. Despite endless efforts by road maintenance crews, who painstakingly scrape away the corrugations, the latter, like an incurable disease, quickly spread again, dimpling the surface into a series of regular ridges. When it's bad your hands and arms tingle from the constant vibration; what corrugations actually do to a vehicle I hate to imagine, but it feels as if it is about to fall to pieces at any moment.

The surface of the road, with its potholes and corrugations, demands the driver's total concentration, but, to begin with, even the passengers will see little of interest. At the start of the journey dense bush lines both sides of the road. Stunted trees, sad and dejected, stand wilting beneath the combined weight of the burning heat and fine white dust thrown up by the wheels of passing cars. It settles like a morbid shroud upon the vegetation, choking it slowly to death.

Gradually the trees begin to thin out and the vegetation alters. Suddenly you realise that a dramatic change has taken place. Before you are endless grasslands and tall, graceful palms, their grey, long-limbed boles reaching up to the sky and holding aloft plumes of feathery fronds. To see and experience the grasslands best, you must leave the main road and take any one of a dozen side tracks that head for the distant horizon. I've crossed the plains many times but no matter what time of year it is, whether wet or dry, the magic of this special place never eludes me.

Long ago as the lake dried out, the water was concentrated in an ever-reducing area. As the surface diminished in size, so the concentration of salt increased and this affected the soil of the land which was exposed by the shrinking waters. In this way zones of vegetation were established. The largest trees, liking salt least, grow furthest from the pans, where aeons of rain have washed the salt from the earth. As the lowest point is approached, the salinity rises, as does the proximity of saline groundwater, and only the hardiest of plants can survive. First the smaller trees give up the struggle, then the shrubs; finally, all that is left is the grass, and it grows in abundance, to the very edges of those vast grey depressions where, filled with salty clay and occasionally water, nothing grows at all.

Perhaps the first thing that will strike you is the enormous expanse of the sky. It arches above your head, so clear and faultlessly blue that you almost expect to see stars in it. Usually it is quite cloudless but, as the season of the rains approaches, daily more clouds appear, great towering monoliths of solid white, tossing between them, in the dry, electric November air, brazen bolts of lightning. They move in stately procession across the parched land, trailing behind them black shadows that patchwork the ground, offering brief relief from glare and heat – but precious little else.

The grasslands appear infinite. In the dry season the grass is short, cropped by animals or wilted to a stubble; goodness, food and strength are stored deep beneath the sun-baked sand or lie dormant in myriad seeds that await only the coming of the rain. In the wet, when the rains have soaked the earth, the grass stands tall and dense, tassled heads tossing in vagrant winds. As far as every horizon, there is only grass. It seems at first a sterile environment, but it is not so. The grass plains are vital to the survival of great migrating herds of game. At a certain time of the year innumerable animals will crowd these plains, which become a chequer-board of black and white, of brown and dun. In a dusty squall of hoof and mane, predator and prey will enact again the desperate battle for survival, and scattered piles of bleached bones will stand as stark monuments to past encounters.

Even when the vast herds have passed, the plains are never empty, but to see its permanent residents needs careful searching and patience. In the early morning you may see a jackal trotting quickly homeward. He will generally ignore you, but he may stop, one paw lightly poised, to glance at you briefly and allow you to admire the glory of his golden coat, caught in the first low rays of the rising sun and etched in shimmering gold.

You will almost certainly see the black korhaan, whose spectacular displays cannot fail to draw your attention. The female of the species is rather drab, compared to the bulkier male in his splendid bib-and-tucker, and is not given at all to the ostentatious aerial displays for which the latter is so renowned. During the mating season, particularly, this flamboyant bird seems to work himself into a fury of territorial defensiveness and hurls himself angrily into the air. His clattering call rises in pitch and speed as his height above the ground increases, borne aloft by rapid, duck-like wingbeats, ill-suited to so ungainly a bird. Then, suddenly, there is silence. The korhaan closes his wings together above his head and, claws extended, plummets to the ground.

Another common and more obvious bird is the Kori bustard, the heaviest flying bird in the world, which tops the scales at nearly 40 kg. This huge bird, with its immense wing-span, is quite unmistakable. Preferring to spend its time on the ground, it reluctantly takes flight if you get too close

and, once airborne, it is a powerful flier. Although it is seen throughout Africa, it is in fact a migrant, but little is known about its movements and we do not know where it winters. The grace and power of its flight are thrilling to watch as the great spreading wings unfold and beat down upon the air and, with no apparent effort, reach up again for the new stroke, thrusting the giant bird into the sky. The male Kori bustard is easily distinguished, especially in the mating season. He is much bigger than the female, and during the time he seeks a mate he puts on a most unusual display. Quite how he does it I am not sure, but at certain times of the year you will see him sternly striding the plains with his throat puffed out to two or three times its normal size. The effect is to make him appear even bigger than he is which, presumably, is intended to deter his male competitors.

The Makgadikgadi plains are not absolutely flat. There are occasional low undulations and, not infrequently, scattered shallow depressions. Century after century these depressions collect the dust and detritus of ages. Small enough to be sheltered from the wind, they begin gradually to fill and, over time, a richer soil then elsewhere develops. First small shrubs take root and they, in their passing, add more organic material to the soil. Eventually trees become established in these reservoirs of richer soil, so that the plain is dotted with widely separated 'islands' of vegetation. These islands create microhabitats as unique and varied as their ocean counterparts.

Exploring one of these islands is a rewarding experience. As the sounds of your arrival settle and the silence of the Kalahari returns, you will experience a sense of all-pervading peace. It is partly the silence, partly the infinity of space about you and partly, too, the sense of total isolation. You are quite alone. No one will come this way for many days and yet there is no feeling of loneliness or vulnerability. It is too beautiful for that and the shelter of the trees provides some subconscious sense of security, reflecting, perhaps, our earlier, hominid association with them.

If you sit quietly for an hour or two, the

island's inhabitants will accept you and, curiosity overcoming their acquired mistrust of man, they will move to investigate or go about their normal day. The smaller birds will come quite close, and the lizards and geckos will come out to appraise you and speculate on your potential as a food source. Bigger birds, resting from their ceaseless search for food, will pause in the upper branches of the trees and perhaps throw you a curious glance. There may be owls, immobile in the deeper shadow, watching you with blinking eyes while they sit waiting for the end of day.

I once came across a hare. It was a youngster, perhaps newly arrived in this forested island, and we met unexpectedly. I was examining the flowers upon a hand-high branch and the hare was crouched in a dense tangle of fallen, thorn-stitched twigs at the base of the same tree. We both froze, I in breathless wonder at so close a contact with this creature, the hare in blind terror. I could see from how it sat, every muscle tense, that it was poised for explosive flight. Its ears were erect and its eyes showed fear and hesitation. In another second it would move, yet I wanted to prolong the contact. Hoping that perhaps it was uncertain as to what I was, I thought to convince him that I was just an animal. I started to 'browse' on the tree, plucking slowly but vigorously at the branches. The effect was immediate. Finding a behaviour that it recognised, the hare promptly relaxed and the tension dissipated. We stayed together for fifteen or twenty minutes, the hare respecting my right to eat from the tree, but prudently declining to leave the shelter of its thorn boma until I had finished.

Early morning mirages build clear, distant mountain ranges, which melt away in the rising sun. If you look about you, just after dawn, you will see on every horizon forbidding, blue-black walls of rock that seem to rise precipitously and encircle you completely. Even if you know the Kalahari and feel sure that nothing of the kind can exist, your confidence may well be shaken. Take powerful binoculars and examine those distant walls and you will find that so clear is the detail that every gully and ravine is visible. Here a major valley breaches the continuous wall; there, along the top, you can see the furry fringe of trees. There can be no doubt – it is a massive escarpment.

But, as the temperature rises, it is the mountains whose confidence crumbles. First they begin to tremble, as if in fearful anticipation of the coming day, whose early light has revealed the barren wastes and lifeless plains they are to command. The burning heat and the endless emptiness seem too daunting a prospect. The first deserters waver and flee. The ranks broken, the army of hills and rocks turns tail. By eight o'clock there is nothing left but the sky and the grass and you.

To the east of the grasslands lie the two great adjacent pans of Makgadikgadi, Ntwetwe and Sowa. Both are vast. Sowa is more than 100 km long and 45 km wide; Ntwetwe, less regular in shape, is even larger. These two pans are the last vestiges of Botswana's once massive super-lake. Fed from the south by the Boteti River, and from the north by several Zimbabwean rivers, the pans today are never completely flooded and only occasionally do areas near the river mouths receive sufficient water for it to stand upon their surfaces.

The surface of these pans is a hard, salt-saturated clay, which for most of the year is firm enough to support a vehicle and can always be walked upon. It is flat, grey and without blemish. Nothing grows upon it and you will find on its surface no grass, no leaves, no stones. Between 50 to 100 m of clay, gravel and accumulated salt lie beneath your feet. The entire pan seems to act like a giant sponge, greedily soaking up such scattered rain as falls upon its surface or meagre waters delivered to its shore, for in the rainy season it is more yielding and you venture upon it in a vehicle at your own risk.

Motivated by caution, driving upon these pans I use a technique which I owe to the literary churchmouse. Never trusting the surface ahead and, at 70 km an hour, having little time to do anything about a mistake in judgement, I prefer to creep around the edges. Staying close to the grass, I resist the temptation to skim across the beautiful pristine bays. I saw a truck go down once. The hard crust of clay suddenly collapsed and the vehicle sank to its chassis. Beneath was a thick, glutinous, black-sodden clay that clung to the wheels, affording them no purchase at all. It took a great deal of digging and hard work to escape. The risks are worth it, however, for there are islands upon these pans of great beauty.

Kubu Island, as it is known by the few hundred people who are aware of its existence, is in the south-west of Sowa Pan. You approach from that direction, following a dirt track that falls from the low escarpment to the south down onto the flat plains of Makgadikgadi. You turn off the road and make your way around or over the patchy islands of yellowed, tussocked grass. A shadowed smudge which looms on the horizon ahead turns into a low headland. From its base a sliver of land juts far out into the pan, at the end of which, tentatively linked by a narrow band of grass, is the island of Kubu. The final approach is across a great open bay. If you know it well, there is a way directly across.

It is disorientating to be in a land so flat and without features, and to cast yourself across this open space can be unnerving. But it is exhilarating too. Impelled by fear and the vague hope that speed may prove an asset on an uncertain surface, the vehicle races over the pan into a world of sky and clay and nothing else. I suppose it is the fear that makes it so exciting and few people I know ever forget the experience, or recall it with anything other than shining eyes and smiling pleasure.

Kubu is an outcrop of ancient rocks, thrust up from deep beneath the clays and sands. It is a small island, rising no more than 20 m above the pan, but the height is enough to offer a view of breathtaking immensity. All about you spreads the harsh, glaring surface, but in the middle distance the pan is clothed in a sombre symphony of muted greys and whites, toned up or down by the shadows of passing clouds, and merging at the horizon into a simple harmony of cobalt blue and grey.

The island is beset with grotesque, stunted baobab trees. Gnarled, usually leafless, their dwarfed and twisted forms suggest the agony of ages spent on salted waters beneath a remorseless sun. Some, seen in silhouette against the stark grey pan, suggest a visit to another world, unutterably remote and lonely.

There is a beacon on the island's low summit. Below and about it, like an encircling tonsure, is a ring of small, water-rounded stones. This is a pebble beach and it speaks of a time long, long ago, when the pan was a sea and waves from the north-east came full-fetch and pounding against this tiny islet, rolling the pebbles into their smooth round shape. There were times when the whole island was deep under water and others when it barely showed, and there were times, like today, when it lay bare and naked to the sun, an island in a forgotten sea.

Man has used this island for aeons. A careful search of the shore will reveal minutely chipped Stone Age tools. On one corner of Kubu is a low, dry-stone wall that erratically completes a shaky circle. It does not match the grandeur of Great Zimbabwe and may be relatively modern. The workmanship is indifferent and the purpose quite obscure, but its presence adds to the magic of this place and inspires the imagination. One well-known writer, on visiting this spot, is said to have been inspired by it to write a popular tale about Phoenicians, inland seas and cities built of stone. I know exactly where, exhausted from their wanderings, his weary travellers heaved their boats ashore – Kubu does that to you.

I once took to Kubu a very dear and valued friend, Ian Marshall, who is an artist with a delicate touch and sensitive perceptions. I wanted to share it with him, whose soul I knew it would touch. We picked a bad time of the year and the heat was excruciating. Nothing perturbs Ian, however, whose equanimity is almost legendary. He and I spent the hottest part of the day in camp-chairs, following, like the hands of a clock, the black block of a baobab's shade, trying hard to pretend we were not dying of the heat. But it was worth it, for that evening the pan treated us to a storm.

It was October, and a time in this part of Africa for occasional titanic struggles between continental air-flows. First the horizon to the north-east darkened, a thin,

Moonrise at sunset on Kubu in Sowa Pan

▲A Landsat image of the Makgadikgadi Pans taken from 930 km out in space. Ntwetwe is on the left, Sowa on the right. Sowa Spit is visible as a distinct line; relic beaches can be seen top centre and stabilised sand dunes top left.▼The salt-stained rocks of some of Sowa Pan's islands

▲Solitary sentinel on Kubu's shore ▼Midnight on the edge of Sowa Pan

End of day at Kubu on Sowa Pan

black band of cloud too small to suggest the elemental violence to which we would soon be exposed. As the bank of cloud grew, I thought of rain and began to put away items that could get damaged. A wind began, gentle at first, but growing stronger by the minute. It plucked at canvas and played with loose sleeping bags but, grateful for its cooling effect, we paid it scant attention. Mounted on a swirling mass of dancing dust and sand, the distant clouds rode towards us from across the pan and soon filled the sky above our heads. The wind gathered strength; the table and chairs rattled; a dish-cloth whisked away. Airborne sand began to sting our arms and legs and we sought shelter among the trees. The sun, setting behind us, and unobscured by cloud, illuminated the oncoming demon with an ethereal, pink-tinged, bloody glow. In a moment, it struck.

With arrogant violence, it smashed through the camp, knocking down everything in its path. It was not possible to stand against it, nor even to consider rescuing the various items that took flight before its fury. Overhead, in sparking anger, sizzling streaks of lightning flashed across the sky and down to a stunned earth. Safe behind our massive trees we did not, could not, move. There was a strangely primitive, thrilling sense of excitement in being there, as if one's innermost self was part of the power and force that raged about us.

Too soon, for me at least, it was over. Silence fell and the dust settled. Not a drop of rain had fallen. The clouds cleared and a gentle velvet night descended. In the flickering light of the camp-fire and the leaping shadows that it cast, we sat together in the peace and warmth, each with his own thoughts. Ian has not forgotten that storm. Nor shall I.

How like the sea the surface of the pan can become. As you venture, on foot, further out upon it you will notice small, plate-sized patches of salty encrustation. Oozing from the mud below, drawn by the sun, the salt sets in bubbled patterns like frozen foam. It is an unreal world for all about you is a mirage; you cannot see what is before you, only the false images offered by the shimmering waves of light.

In the distance the mirage changes the unrelenting grey into a placid sea that reflects the azure blue of the sky and stretches from horizon to horizon. It is limpid and without movement, still and silent on a windless surface. The salt patches, merging with the distance and magnified by it, appear as a line of massive white breakers, surging in silence on the dancing air at the edge of a motionless sea.

Sometimes, when a cloud obstructs the light, the sea becomes again the predominating grey and it takes on a sullen mood, tossing the salty white-caps from side to side.

The capacity of a mirage to mislead is quite extraordinary. One day, running far out across the pan with my small dog Gypsey by my side, I saw ahead of me a full-grown male ostrich. I know these birds well and, amazed as I was to see it there, there was no mistaking it. Clearly I could see the long, balding neck, the pitch-black feathers of the male and the familiar high-stepping gait, curiously in time with my own, of a fast-moving creature. I decided to change course and intercept it. I was less than 100 m from it when it abruptly shrank to a small dot in the sand which, when I came up to it, proved to be nothing more than a small piece of wood, 30 cm long, 15 cm high and half-buried in the sand.

I am not the first to whom this has happened. 'Matabele' Wilson and his friend Arthur Eyre, both highly experienced hunters, set out upon this pan in the late 1880s, stalking the biggest giraffe they had ever seen. As they approached their prey its size diminished and both were disappointed to take for the pot a single, and very small, springbok, a brown and white antelope of some 25 kg.[1]

There are other islands on these pans, all mostly secret and hidden deep within the reaches of their further shores. To visit another one must travel around the south end of Sowa Pan and climb the escarpment marking its southernmost extent.

If the angle of the sun is right, when you approach this slope from the north you will see, cut into its face, a series of terraces, like gigantic steps climbing its gently sloping side. Each of these, if you were

to examine them closely, would, somewhere along their length, reveal another
collection of the rolled stones that tell of an
ancient shoreline from the old super-lake.

Atop the escarpment the countryside is
very different. Here the red sands of the
Kalahari hold sway once more and the
road changes from the smooth hardness of
the pan to deep soft sand. Near the village
of Mosu the road drops down, off the
escarpment again, to the pan's edge, and
for the first time you can look back at the
much more dramatic feature that the escarpment is at this point. Great white cliffs
of bleached and weathered calcrete fall
steeply for 70 to 100 m. What changes
these cliffs must have seen! Once, when
the level of the lake was at its highest,
mighty waves must have crashed against
their base and a view from the top would
have ranged, unimpeded, to the furthest
reaches of this massive sea. Today the area
is dry and dead. Thin, bony cattle search
beneath the struggling thorn trees for a
single blade of grass. Dry, circling eddies
of dust sweep across the face of these cliffs
where once waves washed.

On the east side of Sowa, tucked into a
large bay, is the island of Kukonje. It is
quite unlike Kubu, except in size, and if
Kubu were male, Kukonje would be female.
It is gentle, soft and beautiful, but in quite a
different way. It lacks the hard ruggedness
of the former and is quite without those
fields of bare, grey rocks. Nor does it possess more than a handful of baobabs, and
these are bigger, lighter in colour and
altogether more like the tree we are accustomed to seeing.

Kukonje, too, has been home to ancient
man and piles of his shaped stones are
everywhere abundant. The island is much
further from the shore than Kubu and you
must either risk driving across or walk the
intervening 3 km to gain the island's shore.
Like Kubu, there is no water at all and
everything you need must be taken with
you.

The land is sparsely inhabited but even
so the game has learnt to fear man. During
one visit there we surprised a small herd of
seven wildebeest. They took flight immediately and fled the island, seeking the safety
of the open pan. There, in line astern, the
animals merged with the mirage and looked
for all the world like a line of bobbing
boats, fleeing some inhospitable coast.

There are cliffs on the mainland in the
vicinity of Kukonje. Some are high and
steep and certainly looked down upon this
sea in times long past. Some cliffs, closer to
the shore, are not as steep, nor as high
and, if you 'churchmouse' round the pan,
you can drive across the stubble grass and
mount a ridge to the low cliff-top. Here you
can camp, with the whole of Sowa below
you and at your feet Kukonje Island, sliding
into gold-edged blackness as, at sundown,
it slips into the shadow of the earth. If you
are lucky you will see herds of game
grazing at the edge of the pan and will
watch their shadows slowly lengthen as
the day draws to its close. High up in this
eyrie, above the pan and beside the warm
camp-fire, there is a special feeling of peace
and contentment not commonly found
these days. Here you will feel at one with
the environment, never an intruder.

In the far north of Sowa Pan, where one
of the big Zimbabwe rivers sometimes flows
in, there is a feature called the Sowa spit.
This is a narrow reach of land jutting far
out into the pan from its eastern side, two-
thirds of the way across. It is a low, treeless
sand-ridge, a few metres above the level of
the pan and nowhere more than three or
four kilometres wide. To the north of it
today commercial concerns are exploiting
the soda ash which is to be found in vast
quantities beneath the surface. So much is
there here that this pan alone is thought
capable of supplying the entire world
demand for more than a thousand years. A
pilot project was in operation when I first
visited the area. Powerful pumps suck the
briny sludge from deep beneath the surface
and this is left in the sun to evaporate and
crystallise. The project is of vital importance to Botswana's economy and there is
little doubt that the scheme could burgeon
into a gigantic industry. One only hopes
that the company concerned with its exploitation will remember its responsibility
to the rest of the world and destroy as little
as possible of the nature and form of this
isolated, precious wilderness.[2]

The Makgadikgadi has not remained
untainted by tragedy. About forty years

ago a sad and sickening event took place there, which many of the local people still remember. It was during the Second World War, October 1943, to be precise. Two young pilots, Adamson and Edwards, flying out of what was then Southern Rhodesia, ran out of fuel and crash-landed on these pans.

They did not know the country and were ill-equipped to deal with the fate that awaited them. A group of Bushmen had been hunting, perhaps illegally, nearby. They may have thought that these two uniformed men represented law and order and that they were about to be apprehended. In any event the Bushmen took the pilots into their company and offered them shelter for the night. The offer was accepted but during the night the two men were murdered.

One was shot and the other killed with an axe, possibly his own. The bodies were burnt. It was not until 8 November that the aircraft was spotted and the search for survivors began. Soon much of the gruesome story was pieced together and the evidence led to the arrest of eight Bushmen, five of whom were women. One of the men was a well-known witchdoctor in the Nata area and the investigation acquired a more sinister tone. Eventually the accused were taken to court but, in the absence of bodies and of sufficient evidence, they were acquitted – not, however, to go completely free. The Bushmen and their families were banished to another part of the country and all the others in the area were ordered to hand in what firearms they had. Efforts were then made by the authorities to establish cattle-rearing stations in the district and the police post which is there today was established.[3]

The story to all intents and purposes ended there but strange rumours persist to this day. It is said that the 'white man's justice' was not believed to have worked and that the guilty must still be punished. I have not been able to verify this, but tales persist of the two main culprits being blinded and of the tribal banishment order being, in effect, a lifelong sentence to slavery.

Botswana today is a charming, friendly and surprisingly sophisticated country. One does not hear much of witchcraft now, but it has not always been so, as the airmen incident illustrates. There is another tale, from the early 1930s, where a case of witchcraft was reported from Tshane, far to the south, in the southern Kalahari. An old man had been accused of causing the death of another and the usual village trial had been organised, without reference to the British authorities responsible for civil obedience.

The old man was found guilty and condemned to ordeal. He was tied up in a net, with his head between his knees, and suspended from the branch of a tree. Under the burning sun the net was rotated, while being drawn ever tighter – slowly crushing him. Miraculously, the Officer Commanding Police of that area intervened in time to rescue the man. He held an impromptu investigation but could find no single culprit. He arrested the entire council and, with the aid of two constables, marched the whole party nearly 500 km to the nearest court![4]

On top of the southern escarpment, immediately south of Sowa Pan, lies the source of some of Botswana's enviable diamond wealth. It was in 1967 that the first kimberlite pipe was found. At 113,8 ha in extent, it is the second largest kimberlite pipe in the world, following Tanzania's Mwadui mine, at 146 ha. Thirty pipes in all have been located and all are diamond bearing. In 1968 two more pipes were found at nearby Letlhakane and, although they are not as prolific, the gem-quality rate, at 40 per cent of the diamonds recovered, is much higher than at Orapa, which is only 15 per cent.

Developing the mines was an enormous engineering challenge. There were no roads at all in the area and, more important, there was no water. The latter problem was solved by reaching down, deep into the earth, and tapping abundant groundwater there. In addition, a nearby pan at the end of the Boteti River, which drains the Okavango Delta, was utilised as a reservoir. The valley of the Boteti was dredged in places, as were sections of the Okavango itself and the flow of the water along the Boteti increased. A low retaining wall was built around part of Mopipi Pan and in time a new lake emerged. It has not entirely solved the water problem though and evaporation and the

concentration of natural salts make operating in this inhospitable environment a
continuous battle.

A fascination of the area around Orapa
has been the fossils it has revealed –
probably the first found anywhere in the
Kalahari. When the pipe of kimberlite
punched its way through layers of rock 93
million years ago, it left on the surface a
small crater some 5 km in diameter and as
much as 140 m deep. This crater filled with
water and with successive layers of sediment from the country rock and kimberlitic
debris that formed its sides.

In the crater lake, which was slowly inundated by a film of sediment, fossil plants,
grasses, ferns and insects, including a form
of cockroach and aquatic beetles, were
trapped. Incredibly, many of the insects
are little different from the same species
found today – attesting to the extraordinary
stability among these creatures over vast
periods of time.[5] The age of these fossils
has yet to be accurately determined, but it
is thought that they date from between 18
and 20 million years ago.[6] It is possible for
experts, examining the sediments, to draw
conclusions suggesting times of periodic
desiccation, but again the details of how
long and when, are not yet available. It is
an exciting find but one which involves
scientists in a desperate race against time.
The sediments must be removed by the
mining company before the main diamond-bearing kimberlite can be reached
and although the company has allowed
access to the area and has been more than
generous in the cause of science, the giant
machines cannot wait indefinitely and the
old lake bed will soon be destroyed.

Orapa is not Botswana's only diamond
mine. In 1973 the distinctive three-lobed
pipe at Jwaneng was discovered beneath
30 to 50 m of Kalahari sand. A triumph for
modern prospecting techniques, it is the
largest gem mine in the world. Jwaneng,
with Orapa, makes Botswana the third largest producer of diamonds in the world,
after Russia and Zaire. This wealth has not
come cheaply however. With a total investment approaching P350m, the stakes are
high, but the results have been equally
rewarding. The Botswana Government
owns 50 per cent of the mines, which

account for 50 per cent of her export earnings and between 30 and 35 per cent of
Government revenue. The total production,
in 1983, from both mines was over 10 million carats, which suggests that in that year
Botswana might have exported as much as
2,1 tonnes of diamonds! The mining industry has provided Botswana's nationals with
more than 3 750 new jobs and, with the
infrastructure that has followed development, has helped make significant changes
that have materially altered the face of Botswana and the way of life of its citizens.

Many millions were spent in the twelve-
year search for Botswana's diamonds. Unimaginable mileages were clocked up in
dust-stained vehicles as the surface of the
Kalahari was combed, almost metre by
metre, for the precious trace elements that
betray the diamonds nearby. It is ironic
that the exposed kimberlites at Orapa are
visable on images taken by the orbiting
satellite Landsat. The largest pipe shows
up as a dark mound 1 x 1,5 km in extent.

Unfortunately, in the only Landsat 1
imagery which was available at the time of
the search the exposed kimberlites were
obscured by cloud. So prominent is the
feature that for many years, long before the
existence of diamonds was even suspected,
it was used by trans-Kalahari pilots as an
air navigation marker![7]

REFERENCES

1.  Wilson, W. *The Northern Kalahari Desert*. Rho-
    desia Scientific Association, Vol 5, Part 2,
    1905, pp 29–40
2.  Rhowedder, J. *Sua Pan*. Botswana, No 5 (no
    date) Department of Information, Government
    of Botswana, Gaborone, Botswana, pp 7–14
3.  Hitchcock, R K. Personal communication, July
    1984
4.  Rey, C F. 'Ngamiland and the Kalahari'. In
    *Geographical Journal*, Vol 80, No 4, October
    1932, pp 281–308
5.  Campbell, A C. Personal communication,
    March 1986
6.  Maguire, J. Personal communication, May
    1984
7.  Mallick, D I J, Habgood, F and Skinner, A C. A
    Geological Interpretation of Landsat Imagery
    and Air Photography of Botswana. Overseas
    Geology and Mineral Resources, No 56, 1981,
    p 18

# 4. Of Hills and Hollows

NOTHING in one's experience of the Kalahari prepares one for the approach to Tsodilo Hills. You may fly or drive but either way the first sight of these hills will not fail to evoke a strong feeling of excitement. It may partly be from a sense of achievement in having penetrated to such a remote part of Africa; it may also be amazement at being so unexpectedly confronted with hills in an area otherwise known for the unrelenting flatness of its landscape. For me, however, the excitement comes from the spirit. There is something about those hills that is hard to identify. It is almost as if they have an aura, moving into which somehow sharpens the senses, awakens long forgotten feelings and tells you, unequivocally, that this is somewhere special.

The Tsodilo Hills are found in the northwest of Botswana, on the southern side of the Okavango Delta. There are four hills in the group, the largest of which is named, by the local Bushmen, the Male. Its western face, which is solid rock, has a broad base and rises sheer for over 300 m. To the north of it and separated by a small gap, through which a bush track passes, is a conglomeration of smaller summits known collectively as the Female. Beyond that again is a very small hill called the Child and finally, at the end of the group, the smallest hill of all, that is without a name.

The first time I visited these hills I drove there. From Maun it is a long and tiring journey and can take ten hours or more in a four-wheel-drive vehicle. Leaving the main road (a polite euphemism for 200 km of ghastly track along which vehicle tracks are almost totally obscured in deep, soft sand), the rest of the drive takes two or three hours on a bush track. To begin with, the countryside seems without shape or pattern. Unusual for this part of the world, the track is firm with very little loose sand. The bush is dense and crowds in from either side, scraping against your vehicle as you pass. There are short stretches of mopani woodland but they lack the attraction of the great mopani forests further north which, with richer soils and higher rainfall, give a feeling of lightness and airy spaciousness which is not found among these cramped and stunted trees. Just over halfway, however, the environment begins to change and you move into totally different country. Seen from the air, this part of Botswana is covered with line upon line of ancient sand dunes, lying parallel to one another and now fixed in place by vegetation. They stretch as far as the eye can see and look for all the world like some limitless sea, frozen at a moment in time and forgotten as ages passed them by. It is into this dune country that the track now takes you.

The ridges of sand are regular, with about 1,5 km between the crests, which are seldom more than 20 m high. The valleys between have gently sloping sides. When I was there it was the rainy season and nature had been generous. The valley floors were lush with stands of tall fresh grass reaching almost to shoulder height. There were few trees to obstruct the long green vistas down these valleys to the blue beyond. Having recently emerged from the cluttered bush, a feeling of light and space pervaded the day.

The road followed a line diagonally across the old dunes, so that progress was rather like travelling on a roller-coaster. The sand seemed to get deeper and softer as I approached the crest of a dune; the engine began to overheat and I was obliged to change down to the lowest gear.

Grinding my way over the gently rounded summit, I began the descent on the other side and then approached the next dune. Interestingly, the dune crests are heavily wooded. Here the trees grow tall and widely spaced, and their spreading branches cast a dancing dappled shade across the white sand.

It is from one of these crests that one catches the first glimpse of the Male hill. You will see its summit looming blue-black above the trees, at once beckoning and suggesting, by its very incongruity and size, the mystery and enigma that is Tsodilo. It will take another hour before you stand below it, awed by its presence.

Today two groups of people live permanently at the hills. The first are Hambukushu who live in a small village near the Male hill. They keep a few cattle here, watering them from a deep well they have dug near their dwellings. When the rains are good they will grow a crop of cereals. A representative of Botswana's National Museum will produce a visitor's book for you to sign, for the area is protected, and bureaucracy, in the shape of a stubby pencil and sand-smudged pages, must have its way. I think it unlikely that this group has been here very long, a few generations perhaps, but there have been other Hambukushu here before them, with long gaps between periods of occupation. This tribe is found elsewhere in Ngamiland and, if you ask them, they will tell you that their god Nyambi first lowered people of their tribe to the earth at these very hills. The Museum's custodian will take you to the place if you show interest and there, on the hillside, you will see time-worn footprints of men and hoofmarks of cattle set in solid rock. Historians do not altogether accept this theory and claim that the Hambukushu arrived in the vicinity of the Okavango in about the middle of the eighteenth century, from the Zambezi River in western Zambia.

The second group of residents at Tsodilo are Bushmen of the !Kung tribe. They too have a small village, rather closer to the Male hill than that of the Hambukushu. It is not typical for these people, under natural conditions, to remain permanently in one place all the year round. Traditionally they follow the game and the seasonal ripening of wild foods. However, with the number of visitors to Tsodilo increasing every year, it would appear that they have found better pickings and so choose to remain where they are. Usually there are less than forty of them; they keep a few goats and sell a small range of simple curios. Salt, beer and tobacco are items they crave. No one can tell you how long the Bushmen have made use of these hills. The only certain thing that can be said is that it has been for a very, very long time.

During one visit to their village, I watched an old man making beads from ostrich egg-shells. They were flat, round and about 7 mm in diameter. The bead-maker sat upon the bare ground. On a piece of tatty material laid out between his legs were several large pieces of ostrich egg-shell. These he broke into smaller fragments, each about the size and shape of the smallest finger-nail. Taking one at a time, he would place it on a soft piece of hide and direct down to its centre a sharp metal point. The point was made from a strand of fencing wire and was counter-sunk and bound into a straight length of stick. By rubbing it between his hands, he rotated it, creating a primitive drill with which he bored first through one side of the shell and then, so as not to crack it with the drill, through the other. In time a number of irregularly shaped pieces accumulated, each with a hole through the centre. These he then threaded, side by side, onto a short length of wire. When he had made enough to hold comfortably between thumb and finger, he would rub them up and down on a suitable rock. Eventually, over the years a groove develops in this rock and, by rotating the column of beads as they are worn down, a remarkably circular and delicate bead results.

For as long as we know anything about the Bushmen, beads made from this material have been used for adornment, both personal and for some of their smaller and more treasured possessions. They are still made for personal use today but probably greater numbers are made for sale to tourists, where this is possible. Indeed so great has been the demand, that the Botswana Government has placed a ban, applicable to all its citizens, on taking ostrich eggs for this purpose.

In December 1983 I had the privilege of joining Alec Campbell, curator of the National Musuem, at an archaeological dig on the east side of the Female hill. Alec, who has spent more years than he may care to remember in Botswana, first served with the colonial administration and after independence became a citizen of the new country. His interests are extraordinarily catholic and he probably knows more about Botswana then any other man. This was his sixteenth visit to the Hills. He had conducted several previous digs, one of which was at the same site at which we were to work that December.

The east side of Tsodilo hills is deeply banked with long trailing ridges of sand. Here, in the wind shadow of the hills, the sand had accumulated in deep drifts. According to Alec's earlier research, beneath the shelter of an overhanging rock in this vicinity early man had been living. There is much excitement and fascination in this physical side of archaeology. A square metre on the ground is marked out with pegs and string. Layers of soil, 10 cm at a time, are carefully removed and sieved. My two teenage sons, a friend named Elizabeth, and I joined in. It was tiring and dirty work – but wonderfully exhilarating. Amid clouds of fine black dust that clung to our sweat-sodden bodies, the sieves were gently rocked and the remnants carefully scrutinised. Anything, however small, can be important. Hour after hour the work went on; the sieves were filled, rocked, checked, emptied, filled . . .

Interest began to wane with the rising temperature, but excitement returned to us all when Andrew found an arrowhead, and later Jeremy found ostrich egg-shell beads. The digging continued, down past 10 000 years ago. The boys' sharp eyes missed little. Excavation continued for a further five days, stopping at about 35 000 years ago. Man was not using the cave then but he had been for most of that period.

Almost exclusively during that time the occupants had been Stone Age people, most probably Bushmen. Going back in time for such a relatively short period, we could only hope to find Late Stone Age

tools and there were plenty of these. What exquisitely worked gems of craftsmanship they can be. Andrew found a small crescent scraper which looked as if it had been cut from rose-coloured quartz. It was sharp and crisp and seemed only to have been made the day before. Its length was no more than the width of a finger-nail and from front to back it was half that distance. Yet, small as it was, it had been finely worked. Each side of the cutting edge showed where ten or fifteen minute flakes had been removed to leave a sharp, straight blade. It was truly a work of art.

At another time and place Alec had shown me how to recognise the signs of old and long forgotten village sites. During a break from digging at Tsodilo he took us all on one of many walks, this time around the small valleys and plateaux that abound on the Female hill. The sun was low, the ideal angle for highlighting objects on the ground. Bringing up the rear, I saw a small piece of pottery but had passed it by before I registered what it was. I slowed, looked more carefully and found another piece. Without looking up, I shouted to Alec, 'I think we have a village site here!' and carried on looking. My excitement mounted at the prospect of making a major archaeological discovery. If only I could find a burrow where some animal, making a home for itself, had turned the deeper levels of soil for me. And yes, there it was! On my knees I scrabbled through the soil, yelling again to the group ahead to come and share this discovery. More pottery! A find. A real find! I leapt up in excitement and shouted to Alec. He and the rest of the party were nowhere in sight. I was stunned. They must have heard me, I thought. How could they have ignored me? I caught up with them, angry and hurt that my major discovery should be treated in so cavalier a fashion, only to find them barely able to contain their laughter. It transpired that Alec had spent several years excavating this very site. He had told the others, who thought my excitement a huge joke. At least I had the satisfaction of finding it on my own!

The site in fact was of the Early Iron Age and carbon dating suggests occupation from AD 840 to AD 1200. Prior to that discovery, it had been thought that occupation of Tsodilo Hills by Bantu was sporadic but this site showed continuous settlement for 300 to 400 years. Among the objects found were iron ore slag, fragments of copper and iron and remains of cattle. These finds suggest a Bantu Iron Age people, but who they might have been remains a mystery. Patterns on fragments of pottery and the shape of the vessels themselves provided further evidence of Bantu origins. Typically, the pots had thickened rims decorated with incised or stamped hatching. In addition some had cross-hatched patterns with bands of horizontal and oblique comb-stamping around the shoulder of the pots. Of particular interest was the fact that collections were made of small stone tools characteristic of the Late Stone Age people. This afforded clear evidence of the continued existence of Stone Age man to fairly modern times and, further, that there may have been social interaction between them and the newly arrived Bantu pastoralists.[1]

In a later excavation at a different site in the hills, during the first months of 1985, Alec found evidence of even earlier Bantu occupation, dating from about AD 500. Among the findings were remains of sheep and goats, sea shells, copper and iron. The implication of these finds is far-reaching because it carries the suggestion that these early Bantu were without cattle in AD 500 and that, as shown by the shells, they were trading, at least indirectly, with the coast. The absence of stone tools at this later site – at a time when it is known that Stone Age San (Bushmen) were living in the area – suggests a degree of separateness in their existence. It seems that considerable time was to pass until Bantu and Stone Age man came to share the same hearths, when stone tools of one and cattle remains of the other were to be discarded on the same site.[2]

On another occasion Alec led us on a 'short' nine-hour walk of the hills. In the course of his work for the Museum he compiled a catalogue of the rock paintings at Tsodilo. Systematic surveys have revealed in excess of 2 750 individual paintings, on more than 200 separate sites.[3] The range of style and subject is wide and varies from simple geometric designs, to groups of people and animals. There are silhouettes of animals in natural poses, as well as simple outline drawings of them. The animals most commonly chosen as subjects include eland, rhinoceros, giraffe, gemsbok, zebra and unidentified antelope. Often the artists sign their work; many paintings bear the imprint of a tiny childlike hand, soaked in paint and pressed against the rock. It has been suggested that these handprints are not so much a signature but part of the picture itself. Successive prints are intended to show how the hunter approached his prey on hands and knees. The closest handprint shows the point from which the fatal arrow was fired.[4] There are twelve separate sites where cattle are depicted and this is interesting because it suggests that the artists were acquainted with cattle long before the Hambukushu came to live in the area. There are also important archaeological implications in this fact which will be examined in a later chapter.

The quality of the paintings varies almost as much as the subject matter but some of them are outstanding. I have seen rock art throughout the length and breadth of Southern Africa - in Zimbabwe, Botswana, Namibia, Lesotho and South Africa – and I believe that the best paintings at Tsodilo compare favourably with the best anywhere. High up in the caves of Natal's Drakensberg Mountains there are breathtaking paintings of eland, the artists using subtle shades of blue and grey merging with dark red ochres in a startling depiction that glows with life and movement. But Tsodilo too can boast just such impressive work.

My favourite is a rhino family scene. As you pass between the Male and Female hills you will see a cave on the north side of the road. From it, a faint track leads away, around the corner and into the valley behind. After a kilometre or two it takes you to a low wall of rock. There in front of you stand two adult rhinos with a calf. The outline is in red ochre but, if you look carefully, you will see that the animals have been blanked out in white. The line is exquisite and captures precisely the form and movement of the animals. Their long horns reach up, following the shape of the rock on which they are painted so that an effect of harmony between beast and background is created, reflecting perhaps the harmony that the artist himself shared with these animals and their environment.

Alec, somewhat irreverently perhaps, calls this the Valley of the Dancing Penises, but not without good cause, and a twinkle in his eye. On the other side of the valley is a panel of more than fifteen male figures. Each has an erect or semi-erect penis, through the end of which a short straight line is drawn. This represents a stick and is a practice anthropologists call infibulation. It has to do with sex taboos and initiation but I have not found much written about it and cannot explain why it is done. It looks painful, though, and if it is intended as a temporary deterrent against sex, I am sure it would be extremely successful!

On the way to the rhino site, on the left-hand side of the path and not more than 100 or 200 m from the cave, is a large, upright boulder. There are two paintings on this rock which always attract my eye, one for no other reason than the fact that it is a wonderful caricature of that successful cartoon creature, the Pink Panther, and the second because I find difficulty in persuading myself that it is anything other than a whale. I know it's not a whale, because whales have never existed in the Kalahari but it still looks like one nevertheless. It is probably a fish and may date from wetter times gone by, when the Okavango was larger than it is today and flowing water was much closer to the hills.

Interpreting rock paintings is very difficult. As David Lewis-Williams[5] has recently shown, to do so without a thorough knowledge of the culture, customs and mythology of the artist people, is to do nothing more than dabble in a pointless guessing game that has no serious value at all. This is apparently so because many of the paintings are not created for painting's sake alone. Most have spiritual, religious or mythological connotations which confound simplistic explanations.

Dating rock paintings has also proved to be extremely difficult. There are a number of ways in which this can be done, and all of them have serious drawbacks.[6] Stylistic changes have been relied upon in the past but this method is often subjective and not easily recognised by other researchers.

One painting superimposed upon another may tell you which came first, but not by how long. Similarly, judging age by wear and degree of fading is not reliable because of the many variables involved – the paints used, the type of rock, the degree of exposure to the elements and climatic variations in that particular locality. All can affect how old a painting may appear.

The subject matter of the picture itself does reveal some clues as to age but without yielding a precise date – e.g. men on horses, scenes with cattle or sheep, or paintings of extinct animals. One method employing counts of decaying amino acids has been developed but this has not taken on and there remains a lack of confidence in its accuracy. The most reliable and commonly used methods today are archaeological associations and radiocarbon dating. Using these methods, the oldest examples of rock painting in Southern Africa, from the Apollo II cave in Namibia, have been confidently dated at 26 000 years ago. The most recent were thought to have been executed about 100 years ago. While we have nothing dating back to the 33 000 years which has been established for Western European rock art, Southern African rock art seems to have existed very much longer than its European counterpart, continuing as it has to much more recent times. As to the age of Tsodilo's paintings, little can be said. The small handful depicting what are clearly cattle are unlikely to be older than the oldest traces of those animals found in the hills. This suggests that they were not painted before AD 700–900. For the remainder, we simply do not know how old they are: no date has been established for any painting. They are not likely to be less than 100 years of age, but no maximum age can be suggested.

The question of who painted Tsodilo's art also remains unanswered. Although we can guess it was Bushmen, we cannot be certain. The Hambukushu deny all responsibility while the Bushmen, also denying any knowledge of the original artists, attribute all the work to their god Gaoxa. The

Bushmen say that the animals represent his 'store' and claim that this god once used to keep these animals at Tsodilo. For proof of this they refer you to the hoofprints to be found in the rocks of Tsodilo.[7] They do admit to knowing of a recent ancestor who, they claim, painted some samples in a group containing crude designs. This is significant and may be true, as the paint used in this particular group is powdery and rubs off easily, suggesting that it may be of recent execution.

You will find numerous people in Africa who will tell you, in great detail, just what materials the Bushmen used to make up their paints. You will also find that the closer you get to the bars of civilisation, the more of these people you encounter. Generally speaking, they haven't the faintest idea of what they are talking about. In a recent and splendidly critical article Ione Rudner did much to explode the myths about Bushmen paints.[8] Happily for science, but unhappily for those who need answers, Rudner manages to show that there is no certainty at all about what was used. Through careful and methodical research she has been able to demonstrate that much of what is regarded as 'fact' concerning Bushman paints owes its status to repetition, by one author after another, and that reliable primary sources as to what actually was used are very scarce indeed.

A long list of substances that may have been used includes various plant and animal fats, urine, blood, bile, water, milk, eggs, dung, plant sap, gum, honey, saliva, salt, beeswax, and gelatine. Detailed research lends reliable support to only a few of these substances. Among them are water, animal and plant fats and possibly plant sap and juices which may have been mixed with various pigments. Despite widespread claims to the contrary, there is absolutely no evidence that blood was used as a paint, although it may have been mixed with other substances. The same is true of eggs, with both white and yolk being suggested as binding agents. There is, however, no evidence to support this claim. On the other hand, there is little doubt that the colouring agents used were predominantly earth pigments which included various iron oxides and minerals, clays and accessible

materials such as burnt bone, ash, earths and plant latex. Caches of iron ore and red ochre, as well as evidence of mining for different pigments, are widespread throughout Southern Africa and date back to the Middle Stone Age. So far as can be established, the paints were applied with bone splinters, sticks, brushes made of animal hair or feathers as demanded by the type of paint and the picture to be executed.

The majority of Tsodilo's paintings is found on the Female hill, predominantly along the western base and in the valleys that flow down to that side. To gain the most from a visit there, however, one should explore more widely. There are several springs on the Female, the locations of which are not generally known. I have been shown two of them and cannot help but feel that the permanent existence of so precious a commodity must have added to the attractiveness of these hills as a home for early man. There is no evidence that either the Hambukushu or the Bushmen associate these hills with magic or supernatural powers, yet there is a feeling that it should be so. Laurens van der Post, in his *Lost World of the Kalahari,* captured something of their spirit and there is no doubt, wandering through the valleys and plateaux, that one experiences a 'presence', almost as if antiquity personified is all about one.

There are dramatic views of the Kalahari to be had from these hills. I once walked through them, and over ridges to the north of the Female, westwards to the point where the sheer sides drop to the endless sand. Eventually, I came to a place where a great, grey reach of rock stretched up at an angle to the skyline. It was easy walking but the rock had been worn to weird and grotesque shapes by aeons of elemental assault. Against a sombre background of grey and black lichen glowed more colourful varieties in bright orange, red and yellow. Suddenly, I was at the top and all the Kalahari seemed to lie at my feet.

The rock fell vertically for 60 m to a scree slope that tumbled to the plain below. I was at once struck by the absence of sand dunes in the immediate vicinity of the hill, and soon noticed that the nearest portion of the plain was particularly flat and featureless. It has been suggested that this was once a shallow lake, some 5 km$^2$ in extent, that was filled by run-off from the hills.[9] If you walk out upon it you will see that beneath a thin covering of soil there is a hard layer of white powdery rock called calcrete. This rock contains the skeletons of gastropods – small, hard-shelled creatures, possibly aquatic – that have yet to be identified. The fact that there are no sand dunes across this old pan must mean that it existed after the dunes were formed. The possibilities for further discovery are exciting, but no additional work is being done here as yet, so for the moment the theory remains unproven. Beyond the further shores of this one-time lake the dunes begin again. Row upon row of crest and trough follow each other in endless succession, away to the horizon and beyond.

A faint, narrow track follows a natural fault-line down the cliff and zig-zags to the highest point of the scree slope. There, at the base of the rock wall but still some 20 m above the plain, is a most extraordinary spring. There is an arch-like opening into the cliff, the back of which curves down to enclose, at a level just below that on which you stand, a circular pool of water. Alec says that in all his many visits to these hills he has never found this well dry; the local Bushmen confirm this. Alec has tried to gauge its depth but the space is small and confined and it is difficult to manoeuvre within it; there is no certain answer.

At a number of places in the natural caves and grottoes of these hills you will come across large slabs of stone with a curious pattern of holes in them. No one has been able to explain their significance and yet an explanation seems necessary. All who see them agree that they cannot be natural and must, therefore, have been made by man. Of the two that I have seen, both are almost vertical, with the patterns on one side. One is of living rock, part of the structure of the hill, the other, although large, could have fallen and might, at some other time, have been in a different position. Each has somewhere between 40 and 60 shallow depressions in it. They are circular, smooth, of different sizes and vary between 2 and 5 cm in width. None is more than 2 cm deep. What could they have possibly

been used for? Cracking hard nuts (which abound in the area and formed a large part of the Bushman's staple diet), counting, some obscure game? One suggestion is that they are musical instruments and that the holes are marks where a striking implement was used to produce notes from the hollow-sounding rock, but I was not able to test this.

There are at least two animal curiosities at Tsodilo. One is a small brown gecko, a nocturnal climbing member of the lizard family, which has the singular distinction of occurring nowhere else in the world other than within the limited range of these four hills.[10] Since it requires an expert to tell it apart from all the other geckos, which are plentiful, I cannot help you find him, but one can at least give thought to the extraordinary events that must have led to this remarkable occurrence.

The other fascinating creatures are equally difficult to identify and lack the distinguishing uniqueness of the gecko. However, this does not detract from their interest. They are small aquatic creatures called fairy shrimps, large enough to see easily with the naked eye, and they live in the rain-filled rock-pools of the hills.[11] Members of this genus occur all over the world and are found in the Kalahari wherever there are rocks. That they are able to surmount the incredible difficulties this mode of life presents, is a tribute to the amazing inventiveness of nature.

Fairy shrimps are filter feeders which live on the detritus that accumulates in their pools. One of the fascinating things about these tiny creatures is that they do not live anywhere else but in ephemeral rock pools. Of course, such pools will remain dry for long periods of time – possibly years – and even in the rainy season they may dry out between showers. Yet all this the fairy shrimp can survive. The eggs will not hatch until they have been exposed to the atmosphere and then soaked by water again. This ensures that the current year's eggs will not hatch too soon or, if they do, it will only be after the pool has dried out and will need repopulating. Furthermore, the eggs can survive in the mud at the bottom of a pool for at least six years and can withstand temperatures ranging from 0 °C to 104 °C. The egg contains a kind of built-in oxygen sensing mechanism: if the oxygen level in the water is for some reason too low (below about 1 ppm), hatching is inhibited. It is thought that the distribution of these creatures comes about through the eggs adhering to the feet of waders or by passing through the intestines of birds.

There is another creature whose way of life is very similar to that of the fairy shrimp. This is the dipteran fly, a non-biting midge found widely in Africa, including the Kalahari.[12] The larvae are born and bred in tropical rain pools in exactly the same way as the fairy shrimp. There are several different species of this midge and their larvae are specific to different kinds of pools. For example, the larvae of one kind have physiological adaptations to survive desiccation and therefore are found only in pools of less than one week's duration. Larvae of another, which lack this ability, are only found in larger pools! Never are the two found in the same pools and more research is needed to tell us why. The fact that larvae can survive desiccation at all is in itself remarkable. It is usually the egg that has this attribute; for a living creature to have it is most unusual indeed.

A visit to Tsodilo Hills is a fascinating adventure. There is a great deal there to see and do, much of which is new and as yet unexplored. At the same time there is an awareness that this is a unique and very special place. From the moment you first set eyes on it, it begins to become a part of you, and you will always experience the call to return when you feel a need for peace and tranquillity.

The limestone caves that were shown to Martinus Drotsky in 1932, and which now bear his name, are both extraordinarily beautiful and, from the outside, totally unprepossessing. If ever there were any chance travellers that way, and I doubt if there were many, they may be forgiven for having failed to find the caves, or even being unaware of their existence.

In a way that is unique to the Kalahari, where the beauty of the landscape is so often understated, the approach to Drotsky's Cave in west Ngamiland lulls the senses with its restful vistas and the gently swelling rise and fall of innumerable sand dunes. There is only one way to get there – in a sturdy four-wheel-drive vehicle and six solid hours of battling through deep sand, after the main road has been left behind. The first half of this section of the journey passes through an area that was once inundated by an Okavango Delta much larger than it is today. The track is sandy but through the mixed woodland the nature of the countryside can easily be seen. There are everywhere about you low, uncompleted sand dunes in a winding maze of shallow valleys, which are part of no particular pattern, connected sometimes with half completed ridges, sand bars and spurs. One is left with an impression of some vast body of water meandering without purpose across this featureless land, undecided as to what to do, and finally departing, leaving nothing but the evidence of its indecision.

According to A J Clement,[13] a Mr Craill was taken through this area in 1932 by Martinus Drotsky. He described it as 're-markable country, full of large springs and waterholes'. It is nothing like that today and it seems surprising that it could have changed so in such a short time. The answer has to do with the quantity and distribution of rain. In 1974, at the height of an exceptionally good rainy season, it was described in similar terms, for the pans that lie at the foot of the ridges and hummocks were full of water. Unfortunately, the water remains for only a few short weeks and then is gone. About halfway to the cave the landscape changes abruptly and you find yourself in massive dune country.

No one can tell for certain when these dunes were laid down. The most educated guess puts it within the last 2 million years. These are some of the Kalahari's biggest sand dunes and although they are now covered with vegetation, with grass and trees, and are hard to discern as separate entities, they are big enough to be clearly visible on aerial photographs. They appear as long, black, parallel lines on Landsat imagery, and stretch across this part of the Kalahari far in towards the heart of Namibia.

At one point, towards the end of the

journey, you will cross a particularly high dune and there before you over to the west in the hazy-blue distance, you can see the Aha Hills, which straddle Botswana's border with Namibia. In front lies the valley of the Kwihabe River. 'Valley' is a kind word in the circumstances; whilst it certainly has the shape of one, and an enormous one at that, it is unlikely to have seen a great deal of water in recent times. This is not a high rainfall area, and such rain as does fall soaks into the sand; only the heaviest of thunderstorms might generate any run-off.

The track leads into the valley and follows the river downstream for nearly 30 km. The valley floor is filled with compacted sand and clay, and supports dense thorn-scrub vegetation. On either side the valley walls climb gently to distant crests and one can appreciate how big this river must once have been. If you are watching carefully you might notice a sudden change in the level of the river. The slope increases slightly and in front of you, standing no more than 30 m above the river bed, are two low ridges of sand-covered rock. You have arrived at Drotsky's Cave.

In the immediate vicinity there are six of these low rises, which are composed of dolomite marble and are distributed in close proximity to one another in the Kwihabe valley. Dolomite is a sedimentary rock and, in the case of Drotsky's, of immense age, between 800 and 1 000 million years old, and extremely thick, reaching down into the earth for nearly 2 km. The whole area is part of the Okavango fault system, itself an extension of the great East African Rift Valley. For this reason the rocks have been subjected to much faulting; in fact, the hills themselves owe their origins to it. The fracture zones and joints which were thus created facilitated the penetration of water and the consequent dissolution of the dolomite which formed the caves.

The great attraction of Drotsky's lies not only in the beauty of the formations inside it, but also in the fact that a large system of caves was dissolved out of solid rock by vast volumes of flowing water in a place where, today, flowing water is not found at all. It is even more interesting to learn that the climate has been through such extreme variations that there have been times when

the cave has been flooded, and times when wind-driven sand from a surrounding desert environment has poured in.

From a tourist point of view, the area is totally undeveloped and is exceedingly remote; there is no water and there are no shops or people about. To many this is one of its greatest attractions. The visitor is obliged to be cautious and not to take ill-considered risks, particularly in the caves themselves. Inside it is totally dark and, whilst it is unlikely that you would remain forever lost should you lose your way, accidents can and do happen and there is no outside assistance to call on.

During one visit to Drotsky's I spent many hours alone (except for my little dog Gypsey) in the total darkness, taking photographs with the aid of flash equipment. At one stage I was in a section of the central cavern, had chosen a subject by torchlight, arranged the various flash units and had walked back to the tripod on which the camera was standing to make final adjustments. It was then that I made a silly mistake. Being ready to fire the camera, I leaned over, put the torch down on the ground, and switched it off. Accidentally, my foot caught the tripod, sending it flying. I lunged after it, caught it in time to prevent the precious camera from plunging into the dust, and set it upright again. I reached down for the torch. It was not there! In snatching for the falling camera, I had changed position and was now disorientated. I had no idea where the torch was, nor did I know how to reach the entrance, nor even the direction in which it lay. I was quite helpless, in total darkness.

I had once been trained in the use of aqualungs and searching pitch-black waters. Now the lessons came racing back. Don't panic. Think. I tried to relax. Clearly the torch was somewhere nearby and what was needed was a systematic search. Whatever happened, I must not lose contact with my starting point. Before, when I'd had to do this, there had always been plenty of rope. Now I had nothing. I took off all my clothes and using the firmly anchored tripod as a base, laid them out in a long line from it. On hands and knees I carefully searched an area in front of the line, working from the base out. On the return journey I moved the clothes forward, trying to allow for the diminishing radius of the circle. After fifteen minutes, I found the torch. Never have I been so glad to find something!

Gypsey thought the whole episode was a fine game but I learnt a lucky lesson. Never again did I go into those caves without a second emergency light source, usually a box of matches tucked into my pants.

There are two entrances to Drotsky's and the different systems to which they give access are interconnected. The cave is on two levels, one at the level of the present valley bottom, the other about 12 m above this. There is only one connecting passage. Both entrances occur where the roof of a large cavern has collapsed. Both are boulder-strewn slopes to a flat cavern floor with a low rock roof above your head. Near the entrances sand has accumulated but, as you penetrate further, this material changes to deep beds of bat guano. It is dry, powdery and immensely dusty. The air is fresh and the temperature comfortable. I first visited the caves in the company of Professor John Cooke from the University of Botswana, a man who probably knows as much about Drotsky's as there is to know. Measurements we took together show that the temperature moves hardly at all from a constant 27 °C.

A conspicuous feature at one of the entrances is a curtain of great pillar-like stalactites. Not all of them reach the ground, their bases having been eroded away. Some are cracked through, the two portions slightly displaced. This is the result of ground movements and earthquakes in times gone by. Interestingly, some of the 'wounds' have healed over and are covered by a characteristic white deposit of carbonate. John calls this flowstone. Rainwater, passing through the root zone of plants, picks up biological carbon dioxide and, soaking through the rocks, becomes highly charged with bicarbonates, dissolved out of the material through which it has passed. The air of the cave evaporates the water and the carbon dioxide is lost, leaving the mineral carbonate behind in a new and solid form. Some of the flowstones in Drotsky's, mostly pure white in colour, are unimaginably beautiful. Among these

myriad columns, if disturbed, a host of bats will take flight, filling the air with the beat of their wings and a chorus of high-pitched squeaks. Generally, they will not hit you and they certainly don't attack. I'm convinced that the few collisions that do occur are mutually unpleasant.

Beyond the entrance lies a maze of passages. Most of these were carved by incredible volumes of flowing water that both eroded and dissolved the solid rock. This is quite clearly visible. The walls of the passages are smooth to the touch and the characteristic curves of rock worn by running water are everywhere to be seen. If you look closely, you will see exquisite abstract patterns etched in the stone, where its different chemical constituents have reacted variously to the slight acidity of the flowing water. The result is often a kaleidoscope of subtle colours that stuns the eye and pleases the senses. Some of the passages are huge, as much as 3 or 4 m wide and a good 8 to 10 m high. In some, awesome blocks of stone hang from the roof like gigantic keels, their bases well clear of the ground.

It is an experience to choose a comfortable place and sit down, without any light, quite alone. In some strange way, perhaps because it allows you to be doing things, a light seems to make a cave noisy. Switch it off and you can physically feel the silence. Soon you imagine that you can hear it, a peculiar buzzing in the ear that seems to have no source. You become aware of an uneasy discomfort in your eyes – they are unused to staring so and seeing nothing. Being alone, but safe, in a dark cave such as this, somehow brings you closer to it. You can feel that it's friendly and means you no harm.

I find it surprising that there is no evidence of man ever using this cave system as a dwelling place. It is certain that the Bushmen knew of it – indeed, it was a Bushman who showed it to Drotsky in the first place, but he said that his people did not live in it, and the facts support his claim.

According to Alec Campbell, early man in this part of Africa preferred not to make use of caves, the reason being, as explained by certain Bushmen, that in the warm climate, shelter is not necessary; rain is infrequent and when it does occur, sufficient protection can be found in the simple shelters that Bushmen make. In any dwelling place, dirt accumulates; if the place is a cave, it must be cleaned out. Outside a cave, one can simply move away or allow the rains to do the cleaning. Another good reason the Bushmen had for choosing not to live in caves was the many snakes which made the caves their home.

If man has not lived at Drotsky's, animals certainly have and there are several tales of exciting encounters there with leopard. When E J Wayland, then Director of Bechuanaland's Geological Survey, visited the cave in 1944, he and his companions noticed both leopard dung and spoor trailing across the fine dust surface of the cave. Believing that the creature had left, they ventured on, only to be more than a little concerned on their return journey, to find leopard pug marks on top of their own spoor! Whether there are leopards there today, however, is a matter of some speculation. I know of one that was seen in 1974 and there have been reports of more recent sightings. I should think that probably no more than a few hundred people have visited these caves in the last fifty years but the number is growing and will soon be sufficient to discourage the cats from continuing in residence.

There is no water in the cave – although in the rainy season I imagine there would be drips aplenty. Despite this, they contain a remarkable number of living things. If you lie on your stomach and closely examine the ground you will see that it is positively teeming with small creatures – those whose role it is to break down the products of life and death so that they may be recycled and used again. I don't know what they are but there seem to be many different species: tiny cricket-like creatures, several kinds of small beetle, some a bright red, worms, creatures resembling woodlice, and many more. I suppose that it is the constant activity of these life forms, in endlessly turning the ground, that must explain a curious phenomenon which has often puzzled me. It is impossible to walk through the caves without leaving footprints in the deep soft surface of the floor. And yet a day or so later, all these marks have vanished.

In many places within the cave you will come across flowstone formations that are breathtaking in their delicate form and simplicity of shape. The 'frozen waterfall' is a common feature but well worth a close look. Under artificial illumination, the infinite number of crystals of which it is made up reflect the light, each in a slightly different way, some like prisms. The effect is magical. The whole structure glows and radiates an aura of light, diffused across which are subtle suggestions of rainbow colours. Often, as the mineral-laden water drips slowly over the stone, long icicle-like projections form. These become fluted and some, for reasons far beyond our ken, have rotated slightly as they grew slowly downward.

There is one place in the cave which John Cooke, not without excellent reason, calls 'Dante's Inferno'. It must be the least pleasant place in Drotsky's, but I'm glad, at John's urging, that I went there all the same. Maybe one day I'll have the pleasure of directing someone else to that horrid pit! From the massive central cavern, deep in the bowels of the cave there is a short, vertical tunnel of 3 or 4 m. It leads into the roof of a narrow passage, through which it is just possible to crawl. One side I have not explored but the other leads down at a steep angle and, by means of a most uncomfortable U-shaped dip, passes underneath a ridge of rock via a hole barely large enough to accommodate my sizeable frame. Negotiating this obstacle with armfuls of camera gear was bad enough, but there was another factor which made the task ten times more difficult. I did not know it at the time, but on the other side of the dip the passage opened out into a completely enclosed chamber which was the roost of countless bats.

The situation is not hard to imagine. I was about to violate the home of these creatures who, understandably, were more than a little agitated at the prospect. Many thousands of them decided to leave. However, there was only one exit and I was completely blocking it. I spent some seconds, while bats bounced off my body, thinking of unpleasant things to do and say to John! Once inside the cavern, however, the panic subsided – in both the bats and myself – and it was possible to look around.

The enclosed area was roughly circular and some 10 m in diameter. Every available space accommodated bats. They were on the walls, the ceiling, everywhere, scuttling across the rock like crabs. It was repulsive. Alone in this very deepest part of the cave, it was also frightening. There were at least two varieties of bat, one of which I was later able to identify as Commerson's leaf-nosed bat. Highly adapted for echo location, this animal, in common with many bats, does not always use this facility. In fact it is now well known that bats often rely on memory to fly familiar areas. My penetration of their long dark access tunnel while so many were trying to escape, caused not a few navigation errors.

Inevitably, bats die, and many had done so here. The ground beneath my feet crunched with the countless skeletons that lay upon it. Some of the carcasses were fresh and each was attended by a hoard of insects, busily devouring it.

Dr Reay Smithers, of the Transvaal Museum, is an authority on bats. He has visited this cave on many occasions and acknowledges that much research is still to be done. It is not known for certain which species are to be found in Drotsky's, nor why some should occur only in one part of the cave and others elsewhere. There is another mystery about these bats. Their presence has been recorded here every month except June. In that month, so some reports claim, the caves are empty of the creatures,[14] although others, notably Professor Cooke, have been at the caves in June and have noticed neither an absence nor a reduction in number of bats. If they are absent in June, we do not know why, nor do we know where so many bats might go to.

After years of study, the story of Drotsky's Cave has been partly pieced together by John Cooke, and it makes a fascinating tale. I say partly because, initially, John's work had been within the range of radiocarbon dating which, at its maximum, can only be used to a little over 50 000 years ago. Events before those times are largely a matter for conjecture and some intelligent guesswork. So far as John has been able to

establish, however, the sequence of events was something like the following.[15]

At some stage in the long distant past, the Kwihabe Hills were pushed up, above the level of the ancient surface, by faulting. In a very wet climatic phase the early Kwihabe River flowed strongly, perhaps 25 to 30 m above the present valley bottom. At the same time the water-table would have been correspondingly higher. In this way the higher level passages and caverns were dissolved out of the dolomite. Gradually, the river would have cut down through the bar of rock that initially blocked its course. The water-table in the immediate vicinity would also have fallen, following the river downwards. So it happened that the lower portion of Drotsky's was formed, being for the first time exposed to the relatively more acid waters that are found closest to the surface of a water-table. In the meantime, the caverns above were left dry. However, in order for the Kwihabe to flow so strongly, there must have been a much higher rainfall at that time. It was this copious rain which, soaking through the ground, dissolved part of the rock below and, heavy with its load of minerals, dripped down into the inner empty spaces, depositing on the floors and walls, as it evaporated, the magnificent stalactites, flowstones and, occasionally, stalagmites, some of which can be seen today. John has called these older features Sinter II.

A drier time followed. The caves dried out and quantities of sand entered through crevices and small openings. The climate alternated between wet and dry, and possibly more sinter was deposited in the cave, but generally the trend seems to have been towards increasing aridity. The Kwihabe ceased to flow, the valley was gradually filled in and the climate became drier still. True desert conditions prevailed. The low Kwihabe Hills, and the valley that passes through them, might well have been all but filled in under millions of tonnes of sand during this period of time. Some sand entered the cave, but very little, as the main entrances had not yet been opened up. It is thought that during this period more faulting took place and the blocks of dolomite were lifted vertically. How long this period

A massive rock hanging from the roof in Drotsky's Cave

Storm-cast sunset at Baines' baobabs, near Nxai Pan

A victim of the drought at Lake Ngami

of intense aridity lasted we don't know but all cave-forming processes ceased. Practically sealed from the outside world, it remained lifeless, silent as a grave, while the millennia ticked slowly past.

Somewhere about 17 000 years ago the climate changed again and a major wet period followed, so wet, indeed, that the Kwihabe began to flow again, cutting down to, and through, its old course, following in places the new fault-lines. At first the water-table was high because the valley had been filled in. The original caves were flooded again and there was extensive enlargement. Some of the old sinters were removed by the flowing water. Gradually, however, as the river cut down through the debris of ages to reach the original valley floor, the water-table fell, leaving dry first the upper and then the lower system of caves. Conditions, however, remained wet with the rainfall high. Consequently, new sinter (Sinter III) was deposited throughout the caves, often over the old.

This very wet phase lasted from about 16 000 to 13 000 years ago when, once more, the climate began to dry. At some stage in the next 10 000 years there was yet another period of faulting, and this time the effects were dramatic. The sides of two large caverns collapsed, creating the two entrances that we see today. At the same time the floor of the largest, central chamber collapsed into the passages below it.

Once more the wet conditions returned, about 4 500 years ago. Much of the dune area to the east of Drotsky's reaching as far as the edge of the present-day Okavango Delta, was flooded, suggesting that that river itself had been greatly increased in size. The last period of fault activity – the one which had caused the entrances to appear – had trended along a NE-SW line and it was against this line that the spreading waters of the enlarged Okavango had been halted, some 20 km from the caves. So wet was it during this brief interval, that there was partial erosion of Sinter III in some places, while in others Sinter IV was being deposited.

Inevitably a drier climate returned, alternating, more than ever before, with a wet period, the wettest being between 1 500 and 2 000 years ago. It was at this time that the last of Drotsky's flowstones (Sinter IV) were deposited.

The remarkable history and evolution of this cave that John Cooke has been able to piece together is not only a tribute to his own skills and enthusiasm; it also demonstrates what careful observation, backed by sound technical know-how, can achieve. Thankfully, perhaps, we are a long way from knowing all the answers about our past, but it is an exciting journey and the strides that we have made are as fascinating as the new knowledge we gain.

Some 50 km by road, but within clear sight of Drotsky's Cave, are the Aha Hills. Straddling the border with Namibia, these hills consist almost entirely of limestone, dolomite and marble of exactly the same formation as that at Drotsky's, and are of similar age. They form a low plateau about 245 km$^2$ in extent.

Throughout the area of Kalahari sands lives a species of gecko which, because of the call it makes, is called the barking gecko. This delightful little character, of whom you will read more elsewhere, serenades his mate and vigorously defends his territory in the early evening of the summer months. The Bushmen have called these hills after their onomatopoeic name for this creature, and it is said our English version is a corruption of this name.[16]

The Aha Hills are of interest not only because of their exceeding remoteness but because, being similar in structure to Drotsky's Cave, it is believed that there may exist within them caves of a similar nature. Such exploration as has taken place[17] has shown the existence of two sink-holes, about 15 km apart but apparently unrelated to each other. Both holes are vertical and dangerous. One is about 55 m deep although the bottom has not yet been reached. The other is about 35 m deep. So far no large cavernous systems have been found. The hills remain an example of the many places and features of the Kalahari which are still relatively unknown, have interesting potential for discovery and await exploration.

**REFERENCES**

1. **Denbow, J R.** 'Early Iron Age Remains from the Tsodilo Hills, North-Western Botswana'. In *South African Journal of Science*, Vol 76, No 10, October 1980, **pp 474-75**

2. **Campbell, A C.** Personal communication, March 1986

3. **Campbell, A C, Hitchcock, R and Bryan, M.** 'Rock Art at Tsodilo'. In *South African Journal of Science*, Vol 76, No 10, October 1980, **pp 476-78**

4. **Rudner, I.** 'A Note on the Beliefs of Modern Bushmen Concerning Tsodilo Hills'. In Newsletter No 15, S.W.A. Scientific Society, 3/4 June/July 1974

5. **Lewis-Williams, J D.** 'Science and Rock Art'. In *New Approaches to Southern African Rock Art*. The South African Archaeological Society, Goodwin Series, Vol 4, 1983, **pp 3-13**

6. **Thackery, A I.** 'Dating the Rock Art of Southern Africa'. In *New Approaches to Southern African Rock Art*. The South African Archaeological Society, Goodwin Series, Vol 4, 1983, **pp 21-6**

7. **Rudner, I.** Op cit

8. **Rudner, I.** 'Paints of the Khoisan Rock Artists'. In *New Approaches to Southern African Rock Art*. The South African Archaeological Society, Goodwin Series, Vol 4, 1983, **pp 14-20**

9. **Grove, A T.** 'Landforms and Climatic Change in the Kalahari and Ngamiland'. In *The Geographic Journal*, Vol 135, 1969, **p 203**

10. **Haacke, W D.** 'A New Gecko (*Sauria geckonidae*) from Bechuanaland'. In *Arnoldia*, Vol 2, No 25, 21 July 1966, **pp 1-5**

11. **Hartland-Rowe, R.** 'The Limnology of Temporary Waters and the Ecology of Euphyllopoda'. In *Essays in Hydrobiology*. Edited by Clark, R B and Wooton, R J, University of Exeter, 1972, **pp 15-30**

12. **Cantrell, M A and McLachlan, A J.** 'Habitat Duration and Dipteran Larvae in Tropical Rain Pools'. In *Oikos*, Vol 38, Copenhagen, 1982, **pp 343-8**

13. **Clement, A J.** *The Kalahari and its Lost City.* Cape Town: Longmans, 1967, **p 13**

14. **Smithers, R H N.** Personal communication, February 1985

15. **Cooke, H J.** 'The Palaeoclimatic Significance of Caves and Adjacent Landforms in Western Ngamiland, Botswana'. In *The Geographical Journal*, Vol 141, 1973, **pp 430-44**

16. **Condy, J B.** Personal communication, June 1985

17. **Cooke, H J.** 'The Caves of Ngamiland: An Interim Report on Explorations and Fieldwork 1972-74'. In *Botswana Notes and Records*, Vol 6, **pp 147-56**

# 5. The Kalahari Today

WHAT is the Kalahari and what makes it so different that it deserves a special title of its own? Is it a desert, as it is sometimes called? Simple questions, perhaps, but difficult ones to answer as definitions depend very much on what the person who gives them has in mind. When asked 'What is the Kalahari?', a geologist will offer a very different answer to that of a climatologist or an ecologist. A layman might point vaguely to the map and indicate the western two-thirds of Botswana. It may be as well to spend a moment or two understanding why this confusion arises.

Geologists recognise Kalahari sand by the grades of grain sizes, by the material from which the sand originated, and especially by the tendency of the grains to conform to the rounded shape attributable to their wind-blown, or aeolian, origins. As we have seen, distribution of these aeolian sands in Southern Africa was once very widespread indeed. However, over the enormous span of time that has passed climatic changes, increases in rainfall and the flow of rivers and streams have all combined to remove most of that sand, which now lies beneath the waters of the surrounding oceans on the continental shelf. Within the great internal drainage basins of the continent, however, the sand was not removed. With its distinctive profile of size, coarseness, origins and aeolian characteristics, it remains through vast tracts of country and today is called Kalahari sand. If this sand was used as a criterion for definition, the Kalahari would extend from South Africa's northern Cape through to Zaire.

Some people think of the Kalahari as a desert. Geographers have a number of definitions of deserts. A friend of mine, working on a research project, listed 146 different ones! Generally, rainfall is the criterion and, according to one of those definitions, an extremely arid area is one which receives less than an average 60-100 mm of rain a year.[1] No part of the area in central Botswana, which is sometimes referred to as the Kalahari Desert, receives as little rain as this and therefore does not qualify for the title. Indeed, so far as I have been able to establish, no part of the area covered by Kalahari sands receives less than this amount of rain. There is no such thing, therefore, as the Kalahari desert in the strict sense of the word.

There is, in the central part of middle and southern Africa, a gradient of rainfall such that the quantity of annual rain decreases the further south one moves. That this is so is in no way related to the fact that the ground happens to be covered with sand; it is a function of continental air masses, temperatures, altitude and the influence of the distant oceans. The effect of this distribution of rainfall is, however, quite dramatic. In a very general sense, one can say that the southern limits of Kalahari sand are the driest and receive the least rain and that, as one progresses further north, towards Zaire, the rainfall increases and approaches a level exceeding 1 000 mm a year. It is this fact that makes the area of the Kalahari sands such a wonderfully varied environment, ranging as it does from semi-arid conditions to near-tropical forests.

The closest one can find to true desert conditions is therefore the most southerly portions of the Kalahari sands and these include south-western Botswana, the northern Cape and south-eastern Namibia. Even in these areas, however, the rainfall is seldom less than 150 mm a year and, for this reason, it is more accurate to refer to the drier portions of the Kalahari sands as an arid area or a thirstland. I prefer the latter name because it conveys a more accurate impression of what the land is really like.

The Sahara is a true desert but the Sahel, the arid zone that surrounds the Sahara, is much more like the Kalahari, below about 20° south, in that both have summer rainfall and both receive between 150 mm and 500 mm of rain annually. There is, however, one important difference, and this relates to the rainfall distribution. In the Sahel, and in Sudan, rainfall in some months exceeds the amount of evaporation. In comparable parts of the Kalahari this is not so; the amount of water that is evaporated by the sun always, in every month of the year, exceeds the amount which is delivered by rain.[2] Surface water seldom remains for long under these conditions and it is for this reason that the Kalahari should be thought of as a thirstland.

If it is not a desert, then how did at least part of the Kalahari come to be called one? We should probably turn to history to seek the reason, and examine the impressions of those who first reported upon their ventures into the arid interior and who wrote of their encounters with the deep sand cover, absence of standing water and old, tree-covered sand dunes.

Generally speaking, the area of Kalahari sands exists at an altitude of about 1 000 m above sea level. Although there are many outcrops of rocks, characteristically the surface is sand, but it is not infertile and supports vegetation of a great variety. While it is true to say that the Kalahari is without many prominent features, it is not completely flat, as many think. On a small scale, looking in one's immediate vicinity it is possible to see that the surface is dimpled with shallow depressions and low rises. On a large scale, the Kalahari is divided and intersected by very significant ridges and river valleys. Some, like the Okavango, the Chobe and the Zambezi in the north, are massive, perennial rivers. Others, such as the Molopo, Auob and the Nossob, in the south, only carry water in years of exceptional rain. Still others are relics of a much wetter time and are called fossil rivers. The most impressive of these include Botswana's Okwa and Groot Laag-te, which have distinct valleys, over 1,5 km in width and sometimes as much as 40 m below the surface of the surrounding plain.

The Kalahari is enormously varied, particularly with regard to the vegetation. Nowhere is it devoid of vegetation, and only rarely are there naturally occurring naked dunes. Even in the drier south of the northern Cape, where trees are scarce but not entirely absent, grass and low, shrub-like plants crowd the sands. In southern Botswana and south-eastern Namibia tree-cover increases, as do a number of species of grass. The more arid-adapted shrubs become less common. Among the many beautiful sights in the Kalahari are the open parklands of tall acacia thorn trees, set in uncluttered vistas of tall, golden, end-of-season grass.

The grasses, where the balance has not been upset by man and his grazing practices, are mostly perennial. They have a high nutritional value and exist in great diversity and abundance – a fact that makes the inner reaches of the Kalahari ever more desirable to the would-be cattle rancher.

The distribution and species of trees and grass are not, of course, constant. There are vast areas which support little else but stunted and untidy trees and others which boast a rich diversity of plant life. As one progresses northwards towards more certain rain in greater quantities, the vegetation becomes more lush and varied. The time of year in which one sees it, too, has much to do with the impressions gained. All the Kalahari's vegetation is adapted to survive at least eight months without rain, not to mention several years of drought. To see it at the end of the dry season, when the leaves have fallen and a grey dust coats the stark, bare branches, and when the grass has withered to a powdered straw, is to see it at its very worst. It is worthwhile though, if only to experience the extraordinary contrast which the height of the wet season brings. Then, life bursts forth and shows itself in high, lush grass and trees decked in every shade of green. It happens so quickly that it is sometimes difficult to believe.

The climate of the Kalahari can be surprisingly extreme. Air temperatures of

42 °C are not unusual. The difference between open ground and tree-shaded temperatures, during the day, can be as much
as 30 °C. On a hot day the surface temperature can be as high as 70 °C, but below
the surface it rapidly falls and, at a point
2,5 cm below ground level, will already
have fallen by 10 °C. Throughout the year
there are, on average, more than eight

hours of sunshine a day but temperatures
can still drop to freezing or below in the
cold winter months of June-August.

In 1964 George 'Timber' Woodman,
who served in the Bechuanaland Police,
was married and took his new wife (brave
lady that she must have been) to his station
at Tsabong on honeymoon. George's birthday was on 8 July and in that year nature

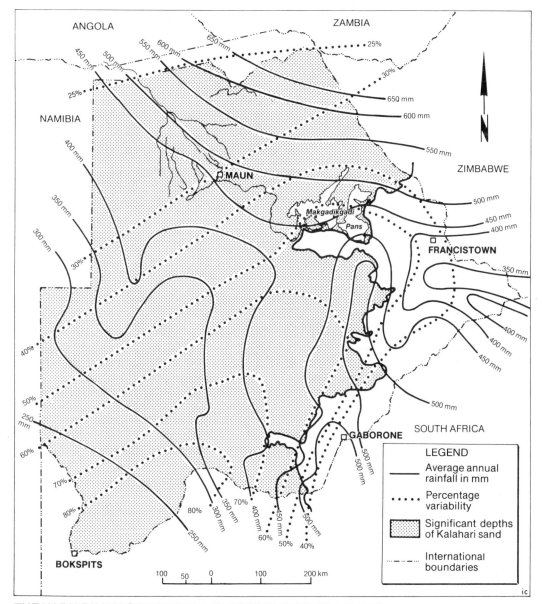

## THE VARIABILITY OF RAINFALL IN BOTSWANA'S KALAHARI

The already low rainfall decreases from north-east and east to south-west, while the degree of variability increases markedly the lower the rainfall.
**Source:** J.G. Pike, "Rainfall over Botswana," *Botswana Notes and Records, Special Edition Number 1: Proceedings of the Conference on Sustained Production from Semi-arid areas*, Gaborone, October 1971, p. 76

helped the couple celebrate this happy
double event of honeymoon and birthday,
by causing it to snow! I am told that Mrs
Woodman was not impressed! George relates that the snow was no more than a
light covering that lasted a few hours.
However, it was real enough and temperatures below —4 °C were not hurriedly
forgotten.[3] The animals and plant life of the
Kalahari must, therefore, adapt to living
with a temperature range of nearly 50 °C.
In the rainy season the extremes of temperature are not usually so great. This is
because the ground, soaked by the rain,
takes longer to heat up and the higher
temperatures, increased by heat radiating
from the ground, are not so common.

Water, of course, is the key to life in the
Kalahari. We have seen how the summer
rainfall varies from north to south. Generally, it falls between October and April but
the variation is great. Tsabong, a small
administrative centre in the south of Botswana, has an average of only 28 rain
days a year whilst Shakawe, 800 km to the
north, enjoys 51 rain days a year. Evaporation also varies a great deal. At Shakawe,
Tsabong and Maun it averages a little over
2,5 m a year but in Ghanzi, on the ridge in
western Botswana, evaporation rises to
over 3 m.[4] It is not just the fact of rain in the
Kalahari that is critical; how and where it
falls are equally, if not more, important.

We have already seen how the average
quantity of annual rain diminishes towards
the southern portion of the Kalahari. Interestingly, as the total amount of rain
diminishes, so the range of its variability
increases. Thus, in the vicinity of the
Okavango, for example, one might expect
approximately 500 mm of rain in a year,
with a seasonal variation of about 30 per
cent. This means that the actual rainfall
could be anywhere between 350 mm and
650 mm. At a place such as Bokspits, the
most southerly tip of Botswana, where the
average annual rainfall would be about
250 mm, the range is 80 per cent. Bokspits
can expect between 50 mm and 450 mm
in a year.[5]

Not only are there these enormous ranges
in rainfall quantity, but there are also wide
variations in the way and area in which it
falls. Widespread rain over the area of the

## TABLE 1

### RAINFALL AT THIRTEEN KALAHARI LOCALITIES DURING 1970

| Period | Tshane | Lephephe | Mabutsane | Mamono | All 13 |
|---|---|---|---|---|---|
| **Jan** | | | | | |
| 1st half | * | * | * | * | X |
| 2nd half | X | X | X | X | X |
| **Feb** | | | | | |
| 1st half | X | X | X | X | X |
| 2nd half | X | * | * | * | X |
| **March** | | | | | |
| 1st half | * | * | X | X | X |
| 2nd half | * | * | * | * | * |
| **April** | | | | | |
| 1st half | * | * | * | * | * |
| 2nd half | X | * | * | X | X |
| **May** | | | | | |
| 1st half | * | * | X | * | X |
| 2nd half | * | * | * | * | * |
| **June** | | | | | |
| 1st half | * | * | * | * | * |
| 2nd half | * | * | X | * | X |
| **July–Sept** | | | | | |
| 1st half | * | * | * | * | * |
| **Sept** | | | | | |
| 2nd half | * | * | * | * | X |
| **Oct** | | | | | |
| 1st half | * | X | * | * | X |
| 2nd half | * | * | * | * | * |
| **Nov** | | | | | |
| 1st half | X | X | X | * | X |
| 2nd half | X | * | X | * | X |
| **Dec** | | | | | |
| 1st half | * | X | * | * | X |
| 2nd half | X | X | X | X | X |
| **Total** | 7 | 6 | 8 | 5 | 14 |

10 mm of rain, or more, during a half monthly
period is marked X. Less than 10 mm is marked ★.
10 mm of rain is considered the least amount to
have an effect upon Kalahari vegetation.

The table shows the principle that chances of a
useful amount of rain falling somewhere in the
Kalahari during a season are much greater than
the chances of a useful amount of rain falling at
any one place.

Source: Parris, R. 'The Ecology and Behaviour of
Wildlife in the Kalahari'. In Botswana Notes and
Records, Special Edition, Number 1, Proceedings
of the Conference on Sustained Production from
Semi-Arid Areas. October, 1971, Gaborone, Bo-
tswana, p 103

Kalahari does occur but, generally, rainfall
is of a very local and patchy nature. It will
rain heavily in one area and not at all in
another just a few kilometres away. Very
often, instead of a gentle, penetrating fall,
the rain is delivered in violent, torrential
storms and has little opportunity to soak in

before draining away to the valleys and depressions.

With this type of rainfall pattern, often scarce, or over-abundant, patchy and unpredictable, one is prompted to ask how it is possible for the Kalahari's game to survive under these conditions. Richard Parris, formerly of Botswana's Department of Wildlife and National Parks, did some very interesting work on this question and showed how it was possible for animals to enjoy constant fresh grazing and a reasonable chance of standing surface water. As shown in Table 1, he recorded rainfalls higher than 10 mm at thirteen separate localities in the Kalahari over a period of a year. Whilst individually each recorded small and occasional quantities of rain, collectively considerable amounts fell over long periods of time. The implications of this are that if game is highly mobile and can detect where rain has fallen, it can move from one rainfall area to another and be assured of good supplies of food and water. Looking at the mammal populations of the Kalahari, it can be seen that those which are not specially adapted to the arid conditions are, in fact, exceptionally mobile. The best example is the wildebeest. Of all the Kalahari's ungulates, wildebeest are least well adapted to surviving without water. They range very widely and during the course of a year may cover as much as 400 or 500 km in search of water and grazing. (See map on p. 238.)

Anywhere in Africa the coming of the first rains in the year is an event that touches the soul. The smell of approaching rain must surely be one of Africa's most evocative smells and one never forgotten by those who have lived there. It is a magic scent – a mixture of moistened dust and dampened soil, as if Africa is releasing all the earth smells of her land in joyous celebration of the coming rain. Before a storm there is a tension in the air. It is not fear but excitement and every living thing appears to share it. The senses quicken and life seems to take on a new and sudden urgency.

After the first rain even the ground itself seems revitalised; it is softened and swells so that it is giving and resilient beneath the feet. It feels alive, as if the first touch of moisture has sent new blood coursing through its old veins and it stirs itself again to pour life back into the trees and plants.

It is incredible how rapidly life responds to the rain. Roadside puddles quickly form and, within days, these are swarming with life. The small black beetles, the water-boatmen, patrol just above the surface of the mud, hardly stirring it at all, and tadpoles soon appear in hordes. Even in the most unlikely places, far from permanent water, frogs will appear and sit by the puddle's edge to croak their evening chorus and search for food. Life in these little, short-lived ponds is necessarily frenzied. There is so little time to emerge, to kill and eat and to complete the purpose of life. In the fine mud at the bottom of these pools you will see the tracks of some foraging bird and, perhaps, the footprints of a small child, thrilling to the feel of warm mud squeezing between his naked toes.

There is often much talk, in Southern Africa, of how the climate is changing, how the rains keep failing and drought is becoming more common. This is not so, however much that may appear to be the case. Professor Tyson, of South Africa's University of the Witwatersrand, has given much time to a study of rainfall patterns in this part of Africa.[6] He has found that there are a number of distinct regional variation patterns in Southern Africa. Within each of these, characteristic and long-term fluctuations in rainfall amounts are discernible. One such pattern embraces the western Transvaal and much of the central and southern Kalahari. Professor Tyson's figures show that in this area there is a 16 to 20 year cycle of above and below average rainfall. His calculations show a distinct trend for approximately 10 years of below average rainfall and 10 years of rainfall well above average. Why this should be so is not known but, over the 80 years for which records are available, it has remained consistent. The model he constructed predicts the 1980s as being a decade of below average rains. It has proved quite correct.

When the rain comes, it does not always do so gently. Sometimes its arrival is accompanied by violent thunder and lightning. Surprisingly, in the Kalahari lightning accounts for as many as fifty to a hundred human deaths a year and more than a thousand head of livestock will be killed by it. In a recent survey carried out in Botswana 76 per cent of those interviewed stated their belief that lightning was supernatural and many of them mentioned a bird as a carrier or initiator of it.[7] It is easy to understand how unsophisticated, rural people, unable to comprehend the physics of lightning, attribute to it supernatural qualities and there is no dearth of tales to support these beliefs.

Early in June 1894 at Maritsane, on the eastern edge of the Kalahari, a party of trekkers was assembled, waiting permission to set out across the great thirstland to take possession of their promised farms at Ghanzi. On a clear day, with but a single cloud in the sky, the leader of the party returned to camp, having been away to purchase sheep. His wife, seeing him approach, ran to meet him. As they embraced a bolt of lightning struck and killed them both where they stood, locked in each other's arms. On a table at their tent door, quite close to them, their baby laughed and cried, unhurt. It was an unfortunate omen for what proved to be an unsuccessful venture.[8]

George Woodman will verify the story of the District Commissioner at Tsabong, in the southern Kalahari. It relates how, in the 1940s, he and his wife were relaxing in the lounge of their house, facing the empty fireplace. Apparently, lightning struck down the chimney and, in some way, was turned across the room, striking and killing the D.C. where he sat. These are the sort of incidents that make lightning difficult to explain, but neither of them equal a more recent incident in which the participants were, fortunately, blessed with far better luck.

It happened in 1973 at Maun, in Botswana, during the period between Christmas and New Year. Being a time of celebration, a number of Maun's business and hunting residents were doing their best to keep it so. Six or seven people were playing poker on the veranda of a house. It was pouring with rain. The veranda was netted, the roof leaked and the concrete floor was wet in places. The poker players sat along either side of a table which was arranged at right angles to the double, gauzed entrance doors, one of which was open. Suddenly an almighty clap of thunder rang out and, at the same time, a sizzling streak of lightning, running parallel to the floor, flashed down the length of the table, between the two stunned rows of blinded card players, struck the wall at the far end and appeared to return from whence it came.

For a moment no one spoke in the sulphurous air. As their wits and their sight returned, one of them broke the silence. When the lightning entered, he had been holding in his hand a glass full of 'Bloody Mary', with a metal teaspoon in it. He hadn't moved a fraction, only now the red fluid was pouring out through a neat hole in the side of the glass, the size of a cigarette stub. The hole was on the side of the glass furthest from the door! That event is still spoken of in Maun today and it serves continually to remind seven men just how lucky they were.[9]

That the area of the Kalahari was once much more arid than is now the case is obvious from the great dune systems that can still be seen today. Called fossil dunes, these vast dune fields pattern enormous tracts of southern and central Africa and, although sometimes difficult to see from the ground, they are clearly visible in aerial photographs and to astronauts circling the earth. All are now fixed in place by vegetation and their shapes change little or not at all, except in so much as infrequent rains may be gradually lowering their height. There are many, now separate, systems; whether they were originally parts of one large desert or whether they owe their origins to different times and events, cannot now be said. To add to the confusion there are what are referred to as 'islands' of Kalahari sand, unconnected to the main body of sand and often in remote and unexpected places, in Mozambique, for example, in the Transvaal and deep within Namibia.

Southern Botswana, the northern Cape and south-eastern Namibia share a common and extensive dune field. Western Zimbabwe and eastern Botswana share another, whilst a third is located in northwest Botswana and Namibia. There is a fossil dune system in the west of Zambia and this undoubtedly extends into Angola. Characteristically, the dunes are seldom more than 20 m high with crests about 1,5 km apart. Alab dunes, such as these, are formed parallel to the line of the prevailing wind, which apparently changed as it moved across the continent, as none of these different dune fields share the same alignment. The lengths of these parallel dune systems are considerable; many stretch for several hundred kilometres before merging again with the featureless sands about them.

Botswana's north-west dune system is considered to be the oldest of the sand features in that country. It was deposited by strong easterly winds which created long alab ridges. These dunes are now strongly degraded. The southern dune system, in which the dunes are smaller, is believed to be much younger and was created by northerly winds. Some researchers believe that these two separate systems may represent two or more generations of dune formation and are the product of two different wind regimes.

Two obvious questions regarding sand relate to its origins and age. Neither can be answered satisfactorily. The Kalahari is described by some as the largest continuous sand body in the world and one estimate places its extent at 2 million km$^2$.[10] A prevailing theory is that the sand has come from alluvial sources, which means that it was deposited initially by water and has since been re-worked by the wind and blown into the dune forms which at one time may have been as high as 60 m. This is substantiated by the work of Smit in 1977 who believes that the Kalahari sands can be divided into four stratigraphic units, only the top one of which is aeolian in character. This upper section, he claims, is rarely more than 20 m deep, there being more clay and gravel mixed with the sand as greater depths are approached.[11]

Questions regarding the age of Kalahari sands also remain unsatisfactorily answered. Many scientists have tried to solve the puzzle but there seem to be as many answers as there have been people trying to find them. Estimates of age range from as long ago as the late Cretaceous

(100 million years ago) to early Tertiary (60 mya), end Miocene (5 mya), Pliocene (between 2 and 5 mya) and some even date the sands as recently as the Pleistocene (1-2 mya). There is no way of ageing a grain of sand nor is there any way in which one can be certain that any sample of sand is necessarily representative of the whole Kalahari. Workers on Kalahari sands in Zaire arrived at three separate dates for three different series of Kalahari sands that lie in a vertical sequence. Those dates ranged from 100 million years down to 2 million years ago.[12]

A clue to the dating of one alab dune system is found in the area of the Okavango, where it can be shown the dune system occurred prior to the delta coming into existence. This is because the present delta truncates the old dune formations which must, therefore, have been there first.[13] This information is not, however, very helpful in establishing when the sand dunes were created. We do not know how much longer they were in existence before the delta was established, nor do we know when the delta itself was first formed, except that it was a relatively recent event, probably less than 15 million years ago.

The red sands of the Kalahari are widely regarded as being typical – but they are not. The sand grains are mostly of quartzite material and range in colour through red, pink, brown, white, grey and buff. The red colour comes from iron oxide which forms on the outer surface of the sand grain. In areas of higher rainfall the oxide is washed off by the rain and this may explain why it is that the redder sands are found in the southern parts of the Kalahari, where the rainfall is low, and the lighter colours more towards the north, where the rainfall is higher.

People often ask about the depths of sand in the Kalahari. This depends very largely upon which particular area is being examined, for the depths vary enormously. As a general rule, it seems that the sands get deeper as one moves westwards across the Kalahari. In the central and southern parts of Botswana, depths seldom exceed 100 m, whilst underneath the waters of the Okavango the sands may be deeper than 300 m. In many places the sand is very shallow, sometimes only a metre or so, sometimes 20 m.

In the southernmost reaches of the Kalahari sands, not far north of the Orange River in South Africa, there is a place called Witsands. Here the white sands display two quite remarkable and, for Southern Africa, unique properties. They rumble and thunder when walked upon, and large quantities of fresh water are found in depressions and hollows within the dunes.

The white sands occur in a small area of about 20 km$^2$ in the south-east corner of the Kalahari. They are set in a sea of red Kalahari sand, standing separate from and well above it, in dunes of 50 to 60 m high. How this can be so, is a mystery. Both the red and white sands are aeolian in origin and probably of Quaternary age, which means they are younger than 2 million years. The Witsands are coarser and this may have something to do with their sound-generating properties. The prevailing winds are from the north-west and west and the white sands have been piled irregularly into dunes against the base of the Langeberg Mountains.

The roaring sound, which is loud and is not dissimilar to the noise of a passing truck, seems to emanate from deep within the dune and is caused by the dryness and polished nature of the grains. In good conditions it can be heard over 500 m away. To cause the noise one has only to walk across the sand or to move it with your hand. If the sand is taken away in a bottle, and kept sufficiently dry, the noise will occur again every time the sand is tipped from one end to the other.

Complete absence of moisture is the first essential for the roaring sound to occur, hence it is not heard in the wetter months of the year, after rain. The roar has to do with the distribution of sand grain sizes, which is completely different from that of ordinary Kalahari sand. Scientists use special sieves, which have carefully measured holes, by means of which it is possible to sort various samples of sand into categories based on individual grain sizes. The roaring sands have the same percentage of coarse grains as Kalahari sand, but only one-sixth of the quantity of very fine material and nearly double the

amount of medium-size grains. The distribution of sand grain sizes is thus very different. Once this secret was discovered, early experimenters were able to produce the same roaring sounds from other, similar materials, the grains of which were sorted in approximately the same mix – they were able to produce an appropriate roar from common table salt, for example. The roaring quality is lost when moisture enters the sand, but it can be restored by heating the sand in an oven and driving off the water vapour.

It was once thought that electrical charges were responsible for creating the roaring noise but this theory was abandoned in favour of another. This is that air, in tiny quantities, is trapped by collapsing waves of falling sand, just as air is trapped beneath waves breaking on a sea shore. The noise is caused by a series of explosions as the trapped air escapes. These are some of the theories put forward to explain this curious phenomenon but most researchers freely acknowledge their uncertainty.[14]

Something similar to the roaring of the Witsands is reported from the Sahara desert and a village called Bilma. There, caravans loaded with cloth from Hausa would call in to trade and barter. If the caravan was a large one, the people of Bilma would have up to two days' warning of its approach, obtained by the sounds emitted by certain local sands. It seems that the caravan, passing in the vicinity of a neighbouring peak, crossed over sands which, on being disturbed, gave out a loud roaring sound. The hills, acting like a natural amplifier, broadcast the sound over great distances, giving the villagers their early warning of the caravan's approach.[15]

The other curious phenomenon associated with Witsands is the large quantity of fresh water found in the dunes. For many years farmers in the area have known of this. They simply scrape a shallow pit in the lowest parts of the inter-dune hollows to disclose, in these open wells, an almost limitless supply of fresh water which meets the daily needs of many thousands of head of stock. The explanation seems to be that there is a perched water-table within the body of the Witsand dunes which is well over 100 m above the general water level in the area, where water is otherwise extremely scarce. The higher water-table is thought to be supplied by run-off from the nearby mountains.[16]

Whatever the explanation, this area of white sands has clearly held good supplies of water for long periods of time since there is evidence that it was inhabited by both Middle and Late Stone Age people. This means that man has lived intermittently at this site for about 50 000 years.

There is an extraordinary optical illusion that is experienced in the Kalahari, associated with its apparent flatness. It is most readily experienced along the 'bush' tracks, many of which are, or have evolved from, what are known as 'cut-lines'.

Geologists mapping the country, and prospecting firms searching it for minerals, must of necessity have access to every part of the Kalahari. Both go about their business in a methodical way and both divide the areas of their search into vast squares or rectangles. Along the sides of these sections perfectly straight lines, often stretching for several hundred kilometres, are cleared or cut through the bush. The cut-line becomes the access route and, sometimes, the main road of the future.

Driving along these cut-lines, you will often notice a gentle but steady rise in the road ahead. Bored, perhaps, with the unrelenting and featureless Kalahari, someone will probably suggest stopping 'at the top of this rise to look at the view'. With an immediate objective in the offing, boredom is alleviated and the viewpoint eagerly awaited. But it never comes. It is the most extraordinary phenomenon. I have travelled with parties of five or six people in the vehicle and all have agreed that we are climbing a gentle slope. Kilometre after kilometre passes – and there is no change in the slope. It is an illusion that I cannot explain. If you should happen to return by the same route, you will often feel that the road is still going uphill, despite the fact that you are now travelling in the opposite direction!

Access to the Kalahari has changed dramatically in the last fifty years. From the horse trails, bush paths and cattle tracks of the past, ribbons of asphalt now circle its edges and gravel roads cut through it. Botswana, which has such a large portion of the Kalahari within its borders, has made particularly dramatic strides in improving the network of tarred roads. In 1966, when the country became independent, there were only 15 km of tarred road; in 1984, there were 2 000 km. Tarmac will take you directly north through Namibia's Kalahari sands to the border with Angola and it will take you through the north-eastern sands of Botswana to the Zambezi River at Kazungula. For the most part, however, road penetration of the Kalahari is limited and confined to sand and gravel roads.

There are two exceptions which are of interest. In a remote part of north-western Botswana, just to the south of the Okavango, visitors are often amazed to encounter 43 km of narrow-mat tarred road, especially when the nearest road of a similar type is 300 or 400 km away. How did this come about? The Botswana Government, in stressing the need for rural development, developed a programme which included the improvement of rural roads. Much of this work was funded by overseas aid, and the story is told of a well-meaning international donor which, seeing an opportunity to help, undertook to complete a gravel road from Sehitwa to Tsao. The work was duly finished and the road, across deep Kalahari sand (which presents especially complicated engineering problems), promptly disintegrated. Repair work was done but before long the road fell apart again. After several further, equally futile, attempts, it was reluctantly accepted that the only way to protect their by now significant investment, was to invest more still. Ngamiland got its first tarmacadam road!

The other exception is in the very south of Botswana where the villages of Tsabong and Werda are gradually being linked with a black ribbon of tar. Again, the nearest tarred road is several hundred kilometres away. Such isolated stretches of good road may seem incongruous but, apart from whatever economic benefits accrue, the psychological, and physical, relief for the traveller from the endless pounding of the gravel roads, is almost immeasurable.

There are enormous difficulties in paving the Kalahari. The deep sands do not provide a good foundation and large quantities of sand must be cleared away and substitute materials found. Most commonly used is calcrete, which is abundant in the Kalahari. Calcrete is a very young rock created when carbonates, leached from the surface sands, filter to lower depths and cement sands and gravels together. The quality of calcrete varies greatly and it is not always found where it is needed. However, where it is available and where the quality is high, it makes a very good road-building material.

Cost is another factor and the low level of economic activity sometimes makes it difficult to justify such significant expenditure. The town of Ghanzi is a case in point.

If you want to experience a bad dirt road at its worst, take a drive from Jwaneng to Ghanzi, across one of the more remote parts of the Kalahari. A well-intentioned Roads Department attempted, once, to gravel sections of this road, but the supply of calcrete was limited and its quality poor. It was only possible to do short sections. The intervening spaces were left as unmodified sand. North-west of Kang, the real challenge begins.

Everything that is produced or consumed in Ghanzi arrives and departs by road. It makes financial sense to move big loads, especially as cattle have to be transported 600 km to the nearest abattoir. Twenty and thirty-tonne multi-wheeled leviathans constantly use the road. Whatever parts of the original gravel surface have not already disintegrated are subjected to woeful punishment and pounded to a powder. Enormous pot-holes develop, growing larger with every passing vehicle. In the sandy sections two sets of parallel ruts are formed. These are so deep and soft that, once in them, it is not possible to leave them, even in a very large vehicle.

A curious aspect of human driver behaviour that one encounters throughout Africa is the belief that the other side of the road is a better driving surface. If two drivers travelling in opposite directions share this belief, no problems arise. Sometimes, however, this is not the case and interesting confrontations have been known to occur! Often the heavier vehicles

travel at night as the searing daytime surface temperatures of sand can cause tyres to overheat and explode with distressing ease and frequency. Sometimes, too, the sand is more moist at night and offers slightly improved traction.

The drag effect of deep sand can be countered by fitting double wheels to big trucks. However, the effect on the road is such that a lighter, more conventional vehicle, travelling behind, finds it almost impossible to move at all. This is because the leading vehicle creates small ridges of loose sand right on the wheel tracks of the one behind. There is now a gazetted agreement that no operator on the Ghanzi route will use double wheels.

Mindful of her responsibilities as a member of a newly formed association of Southern African states, Botswana has agreed to bituminise the 520 km from Jwaneng to Ghanzi. Construction is scheduled to take place in 1990–1991 at an estimated cost of nearly P80m, at today's prices. If you would like to travel to Ghanzi by this route, and there is no pressing urgency to undertake the journey, I suggest you wait until then before making the attempt!

An alternative to a road transport system is, of course, the railway, and railways across the Kalahari have been a dream for nearly a hundred years. Botswana, for example, is quite landlocked and is almost wholly dependent upon South Africa as a route for her imports and exports. There are a number of disadvantages in this arrangement and, more than once, eyes have been cast across the Kalahari to the Atlantic and the possibilities of a trans-Kalahari line have been toyed with. In the past there has been little economic justification for such a huge and expensive project, but today circumstances have changed and the dream may indeed become a reality.

Political factors lay behind the building of the line from Mafikeng, in what was then the northern Cape, through Gaborone and Francistown in Botswana, to Bulawayo. Opened in 1897, it laid the foundations, unintentionally perhaps, for the development of eastern Botswana.

The first proposal for a trans-Kalahari line was made in 1930 and was initiated, not by Bechuanaland, as it then was, but by Southern Rhodesia. There is a railhead in eastern Namibia, at Gobabis, which for many years has been linked to the sea at both Swakopmund and Walvis Bay. Gobabis has always been the focus of any line across the Kalahari. In the 1930s, the Schwarz Scheme (see Chapter 7) was still very much a possibility and it was considered that economic justification for a line through Botswana would lie in the development of vast irrigation projects in the Mababe Depression and Ngamiland generally. The Kalahari was to become the Egypt of Southern Africa and enthusiasm ran high. A major survey conducted by J L S Jeffares in 1931 soon made it clear, however, that the project was simply not economically viable and that Southern Rhodesia would benefit far more than Bechuanaland. The project was shelved.

In 1950 it was resurrected and three routes were considered: one around the north of the Okavango Delta, another around the south, through Maun, and a third crossing the Boteti River near Rakops. This time Southern Rhodesian and South African interests could not be reconciled and the project lacked the support of the British Government. Once again the surveys and reports were returned to the shelves.[17]

In the 1980s the project is again being considered, but this time a number of factors have changed. Botswana's economy has grown enormously; it is sophisticated, well-run and of considerable size. Very large quantities of coal have been found on the eastern edges of the Kalahari and global exporting is a distinct possibility. The mining and manufacture of soda ash is being developed on the Makgadikgadi Pans and this, too, will result in considerable exports. To tackle the project today would be a massive undertaking. It has been estimated that approximately 10 million tonnes of coal would need to be exported every year to justify it and the cost of the line, workshops and rolling stock is placed in the region of $378 million.[18] Four routes are currently being considered. Each of them will cross the Kalahari and the final choice, if the project is to proceed, will be determined by the possibilities for development in the areas through which it will pass. A resolution of the political situation in Namibia is a necessary prerequisite to any final decision but, despite this, the project now looks more likely to get off the ground than it has done at any time in the past.

Much work is currently being done in the United Kingdom on the development of airships and there are many, myself included, who believe that there is a future for these aircraft in the transport industry. Airships could play a vital role in those developing countries which are hampered in their efforts to raise the standard of living of their peoples by vast distances and high cost of infrastructure. They are ideally suited to Kalahari conditions and could provide the solution to many transport problems. At the moment, however, their cost is prohibitive but I am convinced there will come a time when we shall see such craft in daily use above the sands.

## REFERENCES

1. **Louw, G and Seely, M.** *Ecology of Desert Organisms.* New York: Longman, 1982, p 1
2. **Grove, A T.** 'Landforms and Climatic Change in the Kalahari'. In *The Geographic Journal*, Vol 135, 1969, p 191
3. **Woodman, G.** Personal communication, September 1984
4. **Andringa, J.** 'The Climate of Botswana in Histograms'. In *Botswana Notes and Records*, Vol 16, 1984, pp 117-125
5. **Hyde, L W.** 'Ground-water Supplies in the Kalahari Area, Botswana'. In *Botswana Notes and Records*, Special Edition No 1, 1971, p 76
6. **Tyson, P D.** 'Rainfall Changes over South Africa during the Period of Meteorological Record'. In *Biogeography and Ecology of Southern Africa*. Edited by Wergen, M J A. The Hague: Dr W Junk Publishers, 1978, pp 53-69
7. **Devan, K R S and Yeboah-Amankwah, D.** 'The Results of a Survey in Connection with the Study of Lightning in Botswana'. In *Botswana Notes and Records*, Vol 16, pp 150-53
8. *The Great Ngami Trek (By one who took part in it)*, pp 81-102. Author unknown
9. **Paul, S.** Personal communication, December 1984
10. **Flint, R F.** *Glacial and Quaternary Geology.* New York: John Wiley & Sons, Inc, 1971, p 700

11. Dingle, R V Siesser, W G and Newton, A R. *Mesozoic and Tertiary Geology of Southern Africa.* Rotterdam: A A Balkema, 1983, **p 290**

12. Cahen, L and Lepersonne, J. *Mem. Soc. Belge de Geol,* Vol 4, No 7, 1952

13. Baillieul, T A. 'A Reconnaissance Survey of the Cover Sands in the Republic of Botswana'. In *Journal of Sedimentary Petrology,* Vol 45, No 2, **pp 494-503**

14. Lewis, A D. 'Roaring Sands of the Kalahari Desert'. In *South African Geographical Journal,* Vol 19, December 1936, **pp 33-49**

15. Bovill, E W. *The Golden Trade of the Moors.* 2nd edition. London: OUP, 1970, **p 242**

16. Van Rooyen, T H and Verster, E. *Characteristics and Origin of the Sands and Other Surface Phenomena of the Witsand Area.* Proceedings of the Tenth Congress of the Soil Science Society of Southern Africa, South African Government, Dept of Agriculture, Pretoria. Technical Communication No 180, 1983, **pp 107-14**

17. Ngwenya, B N. 'The Development of Transport Infrastructure in the Bechuanaland Protectorate 1885-1966'. In *Botswana Notes and Records,* Vol 16, 1984, **pp 73-6**

18. Shreeve, G. *African Economic Digest,* Vol 2, 2-8 October 1981, **p 26**

# 6. In the Earth Below

IN spite of the extensive area over which they are distributed, the sands of the Kalahari are not always, as we have seen, of very great depth, and even at their greatest depths, they do have a limit. Below them somewhere lies the hard rock which makes up the crustal zone of our planet. Within this rock is sometimes stored considerable mineral wealth. The search for minerals in the Kalahari is still in its infancy. While discoveries have already been made, notably diamonds, copper and coal, that more remains to be found seems quite certain. Large areas have not yet been explored and techniques of mineral exploration are continually being improved.

A recent survey concluded that the true metallic mineral potential of Botswana's Kalahari remains unknown and pointed to considerable geological potential. In the south and south-eastern area, there is the possibility of gold, platinum, manganese, nickel, chrome and tin, whilst copper, lead and zinc are likely in other parts. There is also potential for oil, although this is restricted to the region south-west and northwest of Ghanzi, where a higher proportion of marine formations is present. The potential, in this regard, however, is low. Exploration in neighbouring countries, in similar formations, has been disappointing and there is little reason to expect that results in the Kalahari will be any different. However, there remains a higher possibility that methane gas in commercial quantities may yet be found.[1]

Much of interest lies beneath the Kalahari's sands, although the exploration and study thereof are made more difficult because of it. The sand is seldom uninterrupted in depth and 'lenses' of a white, powdery rock, between 3 and 30 m thick, are fairly common. This material is called calcrete and is of interest to geologists, hydrologists and to those who are responsible for the construction and maintenance of many of the Kalahari's roads. In a sandy wilderness calcrete is often the only rock available and, although its quality varies a great deal, it can make excellent road-building material. It has the advantage of being widely available, deposits are often close to the surface and it needs only to be carried to where it is needed.

What is calcrete exactly and why is it so important? Calcrete, and the closely related silcrete and ferricrete, have been, and remain, the source of much controversy in the scientific world. Calcrete is a rock which is being formed today, but the mechanism by which this occurs is not fully understood. It is thought that long, alternate wet and dry periods are necessary for its creation. Another theory is that calcrete occurs only along old drainage lines but this is a fallacy as, whilst it is certainly found in great abundance in such places, it also occurs along the crests of ancient dunes, as anyone who has driven from Maun to Moremi Reserve will be able to testify.

Lime is the chief component of calcrete. It is formed by the precipitation of this carbonate from soil water. The rock that results is therefore rich in the inorganic components of the soil – what it is is simply soil cemented together by limestone. The process takes place gradually, following a number of distinct stages. By a chemical process that is little understood, calcrete can change into a different kind of rock, known as silcrete. Silcrete also takes many forms, most often that of chalcedony or opal, especially in the Kalahari.[2] Chalcedony is hard and flint-like and was much used by Stone Age people for the small, sharp tools they fashioned. Silcrete occurs under much the same conditions as calcrete.

Calcrete and, to a lesser extent, silcrete hold many secrets of the past, for the material within them has been almost frozen in time. Imprisoned in a cell of carbonate, it is protected from further deterioration and delivered down through the centuries almost unaltered. For this reason climatologists and geomorphologists are greatly interested in the calcrete of the Kalahari. Often entombed within it are the shells of molluscs and tiny crustaceans which can provide many clues to conditions at the time the calcrete was formed. Stone tools have also been found inside this material. One difficulty in unlocking these secrets, however, is that a reliable method of dating calcrete has yet to be devised. Calcrete types are highly diverse and their formation is thought to be influenced by many variables, including the source of carbonate, host materials, time, climate and their geomorphological position.[3] The calcretes of the Kalahari are among the thickest in the world and some are thought to be as old as 5 million years or more.

By far the most currently controversial of the resources beneath the sands of the Kalahari is its groundwater. The controversy hinges on the question of whether or not the supply is being replenished. There are those who claim that there is no recharging of underground waters and that their removal, therefore, is akin to a mining operation. Once the water is gone, they say, nothing will be left. A second school of thought believes that recharging does take place and that there is beneath the Kalahari an almost inexhaustible supply of water. The question is a critical one for the development of the Kalahari. An expensive infrastructure supporting a complex economy cannot reasonably be based upon a resource, the limitations and dimensions of which are unknown. The problem is compounded by the fact that development is going ahead regardless, and there is some concern at the economic and environmental risks that are being taken, especially as the resource that is being exploited is not fully understood.

Most people in the Kalahari obtain their water by drilling boreholes. Water is found at varying depths, ranging from as little as 40 m to as much as 300 m or more. Often it is saline – too much so for human use, although sometimes usable for cattle, which have a higher tolerance level for minerals. Prior to 1929 very little drilling for water took place in the Kalahari. In that year the first of the cattle 'trek routes' were developed and boreholes were drilled along its length to provide essential water to cattle being herded across the Kalahari to the markets in the east.[4] The experience showed that there was water to be found. Gradually, in the years that followed, more boreholes were sunk. The rate began to accelerate and, in the decades of massive cattle ranching expansion, thousands were drilled. Today probably more than 6 000 or 7 000 boreholes exist.

The 'mining' school of thought bases its position on undisputed evidence of the water-holding capacity of sand. It has been shown that 2,5 cm of rain soaks the sand to a depth of 20 cm, which is then said to be at its 'field capacity'. It is then calculated that 81 cm would be required to bring 6 m of sand to its field capacity. The sand below the levels at field capacity remains dry. As there is nowhere in the Kalahari that receives that annual volume of rain, it follows, therefore, that rainwater never reaches further down through the sand than 4 to 6 m.[5] If this is the case, argue the 'miners', there is no recharge through Kalahari sand. Any water found beneath it is 'fossil' water (meaning it is of very great age) and, once this has been removed, there will be no replenishment and the resource will be exhausted.

The 'replenishment' school do not dispute the facts about field capacity but nevertheless argue for widespread replenishment, calling upon nuclear technology to support their case. Tritium is a radioactive isotope of hydrogen. It decays fairly rapidly and has a half-life of just under twelve and a half years. It readily combines with water and, because of its radioactive nature, its quantity in the water can be measured and, because its decay rate is known, the water can be dated for ages up to 50 years. Tritium exists naturally in our atmosphere and the average world-wide level was about 2–

High up on the cliff is Van der Post's panel (the inset is a detail) at Tsodilo Hills

▲View from the Female hill at Tsodilo, across the Child to the Kalahari beyond ▼Drotsky's Cave

4 Tritium Units (TUs). Since the commencement of thermonuclear experimentation, levels of atmospheric tritium have soared. In 1963, when they reached their peak, tritium levels stood at 10 000 TU.

Tritium concentrations can vary seasonally and they are to some extent latitude dependent. These variables can be controlled, however, and tritium can be used to give reliable minimum ages for groundwater.[6] In 1974 one researcher, working on data from 66 boreholes in the Kalahari, found that more than 40 per cent of them revealed tritium levels indicating that recent recharge had taken place. Carbon 14 tests can also be used to date groundwater and data from 72 wells showed that 30 per cent of them had been recently recharged.[7]

How can these two conflicting pieces of hard-won and irrefutable evidence be reconciled? There are several possibilities that have emerged from the claim and counter-claim of scientific debate. One is that samples from the tritium data have in fact been contaminated by direct rainfall seeping down through the soil in the vicinity of the borehole itself. Another is that all the boreholes tested lay next to shallow drainage systems and that they were contaminated by water from these sources. It is unlikely that either of these claims are justified. Many hundreds of tests have now been completed and the data is too consistent to deny the fact of recharge. But the question remains, how does it take place?

One theory is that there occurs in the Kalahari a massive movement of underground water – that it actually flows through the sand, from high to lower levels over considerable distances. It is generally agreed that recharge to underlying aquifers can take place along fault-lines, where rocks emerge through the surface, by following the roots of trees or by flowing down natural holes created by animals and insects. This theory does have some merit. It would explain how run-off is funnelled by hills in and around the Kalahari, deep down into the sands. It would also account for the presence of groundwater in the remote sandy areas where no rocks occur at all. However, there are also grounds for doubting it.

Dr 'Balt' Verhagen, at the nuclear research centre at the University of the Witwatersrand, is intensely interested in this subject and he has researched it thoroughly. He points out that if the 'mass movement' theory were correct, it would demand the presence of a continuous expanse, or several separate but very large expanses, of underground water. The quality of this water need not necessarily remain consistent over its entire distance. Indeed, an increase in salinity could be expected the further removed one was from the source of re-supply. What one would not expect to find, though, but which does in fact occur, is a totally random distribution of salinity, which was shown in a line of test boreholes running from the edge of the Kalahari towards its centre. The first well might be very fresh water, the second saline, the third less so, the fourth fresh, the fifth saline and so on. How then can this be the same body of water? Dr Verhagen is of the opinion that massive underground movement does *not* take place and that beneath the Kalahari is a series of discrete and unconnected aquifers, each recharged by a separate supply, some possibly overflowing into others in time of great abundance. Others, for some reason, may be cut off from recharge and lie as fossil, saline waters.[8]

Another interesting personality doing research in this field is Dr John Vogel, at the Council for Scientific and Industrial Research in Pretoria.[9] He has a theory concerning groundwater recharge that I have heard nowhere else, and it has about it an attraction that is intuitively appealing. Dr Vogel is quick to point out that, despite the theories on field capacity of sand, no matter how deeply one digs, one will always find a certain amount of moisture. The sand will be damp to considerable depths. Kalahari trees are often deep rooted and they would not be so if there were no water in those regions.

Dr Vogel's theory involves 'layers' of water: Rain falls and soaks the sand to its field capacity. The sun comes out, the moisture evaporates and the lowest level of saturated sand moves upward towards the surface as water from the top is drawn off by the sun. However, it must sometimes happen that it rains again before all the water has been evaporated. When this occurs the new rain falls upon the surface and, as before, soaks down into the sand. As it does so, it drives to deeper levels the moisture that remained from the last fall. In this way two 'layers', each from different but successive periods of rain, now 'lie' one on top of the other, within the sand itself. The process is repeated indefinitely, and moisture is 'pushed' deeper and deeper down into the sand. Eventually two things happen. The lowest levels reach the water-table, which is thus recharged and, before this happens, the deeper levels of soaked-in rainwater are driven down to a point beyond the reach of the sun. They are no longer drawn by the capillary action of evaporation. No matter how much time passes, the water will not be lost. It will not evaporate nor will it be pushed to lower levels and the water-table, until new water appears on the upper surfaces. The way I understand Dr Vogel's theory, the process is slow but inexorable and it seems to me quite logical. It could account for ground-water recharge in areas devoid of the accepted mechanisms, such as rocks and fault-lines, by which it is otherwise thought to take place.

There are several other possibilities that might explain the direct, vertical recharge model for Kalahari sands. One is that grain sizes in the sand vary enormously and it stands to reason that the field capacity must also vary accordingly. Perhaps, in some cases, the lower level of field capacity is beyond the reach of the sun? Another possibility stems from simple observation in the Kalahari itself. Despite the fact that the Kalahari is renowned for its flatness, it is not completely flat. Everywhere across its surface there are shallow drainage patterns, and even where these are not noticeably present, the sand itself is not absolutely flat. At a micro level, the surface is undulating and dimpled. When rain falls at a rate faster than the water can be absorbed by the sand, run-off occurs and collection in the hollows begins. In this way, although the average rainfall on an area of 100 m$^2$ may, for example, have been 300 mm, because of the way the rain might accumulate in some areas and be dispersed by small gradients from others, the distribution would be different across the surface. Some parts of that 100 m$^2$ may have received an effective rainfall that was double that which actually fell, whilst others would have received only half that amount. This must surely impact upon the dynamics of field capacities and ground-water recharge.

As development in the Kalahari speeds up, so too does the demand for water. The problems that this creates are nowhere better illustrated than in the case of Jwaneng diamond mine.[10] When a fabulously wealthy pipe of diamonds was found deep in the Kalahari the decision was taken to open a mine. There was no water at all in the area, however, and a firm of consultants was called in. Their brief was simple. They were allocated 12 500 km$^2$ of the Kalahari and were asked to find a reliable supply of 15 000 m$^3$ of water a day. This was a daunting task to say the least and nothing on a similar scale had been attempted before. Every modern technique was used and eventually, after a long search, a supply was found in July 1977. At 71 m water was struck and the supply increased with depth. Drilling was halted at 206 m. The well yielded volumes of water never before heard of in Botswana. As the extent of the aquifer was explored, more wells were sunk. In the end there were 17 wells, 14 going below 220 m. But the water had been found and it was soon piped the 50 km back to the mine, the fate of which until this moment had hung in the balance – no water, no diamonds.

It was, of course, critical to evaluate the reliability of the resource and sophisticated computer models were employed to predicate the draw-down rate. A 30 m fall in the water-table level at the centre of the field was predicted after three years of operation. In the event, after three years it had only fallen 3 m.[11] The prediction was wrong and underlines how little we understand the Kalahari's groundwater, how much there still is to learn, and what incredible risks are taken.

The feasibility of deliberately recharging boreholes by channeling rainwater to them during the rainy season has also been investigated. It was tried, with very little success, in the southern Kalahari, in Gordonia, south of the Molopo River. Here an enterprising farmer tried to improve his borehole by adding rainwater to it. During the 1975-6 wet season he pumped into the borehole fresh rainwater that had accumulated in nearby pans. The borehole normally yielded very saline water and he thought that by mixing the two he might improve the quality. He pumped for five months but, for practical purposes, the experiment was a dismal failure. Normal pumping brought only the usual saline water to the surface. Quality could be improved only by pumping at a very slow rate.

There is an interesting explanation for this. Fresh water and saline water have different specific gravities. Fresh water, being lighter, floats on top of the heavier saline water. They do not mix. Depending upon the exact location of the junction between these two layers of water in relation to the end of the borehole pipe, pumping causes a 'cone' to develop. Drawn by the upward pressure, caused by the pumping, the heavier saline water rises in a cone towards the base of the pipe. If the pumping pressure is high, the cone fills the pipe and excludes the fresh water. Only by dropping to a very low pumping rate can fresh water be drawn in too. This same situation occurs in all sea-level towns where fresh water lies on top of the saltier seawater, and the same slow pumping rate is required to extract only the fresh water.[12]

Paul Larkin runs his own consultancy in Gaborone and specialises in locating groundwater.[13] It is his business to know the practical side of this work and he is convinced that direct groundwater recharge does take place through Kalahari sands. He believes that there is at least patchy recharge and, like others, points out that sand grain size is not uniform across the Kalahari and that recharge is thus possible. He too holds the view that there are vast water resources beneath the Kalahari and that we are still a long way from understanding how they come to be there or how they are replenished. It is his opinion that one reason why recharge may not be taking place is that many of the aquifers are full and there is no room for more water.

Dr 'Co' de Vries, at the University of Botswana, is another who subscribes to the theory of almost unlimited supplies of water in the Kalahari and he firmly believes that there is enough to allow for the utilisation of the whole Kalahari for cattle ranching.[14] To some, who are concerned at the poor standards of range management that are associated with the cattle industry in Botswana, this is disturbing news. It poses an ecological threat of immense proportions and further complicates the political, social and economic consequences of exploiting the Kalahari's groundwater.

That some of the Kalahari's water is ancient is beyond dispute. What is less clear is whether, as Paul Larkin claims, this is so because the aquifer is full or, as others would have it, because recharge no longer takes place. In Gordonia a test was conducted to establish the age of the water in a number of the 168 boreholes in a particular area. It varied greatly. Some boreholes contained water which was less than 155 years old. Other aquifers showed water of 14 000, 19 000, 25 000 and 30 600 years of age. Interestingly, aquifers of vastly different ages were often adjacent to one another. One with water 2 000 years old was only 15 km away from another whose waters were older than 30 000 years.[15] Examples of this type are numerous in the area and go some way towards supporting the theory of Dr Verhagen that massive groundwater movement is not a common feature in the dynamics of underground water distribution in the Kalahari.

Ancient water certainly exists in Botswana's Kalahari. When Orapa diamond mine was established considerable hydrological survey work was carried out on the site. In one case, an aquifer which was completely contained within what is known as cave sandstone was penetrated. The water was devoid of tritium and very low in Carbon 14. This indicated that the aquifer was neither leaking nor was it being recharged. The water was older than 15 000 years.[16] This information tends to indicate that there may well be two sources of Kalahari water. One is ancient in origin and is a remnant of wetter times. It is uncontaminated by modern isotopes, which suggests that it is either isolated from them because its recharge mechanisms no longer work, or it is so full that it cannot absorb any additional water. The other source of water in the Kalahari comes from aquifers that are being actively recharged today. The puzzle for the future is to discover how and at what rate these aquifers are being replenished and, above all, to establish how much can safely be drawn off.

In the course of meeting some of the many fascinating people involved in the controversial question of the Kalahari's groundwater, I came across a most unusual phenomenon. It concerns a borehole at a village called Remotswa, on the eastern edge of the Kalahari. (I have been reliably informed that the phenomenon is universal and that Remotswa happens to be a particularly good example.)

The borehole there penetrates some superficial sand and then strikes down deep into heavily fractured, ancient rock. The information that I saw was a graph that recorded water levels in the borehole. I looked at it in amazement for there occurred two high peaks and two troughs in the level every day. At its greatest extent the range of movement was more than 20 cm. Not only that, but the range diminished during a given month to a point where there was almost none at all, and then increased towards the end of the time period. Dr De Vries had shown me the graph and I asked if it was tidal movement, and therefore linked to the phases of the moon. It was, but extraordinary as it may seem, it had little to do with the moon's effect on the water. It was the rocks that were responding to earth's natural satellite! They are drawn towards the moon and the gaps between them open up, causing the water level to fall. As the gaps close, the water is 'squeezed' upwards again and the level rises. The strength of the gravitational pull alters in accordance with the relative positions of sun and moon and thus the level of fluctuation alters also. They correspond exactly to the tidal movements of our seas. This is known to happen in the Jwaneng well-field and at many other places in the Kalahari. I find it fascinating because it demonstrates the pervasiveness of extraterrestrial gravitational influences as well as the amazing flexibility of our so-called solid earth.

Development in the Kalahari will not abate. If anything, it will continue to accelerate. The lot of the rural people there will be improved and this necessarily means development. It also means increasing demands upon the area's water resources and the consequent improvement of techniques for location and extraction. This poses two serious threats: one being that cattle-ranching will increase and with it the further mismanagement and abuse of the range-lands. The other is the possibility that the Kalahari's water is indeed being 'mined' and that it will eventually run out. Development therefore compels the acceptance of awesome responsibilities. I hope they will be lived up to.

## REFERENCES

1. **Pretorius, D A**. 'The Contribution of the Aeromagnetic Interpretation to an Assessment of the Mineral Potential of Botswana'. In *Reconnaissance Aeromagnetic Survey of Botswana, 1975-1977*. Geological Survey Department, Government of Botswana, pp A14-A50
2. **Dingle, R V, Siesser, W G and Newton, A R**. *Mesozoic and Tertiary Geology of Southern Africa*. Rotterdam: 1983, p 294
3. **Watts, N L**. 'Quaternary Pedogenic Calcretes from the Kalahari (Southern Africa): Mineralogy, Genesis and Diagenesis'. In *Sedimentology*, No 27, 1980, pp 661-86
4. **Boocock, C and Van Straten, O J**. 'Notes on the Geology and Hydrogeology of the Central Kalahari Region, Bechuanaland Protectorate'. In *Transactions of the Geological Society of South Africa*, Vol 65, Part 1, 1962, pp 125-70
5. **Ibid**, p 159
6. **Jennings, C M H, Sellschop, J P F, Verhagen, B Th and Jones, M T**. 'Environmental Isotopes as Aid to Investigation of Ground Water Problems in Botswana'. In *Botswana Notes and Records*, Vol 5, 1973, pp 179-90
7. **Mazor, E**. 'Rain Recharge in the Kalahari - A Note on Some Approaches to the Problem'. In *Journal of Hydrology*, Vol. 55, No. 1, February 1982, pp 137-44
8. **Verhagen, B Th**. Personal communication, May 1984
9. **Vogel, J**. Personal communication, May 1984
10. **Stepto, D**. 'Desert Water'. In *Botswana*, No 6, Ministry of Information Services, Government of Botswana, Gaborone, pp 43-7, (no date)

11. **Buckley, D.** Personal communication, August 1984

12. **Levin, M.** *A Geological and Hydrochemical Investigation of the Uranium Potential of an Area between the Orange and Kuruman Rivers, Northwestern Cape Province.* Vol 1, April 1980. Atomic Energy Board, Pretoria, South Africa, p 31

13. **Larkin, P.** Personal communication, Sep., 1984.

14. **De Vries, J J.** Personal communication, June 1984

15. **Levin, M.** Op cit, Vol 2, map 8

16. **Mazor, E, Verhagen, B Th, Sellschop, J P F, Jones, M T, Robins, N E, Hutton, L and Jennings, C M H.** 'Northern Kalahari Groundwaters: Hydrologic, Isotopic and Chemical Studies at Orapa, Botswana'. In *Journal of Hydrology,* No 34, 1977, pp 203-34

# Part 3
# The Last Frontiers

# 7. Okavango

LIKE a giant hand laid across the heart of the Kalahari, the Okavango River pours its precious liquid out onto the burning sand, forming one of the largest inland deltas in the world. The river once flowed on, but it does not do so now. Ponded back by rising land in the east and trapped between deep fault-lines, it is slowly choking with its own sediment. The vast area of water stands almost motionless beneath the tropical sun; most of it evaporates, some sinks into the sands below, while the remainder fingers its way along imperceptible gradients before its energies are finally sapped by sun and sand and nothing remains but a damp patch upon the earth.

The Delta is one of the most beautiful places in Africa, with its sheltered waterways, islands of towering trees and its exotic range of bird and animal life. It is formed by the Okavango River which rises on the Benguela plateau, near the town of Nova Lisboa in Angola. In this mountainous area the rainfall is high, averaging between 1 200 mm and 1 500 mm a year. The large and powerful Cubango River, as the Okavango is known in Angola, flows south-east to Angola's southern border, turns east along it, then crosses the Caprivi Strip to enter north-west Botswana. Nearly 1 300 km of this journey lies over Kalahari sand.

The great delta does not begin immediately once Botswana's border has been crossed. There is first a feature known as 'the Panhandle' (see map on p. 86) which extends for 95 km and within the steep banks of which the river is confined. The Panhandle is actually contained within two deep, parallel faults in the earth's crust, concealed beneath the sand, and which serve to create a valley, barely discernible with the naked eye, some 10 to 15 km in width. The gradient of this valley is extremely flat and the river meanders back and forth across it so that river distance is about three times the direct route. It is usually possible to see the river only at those places where it swings in close to the bank; otherwise the view is nothing more than a dark green sea of tall papyrus reed which blankets everything. Where the river touches the bank villages have been established, with names such as Sepopa, Shakawe and Seronga. Standing upon the loose white sand are the thatched-hut homes of the Hambukushu and Bayei people. Precise, neat and tidy, the houses are often surrounded by a pallisade of long reeds. Carefully bound and accurately trimmed, they glow a rich gold in the low sun, suggesting the warmth and happiness of these people who live at the edge of a paradise.

Life in these villages revolves around the river. Echoing the rains in distant Angola, the river floods once a year. The receding waters leave behind soaked pastures which feed large herds of cattle. Rainfall in this region is higher than in the more southerly parts of the Kalahari and crops are quite successfully grown in fields not far from the river. The river itself is the most important element, however. It provides water for drinking and a place to bathe; it offers a route for transport and an abundant stock of fish. All the people of the delta are great fishermen. They set out in their wooden canoes, called mekoro (see Chapter 16) and fish with nets, as well as hook and line. Sometimes a technique of fishing with baskets is employed and the catches provide variety in an otherwise subsistence-level diet.

Fresh fish can always be purchased at

any of the villages but you need to keep your wits about you as there are pitfalls for the unwary. Sometimes there is a definite difference in perception between salesman and customer as to what exactly a fresh fish is. The matter is complicated by apparently different ideas about time, and by an endearing habit, common among the locals and born only from a desire to please and be polite, of always giving the answer they think you want. Thus it is that the smiling, kindly old man, whom you wish to befriend as much as benefit by purchasing the large bream he is offering, will blandly assure you that it was caught 'this very morning'. Inexperienced perhaps, and unwilling to distrust him, you might accept it, only to discover, much too late, just how unpleasant the three-day-old rotting insides of a fish can really be. The trick is, I am told, to examine the fish's gills. If the fish is fresh, they will be bright pink. If they are not, you should avoid it.

If the river tends to follow a single channel in the Panhandle this is not to suggest that everywhere else in the valley is dry land. The whole area is in fact a mass of papyrus reed and lagoons, connected by small channels. Papyrus floats and does not seem to care for swiftly flowing waters, but there are vast stands of it in shallow places and the water gently flows among its loosely packed roots. In this way huge areas are inundated and travelling through these wetlands in anything but a boat is almost impossible. You can walk through papyrus but it is not a pleasant experience. It gives under your weight and you sink to thigh or waist level in muddied water. Progress becomes a desperate struggle and not one to be undertaken for pleasure. Because it is closed in and you can see nothing but a forest of thin green towering stems, it is easy to start panicking and I do not recommend the experience.

Unappealing as it is to us, the papyrus is, however, the favourite haunt of one of the world's rare animals – the shy sitatunga. This medium-sized antelope has become specially adapted to an aquatic environment. Its hooves are deeply splayed to give it more support in soft mud and matted beds of vegetation. The animal is subject to controlled hunting and hunters often burn small areas of papyrus, as the sitatunga has a passion for the new green shoots which quickly appear. The sitatunga is wily, though, and if its suspicions are aroused and it becomes alarmed it will submerge itself completely in the water, with only its nostrils showing, making it impossible to find. The number of sitatunga in the Okavango is not as great as it once may have been. Eradication of tsetse fly has allowed man and cattle to spread into some areas where it once flourished; the sitatunga does not fare well in competition with man and its range has accordingly been reduced.[1]

The crystal clearness of the Okavango's water is often remarked upon and, generally speaking, this is justified. Further south in the Delta the waters move so slowly that no sediment at all can be carried and it is amazingly clear. In the northern parts, however, the water is not always as clean, especially in the main river itself when in flood. I have seen it a turgid brown, thick with clay and mud and there is no doubt that much sediment is being carried into the Delta every year; one calculation suggests that over 660 000 tons are delivered annually.[2]

The upper river is the haunt of the Okavango's big crocodiles. Once they were hunted, almost to extinction. Between 1957 and 1969 it has been estimated that in excess of 10 000 crocodiles were killed and taken. The population has never fully recovered from these depredations.[3] John Seaman was one of those hunters. It was a business then and no one gave much thought to the future, or imagined that the crocodiles might ever 'run out'. John is a great, burly, humorous man, whose fund of stories seems never-ending. He and a man called Bobby Wilmot halved the Delta between them and, in those years, systematically hunted every crocodile they could find. They had teams working for them and John's team alone accounted for 14 300 animals. Probably the total number of crocodiles taken from the Delta was very much higher than has been suggested, perhaps as many as 25 000 in the twelve-year period. Inevitably, the supply of crocodiles diminished. Bobby met a tragic death from snake-bite and John moved away to different pastures. He recently returned and now, ironically, runs a crocodile farm. Some animals have been captured to build up the farm's breeding stock and some are exported. Eggs are also collected from the wild and hatched.

John tells a delightful story of a crocodile catching expedition which illustrates the wonderful sense of camaraderie that is such a feature of life in this rather out of the way part of Africa. He had heard of a number of crocodiles, far out in the bush, well away from the Delta, that had been caught in a drying pan. They were likely to die unless rescued and John had a permit to capture them. Rope, planks and the inevitable Toyota Land Cruiser were assembled for the task. To begin with, all went well. Planks were laid across the drying mud and loops of rope were tightened around the snouts of the smaller creatures, which were then hauled by the truck into captivity. The larger ones were a problem, however. As soon as they felt the tug of the vehicle they stuck their snouts into the mud and were soon buried so deeply that it was impossible to move them. Some method of keeping the jaws out of the mud was needed and there seemed nothing available which was suitable for the task. But this was Ngamiland and strange things always happen there. Just at that moment, a helicopter was passing overhead. As is the way in Ngamiland, seeing the group of people around the pan, the pilot dropped in to have a look. He happened to be a friend of John's and, sizing up the situation, he offered to help. Using the helicopter's splendid sky-hook, it was a simple matter to run a loop along the hauling rope and attach it to the helicopter. By hovering at the right height, the tension upon the rope was sufficient to prevent the bigger crocodiles from digging in. One by one they were hauled across the slippery mud. Everyone was very pleased with the success of the operation – except, perhaps, the crocodiles.

Despite their justly deserved, fearsome reputation, the crocodile is a fascinating creature. The female makes a nest and lays eggs in the deep soft sand, not far from the river bank. There will be anything from 20 to 90 eggs and they will incubate in the warm sand for about three months. Interestingly, when they are ready to hatch the young begin to call and, although the sound emanates from under the sand, it can be heard by humans nearly 2 m away. The mother will help uncover the nest and will carry the young in her mouth to the water's edge.[4] A remarkable recent discovery about crocodiles has to do with the matter of sex determination in the young. Extraordinary as it may seem, it looks as if temperature is the most important single determinant. Typically, eggs are laid in three layers in a cone-shaped hole in the sand. Understandably, there is a temperature difference of about 4 °C between the bottom and the top of the clutch. The young from the warmer area at the top turn out to be males and those from the bottom are females.[5]

Crocodiles do not like the cold and, even in the warm Okavango, are much less active during the winter months. They seldom eat then and spend most of their time in semi-hibernation. They are therefore less of a risk than at other times of the year but never should they be underestimated. John has some rather unpleasant facts about these creatures, most of them discovered through personal experience. A man cannot, he claims, out-run a crocodile on dry land. They are exceedingly fast and, if the man is at a disadvantage – surprised, unprepared and usually on sand – he has little prospect of getting away. It is unwise, says John, to be over-confident about a crocodile at the water's edge for it can throw itself one and a half times its own length out of the water.

In addition to being an opportunistic feeder, a crocodile will sit and watch and, if it detects a regular pattern, it will prepare an attack. Ursula Wilmot, daughter of Bobby Wilmot, who still lives in Maun at the base of the Delta and runs a small business there, can verify what John says from her own terrifying experience.[6] In 1983 Ursula was caretaking one of the most beautiful safari camps in the Delta, a place called Xugana. She was alone in the camp which is set beneath tall trees on the edge of a deep and beautiful lagoon. She had a pet fishing owl and needed fresh fish daily to feed it. Moored nearby was a large houseboat which is used to show the Delta to visitors. Ursula had laid her line from the end of the houseboat and checked it regularly during the day. Fishing was bad and she caught nothing. She returned several times that night to check again. At about 9 o'clock, she made her last visit. It was then that the crocodile attacked. It leapt out of the water at her as she was checking the line and she would certainly have been taken but for the light metal railing around the deck. Drenched and shocked she fell back against the side of the cabin, only to be doused again almost immediately by a second attack. Fortunately she was unharmed and owed her life to the railing, the scarred paint of which showed where the crocodile's jaws had struck. Crocodiles are well known in Xugana's lagoon and one in particular, a large creature some 2,5 m in length, is regarded almost as a pet.

As one emerges from the Panhandle, the nature of the waterway changes and the true Delta begins. This is not perceptible from the ground, however, nor on the water, but a map will show that the Okavango divides into several main channels which work their way across interminable flat sands to the south-east and the Thamalakane River. In addition to the main channels there are countless smaller ones and everywhere the water, gently flowing, pushes its way through reed-beds and papyrus, sliding gently round innumerable islands, returning again and again to the main channels, only to leave them once more to meander over the land. The shape of the Delta is roughly triangular or cone-shaped and the distance from the apex to the base of the cone is about 175 km. Like the Panhandle, the slope is extremely gentle and although it varies within the area on average the fall is about 1 in 6 450. It is in this region where the Delta is at its spectacular best. It is a true wetland wilderness and there are places within it that man may yet not have visited.

The islands are this area's most characteristic feature. They vary in size from a small anthill, perhaps supporting a single tree, to the vast Chief's Island, 40 to 50 km long and 10 to 15 km wide. Because of the ever-changing water level, rising and fal-

ling with the annual floods, some islands are only temporary, losing their status as the water recedes. Many are incredibly beautiful. Jessie Neal, who runs Camp Okavango, regularly takes her guests for an evening barbecue on Lopis Island. Unusual for the Delta, the banks of this island stand nearly 2 m above the water level. It is set with huge evergreen trees, many of which stand close to the water, some reaching far out across it where a wide bend in the river incises deeply into the land. The trees have high dense canopies and the trunks stand bare and straight. The ground beneath is free of vegetation so that only leaf litter softens the footfall as evening approaches and the long, low rays of the departing sun set the distant papyrus tops afire and bathe the tree trunks in a warm, ruddy glow. No guest, tempted with the finest wines and a succulent meal, can ever forget such an evening in the Okavango.

The lagoons of the Okavango are another of its magic features. Locally called madiba (sing. lediba), they are found in great numbers throughout the Delta. Often a channel simply opens out into a great stretch of water. Sometimes they are isolated from the main flow, many kilometres from it, and access is by a narrow, secret way that winds through tall, dense papyrus and is known only to a few. No one knows how the lagoons came into being but they seem to change little and are an enduring feature of the Delta. Their edges are mostly deeply lined with floating papyrus but some have a short section of high bank, overgrown with trees, where the fringing reed is less dense.

In one of these places, in the cool clearing beneath the trees, it is possible to camp, watching out over the waters as the day draws to a close. The days are sometimes windy but at dusk the wind usually dies away and the lagoon surface stills, taking on a mirror-like quality, the reflection of which is so perfect that it is hard to tell 'up' from 'down'. Islands seem to hang suspended in the clouds which themselves appear to plunge upwards from the depths. The change in colours, as the day comes to an end, is always dramatic. The blue-sky surface becomes metal grey and throws back the pinks and oranges and reds of the sunset. And when the sun has gone a soft mauve lingers on, gradually fading as the last light leaves the sky. And then the stars appear. They shine as brightly on the water's surface as they do in the sky above and they bob up and down in the gentle swell from the wake of some passing nocturnal aquatic creature which has silently begun his day.

The total quantity of bird and animal life in the Delta, although huge when measured in thousands, is in fact relatively low when compared to a similar dryland area with adequate water resources. The pattern of utilisation by mobile and grazing wildlife is seasonal and the Delta is not the preferred habitat of many species. It is used in the dry season when grazing outside the Okavango is scarce, but as soon as the rains fall the elephant and buffalo move out to more palatable pastures on the mainland. Two separate estimates of animal numbers must be taken, therefore, one for the dry season and one for the wet, and some animal populations fluctuate very widely.

Elephant, for example, vary from about 200 to 4 100, while giraffe, at about 6 500, vary hardly at all. Many buffalo remain in the Delta throughout the year but at the end of the dry season, their number may double to about 35 000. The beautiful sable antelope may number as many as 2 500 when concentrated into parts of the Delta, and less than 100 when they disperse with the rain. Permanent residents such as lechwe, tsessebe, impala, kudu, warthog, reedbuck, baboon and hippo, never leave the Delta at all and their overall numbers remain quite stable although their distribution within the area may change a great deal as they follow seasonal changes in vegetation. Excluding baboons, of which there are over 200 000, it is said that the large mammal population of the Delta, at its maximum, does not exceed more than 176 000 animals, of which 60 per cent are antelope.[7]

This sounds a great deal but it is not, relatively speaking, a high figure and one is often hard put to find game in any quantity within the Delta itself. The total area of the Okavango Delta where sand is, or has been, redistributed by flowing water, is some 22 000 km$^2$ but not all of this is covered with water today. The perennial wetlands are only about 6 000 km$^2$ in extent, which doubles in size during flood to about 13 000 km$^{2}$.[8] The dominant vegetation consists of papyrus and phragmites reeds and whilst a wide range of trees, shrubs and grasses occurs, the amount of edible vegetation for grazing species is not comparable to that of dry land. This perhaps suggests why mammals are not as numerous as one might expect and why the Delta appears to be used as a dry season refuge by the migrating species who wait there until the rains restore the lushness of their dryland habitat.

Surprisingly, fish are not as numerous as one might expect either and fish stocks are not as high as in other, similar, tropical habitats. However, there is a good, though curious, reason for this. There are between 70 and 80 different species of fish recorded in the Okavango Delta but their distribution is unusual. Seldom are more than 15 or 20 different species found in any one community and usually only 3 or 4 species will comprise the largest proportion of the population. The major food source for these fish comes from vegetation and detritus; insects and other invertebrates, although they are widely consumed, provide only a small proportion of their total diet. Breeding is affected by food supply, but it is also influenced by water temperature. In other, similar systems, such floods as there are usually coincide with the warm season, but in the Okavango the reverse is the case. Here the floods are powered by seasonal rains in Angola and by the time they reach the fish-breeding grounds of the Okavango, winter has set in and temperatures have fallen to between 13–21 °C. In fact, most fish breed in the warmer months of September to January, at a time when the waters, far from rising, are falling to their annual low and at a time, therefore, when food resources are dwindling, not increasing.[9]

Despite these limitations, the Okavango is justly famous for its fishing. Although mainly tiger-fish and bream can be found in most lagoons and channels, the larger fish of this type are caught further upstream in the Panhandle and several thriving fishing safari camps cater for the enthusiast. I am not a fisherman and my few attempts have nearly always been crowned with disaster. Several times, however, I have been persuaded to try fishing on the broad Okavango and I can attest to the thrill of holding a fighting tiger-fish as the line screams off the reel and curves, juddering, through the water, following its victim. (I can also tell you of sunken trees and how they can snag lines, of the fragility of fishing line when it gets near the propeller of a boat and about a certain record-breaking tiger-fish, that I didn't actually see, that got away just as . . . !)

Barbel is another common fish of the Delta. Favoured mainly by the local people, it is not generally sought after by fishermen as the flesh is rather bland and sometimes has a muddy texture. (Barbel are bottom feeders, which probably explains this.) What makes barbel interesting to me is their extraordinary migrations. Mike Gunn is a man who lives and works in the Delta and, among other things, he conducts visitors to parts of it that they might not otherwise have seen, for Mike knows the Delta well. He has witnessed several barbel 'runs', a mysterious phenomenon about which little is understood. In October or November, in the upper river, some weeks before the early floods arrive, the fish begin to congregate and swarm the water in huge numbers. The papyrus mats on either side of the channels become alive with flopping, slapping fish, as hundreds of thousands of them seem to be working their way towards the main body of water. So numerous are they that the surface of the water fairly boils with their movement and the occasion signals a feast-day for all. It seems that every fish-eating bird of the Delta gathers here and a barbel run can often be located at some distance by the column of predatory birds circulating above it. The general movement is upstream but the triggering mechanism is not known for certain, although some think that it might be the arrival of the first new rainwaters from Angola. The run sometimes persists for as long as a week and its slow progress can be followed by boat along the waterways of the Okavango.

Birdlife in the Okavango is prolific and enormously varied. Happily for the visitor, the variety is greatest along the edges of the Delta where the wet Okavango habitat meets with the dry thorn-scrub of the Kalahari. A particular favourite is the great African fish eagle. With its white head and shoulders and dark brown body, this majestic eagle, which occurs so widely along the rivers of Africa, is one of the Delta's most evocative sights and sounds. Its haunting call is uttered with the head thrown backwards and even in flight this same attitude is adopted.

Fish eagles are territorial and pairs will be seen perched on high trees along the river channels and waterways, jealously guarding their hunting rights. They will not hesitate to attack an intruder and have often been seen locked talon to talon with another fish eagle, plummeting from the sky, breaking the hold at the last possible moment as they struggle for dominance. As their name suggests, they feed almost entirely upon fish. They will eat dead or dying fish cast upon the shores but it is their hunting of fish that venture too close to the surface of the water that is especially exciting to watch. The fish eagle will swoop from its perch, plunging its talons deep into the water, to seize the luckless fish, while the enormous wings powerfully beat down to thrust it and its quarry back into the sky. Sometimes it will misjudge the size of its prey; one eagle was seen 'dragging' a 2,9 kg fish across the surface and another, which made a catch close to the shore, 'paddled' its way to the bank with a fish that weighed just over 3 kg.[10] Fish eagles are wonderfully regal birds as they sit in splendid solitude atop their high perches or cruise the open water with graceful ease, the tips of their primary feathers curling and spreading as the air slides over their motionless wings.

The fish eagle is not the only large predatory fishing bird of the Delta. It is also the territory of the remarkable fishing owl. Named in 1850 and from West Africa, little has been discovered about this bird since then. Although widely distributed in Africa, south of the Sahara it is extremely elusive. Tim Liversedge, who lived in the Delta for three years, had the good fortune to be able to locate and observe ten nesting pairs in the Panhandle region of the Okavango.[11] The information he was able to gather has provided much of what is known about these birds in Southern Africa.

The fishing owl prefers areas of dense riverine forest and is found more commonly in the Panhandle, although it does occur throughout the Delta. It is a nocturnal creature, spending the hours of darkness perched on a branch overhanging a stretch of water. Its plumage is a beautiful dark brown flecked with black, and the head and bib are a light tan colour, shading to cream. Obvious adaptations to its fishing habit are the absence of feathers on the legs, and the long claws and feet with rough soles which seem especially suited to grasping slippery prey. The fishing owl apparently relies less on sound than other owls, and it also lacks the characteristic facial shape. Nor does it have the specially modified feathers which permit other birds their silent flight. From its perch, one to two metres above the water, it drops suddenly down and clutches from the water any fish swimming close to the surface.

The fishing owl is a large bird, standing 30 to 40 cm high, and is clearly a powerful flier since it can lift a fish weighing 2 kg from the water. Sometimes the owl is pulled deep into the water by too large a prey, yet it seems capable of taking off again, although its feathers might have been completely saturated. Despite Tim's pioneering work, the fishing owl remains under-studied and its hunting techniques seem to me a fascinating field for further research. How, in the total darkness of a deeply shaded stretch of water, does a bird, even an owl with its remarkable sense of sight, detect a fish beneath the surface? How can it differentiate between fish and other aquatic creatures?

Among the delights of silently following the waterways of the Delta are many different birds one surprises on waterside perches. The tiny malachite kingfisher with bright red bill and white bib, orange chest and coat of iridescent blue, eyes you suspiciously before flying on 20 m or so to another perch, from where he watches you again. Cormorants, darters, ducks by the million, egrets, herons of a dozen types

and the bee-eaters, newly arrived from northern climes, are but a few of the hundreds of species to be seen.

As their name suggests, bees are part of the bee-eater's diet, but they are by no means all they eat. Any flying insect will be consumed and their dexterity on the wing is a wonder to see. Among the most startling of these birds is the carmine bee-eater. This crimson, cochineal-coloured bird nests in tunnels bored into the sandy banks of rivers. Several hundred of them will live in a colony and when they take to the air the river bank seems to explode in a cloud of red. It is a marvellous sight.

Over 350 different species of bird are listed as occurring in the Okavango Delta and indeed birds are everywhere abundant. Some friends of mine once watched a grass fire raging along the banks of an Okavango river. The fire attracted a huge number of birds seeking the insects that fled before the heat. Among them were fork-tailed drongos, the arch acrobats of the avian world. The drongos would swoop down, almost into the very flames themselves, seize an insect and then, while still on the wing, appear to dip their breast feathers in the river before returning to the feast. What exactly the birds were doing is intriguing. Cooling singed feathers perhaps, wetting themselves first so they didn't get singed, or dunking cooked insects that were too hot to hold?

It is the secret byways and narrow water passages that add so much to the intrigue of the Okavango Delta. As we have already seen, the water not only flows along the main passages, but meanders through a million smaller interlinking channels in a complicated maze, and it is only by trial and error that you will learn to find your way. There are no maps showing these tiny trails, and the tall papyrus shields them from the aerial photographer who seeks to lay bare the Delta's secrets. There are some men who know their way about the Delta well, but they have learnt the hard way, and there are only a handful of them. Nowadays, however, with more sophisticated boats and engines and a growing overseas tourist demand to see the Delta, their number increases yearly.

It is always fascinating to accompany

someone who knows his local area well. I once went across with Mike Gunn from Seronga to a lagoon on the southern side of the Delta, about three hours' boat ride away. We were supposed to be following another boat but it quickly disappeared from sight, leaving us behind. I tried to use the sun as a guide but, without any landmarks and nothing but a solid wall of papyrus to be seen, it was no assistance at all. Even more confusing, it seemed to wander aimlessly about the sky as the narrow channels twisted, turned and doubled back upon themselves. Mike seemed unperturbed and I asked him how he could follow a new route so confidently. He pointed to a barely visible thin line of foam on the down-current side of the channel we were in. This line is left by the churning propeller of an outboard engine and takes about an hour to subside. Further on we found ourselves in a lagoon, and he pointed to some water-lily leaves in a sheltered spot, protected from the wind, which were up-turned and tilted on their sides. They had been upset by the wake of a passing boat, he explained, and it could take up to two hours for them to settle. Some of the channels in the Delta are so narrow that a boat will have to force its way through tightly packed papyrus – and there, on the stems, at just the right height, was the bruising that indicated the contact of constant passage.[12] When you begin to look the signs are there to see and it seems that tracking on water is no less of an art than it is upon the land.

Mike was once working on an island near Seronga and one day I paid him an unexpected call. The only way to get across to his home was by mokoro, the traditional dug-out canoe of the Okavango. The mokoro is hewn from a single tree and may carry anything from two to five or six persons. It is narrow and has a rounded bottom with no keel and this makes it especially unstable. It is propelled either by paddles or by poles, depending on the people who use them and the part of the Delta one is in. I was in the poling part – which generally means that the water tends to be shallow, a fact for which I was grateful. There is rather a lot of me and, with my dog Gypsey and two rucksacks, one of

which was full of precious photographic equipment, we represented rather a large load.

The mokoro owner I hired happily piled us all into a single, rather small craft and we set off over a flooded meadow, covered with barely half a metre of water. This first stage was not a success. Less concerned about myself than the cameras, I apprehensively eyed the 5 cm of freeboard and the rapidly rising level of water in the bottom of the boat. I prepared for disaster and nervously grabbed at the straps of the camera bag. This was not easy to do and I soon realised just how unstable these wooden vessels could be. A series of wild oscillations followed, together with a sternly disapproving look from the owner. Resigned, I lay back and silently prayed, learning, at the same time, that the lower one's centre of gravity, the less insecure one feels. However, the rising water took its toll and my custodian, recognising the inevitable, poled to a nearby island and minutes later, after some lusty shouting, a friend appeared with another mokoro. To this my luggage was transferred and then, with 7 cm of freeboard, we set out into the papyrus and the lagoons beyond.

I relaxed enough to examine the boat more closely. The poler, I later learnt, was called Bwatumitse and, despite my unsteadying influence, his balance was not shaken at all. With easy strokes he pushed the long pole deep into the water ahead of him and, standing in the rear of the boat, rested his full weight upon it as he pushed the boat forward with his feet. The bottom of the boat was leaking but this did not seem to concern him. I noted that, as is common practice among all the mekoro people, Bwatumitse had thoughtfully snapped off several papyrus heads and laid their bushy fronds down as a seat for my comfort. Since they were squashed quite flat by my weight and since the level of water was, by this time, a centimetre or more in depth, the seat did nothing to keep me dry, and precious little to cushion me from the hard wooden floor. Nevertheless, the thought was appreciated.

In the bottom of the boat was an empty plastic bottle and I found it disconcerting to watch it rolling heavily from one side to

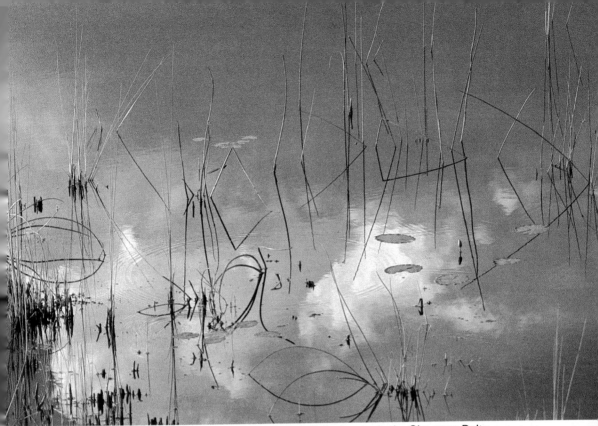

▲Reed reflections in the Okavango Delta ▼A backwater in the Okavango Delta

Smoky skies at Seronga

▲Dragonfly, Okavango

▲Water lilies, Okavango

▲Sharp-nosed reed frog, Okavango

▲Salvinia, Chobe River

▲Freshwater crab, Okavango ▼Stapelia, Ngamiland

▲Grassland striped frog ▼Camouflaged grasshopper

the other and then bobbing lightly on the surface as the water level rose. It made me think again about the water-proofing on the cameras. Near it, at the high end of the boat, where the water had not yet reached, lay a dead fish. Quite why it was there I am not sure. It looked decidedly sunburnt and I had the impression that it had been there, along with the cloud of flies that seemed to be attached to it, for several days. The other canoe was some distance ahead but the two men carried on a friendly conversation, which I am sure could have been shared by anyone within several kilometres.

We crossed a large lagoon without incident (I wondered if my thoughts on levitation helped) and entered a narrow papyrus channel on the far side. Here I felt safer – there was always the papyrus to prevent us from tipping over – and shortly we emerged onto another meadow and sodden grasslands leading to the island that was our destination. I gratefully left the mokoro with renewed admiration for them as a craft, and for the people who guided them with such skill, but with a determination not to travel in one again unless I really had to!

The shallower lagoons, of which there are many hundreds, are often densely packed with beautiful water-lilies whose round, dark green floating leaves carpet the surface and create a perfect backdrop to their exquisite flowers standing proud above the water. Their centres are golden yellow and the petals either cream or a delicate translucent blue, although sometimes, red and orange ones are found. The leaves of these plants usually lie flat upon the water, but when they are caught by the wake of a passing boat or a gust of wind they are flipped over onto an edge. This can be a little disconcerting, especially if seen out of the corner of the eye, for the up-turned leaf has a deeply serrated edge and is large enough to suggest the sudden appearance of a school of hippo or the Delta's equivalent to the Loch Ness Monster!

In the less exposed areas of a lagoon or river, it is across these leaves that you will see the African jacana, or 'lily-trotter', sprightly stepping. Its elongated toes so spread its weight that a single leaf will support it as, with nodding head, it searches the aquatic vegetation for the insects, snails and seeds upon which it feeds. The nest of this beautiful bird is cunningly hidden in a clump of floating vegetation. The jacana usually has two to four young and within minutes of emerging from the nest they can walk and forage like their parents, though they stay close to them for several months. The mother when alarmed will stoop down with wings raised, and call to her young. As they scurry to her side, she clamps her wings over them and carries them off at a rapid walk, away from danger. It is a most amusing sight to see, the female striding along with four pairs of young and rather gangly legs protruding from beneath her wing feathers.

Another inhabitant of the rivers and lagoons is the pygmy goose. Not a goose at all in fact, it is one of the most brilliantly coloured ducks in the world. Often seen in pairs and sometimes in small flocks, this duck prefers to roost and nest in trees, and there are numerous reports of nests discovered in holes in trees. The young have very sharp claws and when the day comes for them to leave the nest, they back out of the hole and try to cling to the bark as they scrabble backwards down the often vertical trunk to the ground and the water beyond. Sometimes, they fall to the ground. I know of one nest in the Okavango in a tree 5 m from the ground. Out of this the fluffy, down-covered chicks would fall, because the bark was too slippery for them to hold. Despite the fall, they were quite unharmed and under their mother's careful eye were shepherded to the water's edge.

As we have seen, the Okavango River may at one time have continued its flow to the east, across northern Botswana, and entered the Limpopo. We have seen how continental warping raised the outer margins of the African sub-continent and how the inland areas tended to remain at about the same altitude so that a saucer shape was created. Inevitably, these movements of the earth's mantle placed stresses on the continental crust which were most likely to manifest themselves in areas of existing weakness. Down the length of Africa, from the Red Sea through Kenya, past the Great Lakes of East Africa, splitting to include

Malawi on the one side and Zambia and the Zambezi Valley on the other, the Great Rift Valley system of Africa divides the land. It has not appeared simultaneously along its entire length. In places its appearance has been relatively sudden; in others it has been a gentle submergence of rock along existing lines of weakness. The northern end may have developed first, with sequential sections added as the milennia have rolled past. It is now widely accepted that the Okavango Delta is the most southerly end of this massive continental fault. It is what is known as a developing graben and can be envisaged as a sheer-sided valley in which the middle section has dropped. In the Okavango, the extent of this drop is between 320 m and 360 m at the deepest, south-western end, although it is more shallow as one progresses upstream.

The geological genesis of the Delta is not precisely known; indeed, it remains a matter of great speculation since the dates of important geological events remain uncertain. The emergence of the Rift Valley system is thought to have first occurred during the period of intense crustal warping that took place in the mid-Miocene, about 10 to 15 million years ago. The Okavango Delta is likely to have formed very much later than that date. The Delta was clearly greater in extent than it is today and there is evidence of where, in the past as well as in more recent times, the flowing waters cut through and truncated the extensive dune fields that cover much of north-western Botswana. Therefore, the Delta is plainly younger than the last period of dune formation. This does not help with a specific date, however, since the age of the dunes is also the subject of much speculation. It is thought, however, that the climate was exceptionally dry at the end of the Tertiary period, about 3–5 million years ago and that this was when the great dune fields were formed.[13] This then suggests a much younger date for the Delta, of less than 3 million years. As we have seen, the super-lake was probably drained by continental tilting, nudging the waters northwards to escape into the Zambezi, and the earliest time when this river, in the vicinity of the Victoria Falls, could have been established

was about 5 million years ago.[14] Other scientists put this date even later, at 3,3 million years ago.[15] It was at that time that major fault-controlled realignments of the rivers in north-western Botswana took place and, since the faults are all part of the same system, those that form the Okavango, further to the south, are likely to be younger still. At most, the Okavango Delta is probably not more than 2 million years old and it may be less than that.

For as long as the trough astride its course has been in existence, the Okavango River has been filling it with sediment, mostly sand and clay, carried on the incoming water. Today the whole trough has been filled, although the depth of the sediment varies. In the south-eastern end of the Delta it is well over 300 m deep; in the north-west, as the Panhandle is approached, the depth decreases. How this filling up process took place is unknown. Whether the rock beneath subsided at the same rate as sedimentation took place, or whether the Okavango cascaded over some forgotten precipice to form a lake in the valley below, may never be known. Today, however, the trough lies completely buried beneath the sands. The fault-lines, which have played so important a role in the development of the Delta, cannot be discerned with the naked eye and all lie beneath a concealing blanket of sand. The south-eastern end of the Delta is abruptly truncated by two long parallel faults. Like a massive drain, these faults contain between them the Thamalakane River which collects all the outflow from the vast wetlands and channels it, via a junction along its course, either to Lake Ngami or along the Boteti River, far out into the Kalahari.

Enormous quantities of water flow into this delta system. Formally defined as 10,5 $\times$ 109 m$^3$ of inflow with another 5 $\times$ 109 m$^3$ from rainwater, these rather intimidating figures tell us that something in the range of 15,5 km$^3$ of water enters the Delta every year. To put this figure into perspective, this is about the same as the total amount of water used in England and Wales in one year.[16] The mean annual discharge of the Okavango is also equal to about one-fifth of the total run-off in the Republic of South Africa.[17] These figures are important and we will return later to their implications for the future of the Delta. Not all this great volume of water leaves the system via the Thamalakane River. A staggering 95 per cent is believed to evaporate. About 2 per cent sinks through the sands to become groundwater and the remaining 2-3 per cent finds its way into the Thamalakane.

The distribution of this vast flow across the area of the Delta is constantly changing. Despite its widespread nature, main channels right down to the end of the Delta do exist and, for a hundred years or more, the abrupt switching of flow from one to the other has been a mystery. The Thaoge River, one of the main drainage lines in the south-west of the Delta, ceased to flow in the 1880s. Until then it was the main source of supply for Lake Ngami and was a massive river. In 1854 the explorer Andersson boated up it from the lake for over 100 km and only in a few places did he find the water less than 2 m deep.[18]

The Boro River, a central drainage line just south of Chief's Island, suddenly started to flow in 1953 for the first time in living memory.[19] As recently as 1984 Maun residents were commenting on the inexplicable shift in water distribution, noting that the bulk seemed to have gone, unusually, to the western side. In the early days all sorts of explanations were offered for this phenomenon. It was noted, for example, that the papyrus growth in some channels would increase and it was thought that the reed was responsible for the blockage. To some extent this may have been so, but later research showed that this was not the major cause. Many of the Delta's indigenous peoples were in the habit of cutting large rafts of papyrus which they used to float themselves across the waters. When no longer needed, the rafts were abandoned and they would eventually come to rest, blocking, or helping to block, an already restricted channel.

Hippo were regarded as an important means of keeping open, by their continual tramping along certain routes, some of the narrower channels. Hunting of these animals and the subsequent decline in hippo population was also blamed for the many blockages that frequently occurred. The real explanation for these strange changes

is far more dramatic than either of these, for it seems directly linked to the turbulent forces that broil within the mantle of the earth.

The whole of Ngamiland is tectonically unstable. This means that the particular part of the earth's crust upon which it is located is susceptible to movement at any time. The movement, which probably consists of warpings, tilts and gentle twisting, is not generally sudden and is quite imperceptible to humans. There is no doubt, however, that it is constantly taking place and that it accounts for the strange behaviour and flow of much of Ngamiland's waters. Associated with this movement is a high level of earthquake activity. This is merely the physical manifestation of the region's instability and represents sudden change which may not always affect surface features. Seismicity in the Delta was first recognised in 1952 and since then several studies have been carried out. Between May 1952 and May 1953, for example, 22 earthquakes were recorded in the vicinity of the Delta. One, in October 1952, was of magnitude 6,7, and the others were magnitude 5 events. The October earthquake was strong enough to cause damage to buildings in Maun and is believed to have resulted in a change in the drainage pattern of the Delta.[20] It is possibly the explanation for the reopening of the Boro River in 1953.

These events cause less damage than might be expected, because of the relative absence of large or tall buildings, but their occurrence has considerable implications for the long-term development of the area. From September 1965 to August 1974, 38 events were recorded and this level of activity continues to the present day.[21] There seems no reason to doubt that this activity, together with less violent flexings of the earth's crust, are the cause of major changes in the pattern of water distribution within the Okavango Delta.

Generally accepted today, this was not so in the past and at least three memorable characters[22] have been involved in trying to keep the river channels clear of papyrus. They did not know that these were being blocked by shifting land and not by the papyrus. As part of a scheme to develop

Ngamiland, strenuous efforts were made at one time to restore and improve the flow in some of the Okavango's channels. Until then pristine and quite unspoilt, the colonial period ushered in an era of change and plans were laid to develop the Okavango as a water resource, not only for Botswana but for much of Southern Africa.

The Thaoge River, so recently dry, occupied the attention of water engineers in the 1930s, 1940s and 1950s. Martinus Drotsky, working with hand labour, hacked, slashed and cleared his way through many kilometres of papyrus. The men would stand in the water, often up to their chests, cutting and clearing the reed. Sometimes Drotsky dug shortcut channels across large loops in the river. In all, thirteen channels were made, covering a distance of 14 km, reopening a total of 112 km of flowing water. It was an outstanding effort and in 1972 those channels were still clear and unobstructed. It was all to no avail, however, as money for the project ran out and the water never flowed beyond the remaining obstruction.

Brind, who was engaged to conduct a survey of the Delta in the 1950s, conceived the idea of a papyrus cutting machine. It was approved and, to this exceedingly remote and particularly inaccessible part of the Delta, came 45 tons of floating metal monster. It could cut a swathe 7 m long by 1 m wide. The cut material was raised onto a platform from where it could be mechanically moved to one side. The whole contraption was 8 m wide by 8 m high by 9 m long and it took three 5-ton lorries four weeks to carry from the railhead at Francistown 750 km away. It was a magnificent idea, monumental in its execution – but the trouble was it did not work. To design a machine of that nature and to expect to get it right first time, was perhaps asking too much. Weak components prevented the machine from being given a fair trial and breakdowns put it out of action very quickly. The logistics of replacing parts over such an enormous distance, coupled with the fact that money had, once again, run out, meant that the machine was left to rot, even though the modifications and repairs were minor. It was a great pity. Drotsky and Brind, between them, share

the honours for real effort and determination to tackle the problem of the Okavango's changing waterways.

The third character, whose name is associated with these attempts, was of a different mould entirely. Charles F Naus was a most extraordinary man. Gullible, naive, and perhaps a charlatan, he was obviously earnest and very convincing. His heyday in the Delta was in the early 1930s when ideas for developing its waterways were in their infancy. He claimed to be an architect and an engineer, as well as a retired colonel – but of what we do not know as his antecedents were at best somewhat cloudy. He had several schemes for clearing the waterways of the Okavango and opening it up for traffic and development. He offered his services to the British Government but they were not convinced and his offer was turned down. Naus persevered, however, and won the ear of the Resident Commissioner, Colonel Rey, who took a liking to him and considered his ideas feasible. He was given the go ahead in 1933, and for four years, supported by the Colonial Development Fund, he worked at clearing the waterways.

Naus's idea was to clear the papyrus by fire. This was not new and had been tried extensively before, but Naus had a different approach. He planned to build a series of small dams that would deflect the flow of water, thereby exposing the papyrus right down to its roots. Deprived first of water, and dried by the sun, Naus was convinced that burning them thereafter would completely eradicate the menace. His first dam was 300 m long, 8 m wide and 4 m high – in itself a significant construction. It was as the project was nearing completion that Naus struck on the idea which impelled him into the pages of the Okavango's book of fools.

Naus began construction of his dam simultaneously from opposite sides. As the two ends approached each other, in the middle of the stream, and were only narrowly separated, he noticed how the water level on the upstream side rose and how the speed of the water increased as it rushed through the remaining gap. He suddenly realised that here, in this simple phenomenon, hitherto unnoticed by anyone, lay the solution to the whole problem of clearing the Okavango's waterways. If the water flow was increased by leaving narrow gaps in low dams, he reasoned, a series of such dams at critical points all over the Delta would be the answer. Each would speed up the flow of water which, with its new-found power, would punch and scour its way through all obstructions, clearing the Delta forever.

Excited by his discovery, he hurried back to Maun and triumphantly revealed his plan. Convinced that dams with gaps in them somehow increased the total flow, he had completely overlooked the relationship between volume and speed. The speed of the water did indeed increase, but the amount that passed through was reduced and he would in fact have achieved nothing. The Government engineer recognised the foolishness for what it was and advised against the adoption of Naus's scheme. The engineer seems to have been the only opponent, however, for Naus again had the support of Col Rey and he was given authority to build five more such dams. He started with three dams across rivers near Maun. The more certain the Government engineer became that the project was completely unfeasible, the more certain were Rey, Naus and all the residents of Maun that it was actually working (in spite of the fact that it was not), so infectious was Naus's enthusiasm. The whole episode was reminiscent of the fairytale of the emperor's clothes, with only the Government engineer seeing the truth. There must have been other non-believers, too, though, for a commission was appointed in 1935 to investigate the matter and submit a report, and a second appointed later in the same year. It was not until the retirement of Col Rey, however, that sanity finally prevailed and Naus's project was abandoned.

The time and money spent were not altogether wasted for three of the dam sites provided foundations for road bridges which still exist today. Naus, who went on to work for the first Director of Public Works in the Colony, resigned soon thereafter. This was not surprising perhaps, for the holder of this high office was none other than Brind, who had been the Government engineer in Maun.

Inevitably, man has been excited by the possibilities of exploiting the Okavango Delta. Such huge volumes of water in the heart of so arid a land have stirred dreams of fantastic local irrigation projects or, in a generally arid sub-continent, of supplying almost unlimited quantities to neighbouring states whose thirsty needs threaten to exhaust their own meagre supplies. Without doubt the most infamous, ill-considered and foolhardy of these ideas was what has become known as the Schwarz Scheme, which, like that of Naus, raised the hopes and expectations of millions of people. It took nearly thirty years for the scheme to be recognised for what it was.

Professor E H L Schwarz first published his proposals in 1918 in a Johannesburg newspaper. His scheme was almost continental in its extent and encompassed the diverting of certain rivers so that the Kalahari would become the most fertile region in the world. Schwarz suggested diverting the Cunene River (between Namibia and Angola) so that it flowed into and filled the Etosha Pan. The overflow would find its way into the Okavango River which, together with the Chobe River, was to be channelled into the Boteti River, which would in turn refill the old super-lake.

The recreation of these two vast lakes, Etosha and Makgadikgadi, would revolutionise the climate and economy of Southern Africa. Schwarz calculated that after ten years the climate would be changed by the addition of 250 mm of rainfall to the existing average. This would come about as a result of increased evaporation caused by the creation of the two lakes. The increased rainfall would in turn enlarge the rivers, which would enlarge the lakes... There was no denying the beautiful simplicity of the scheme. The super-lake, once full, would overflow to the south, re-establishing an ancient waterway which, claimed Schwarz, would bisect the Kalahari and, after joining the Orange River, would provide a water-transport route from the Atlantic to the very heart of the Okavango Delta.

In addition to all these benefits, over a quarter of a million km$^2$ of land would become available for irrigation and, in Southern Africa 'the condition... would be restored to that of some two or three hundred years back, when the Karoo was a flower garden, supporting vast herds of game, and the present dry rivers ran throughout the year' .[23] Twenty per cent of the water in the new lakes would seep into the ground and would replenish and strengthen springs and wells right down to the very coasts of Africa.[24] It was a grand, exciting and inspiring scheme and could hardly fail to capture the imagination. That it could be achieved, as Schwarz claimed, for as little as £100 000, assured it of popular acclaim and for some years Schwarz acquired the status of a demi-god, saviour of Southern Africa.

That Schwarz had never actually visited any of the areas of which he spoke when his grandiose plans were first published was, apparently, overlooked, or considered to be of little importance.[25] Even in the 1920s the area was remote and little known. Maps were sketchy and data upon them highly unreliable. It soon became apparent that Schwarz's arguments were based on complete ignorance of respective ground levels, on extremely unsound meteorological theory and, at times, highly dubious mathematics! In the face of criticism, his responses were vague and unsatisfactory but his overwhelming enthusiasm ensured that his public accepted him completely.

A violent controversy emerged which necessitated two public enquiries to resolve. The first was in 1925 and included Schwarz himself, although he chose to take no active part in it. Its report failed to entirely dampen support for the scheme as many of its members were themselves infected with enthusiasm for its ideals. The more pragmatic and technical of its number were, however, quick to condemn it in its entirety, although even they accepted that some irrigation potential did exist. This equivocation served to fuel continued support so that, in 1946, a second survey was undertaken which finally laid to rest the theory that the Kalahari might become the bread-basket of Southern Africa.

Although the Schwarz Scheme is now a thing of the past, dreams of exploiting the Okavango have persisted to the present day. In 1960 it was suggested that a canal could deliver large quantities of water to Rakops, on the Boteti River, there to be used for irrigation purposes. A plan to sell water to South Africa has been suggested more than once in recent years. Less ambitious, perhaps, ideas such as these continue to crop up from time to time and, for a number of years, the United Nations, through its Food and Agricultural Agency, has studied and reported comprehensively upon the potential of the Okavango Delta as a primary water resource for Botswana.[26] A number of possible schemes have emerged from these reports, graded in size from small to large agricultural projects. One project is being considered at this moment and involves the construction of dams on the Thamalakane River which would create a reservoir of considerable size and may make available as much as 10 000 ha of irrigable land. Another is to restore the flow of the Thaoge River – the task so bravely attempted by Drotsky and Brind so many years ago. No direct mention is made of any specific plan for large-scale withdrawal of the Okavango's water. Although any attempt at utilising the Okavango as a water source or for agricultural purposes raises real fears for its future among the world's conservationists, large-scale extraction is what is feared most.

The Okavango is unique in this part of Africa. It is a pristine wilderness, largely unspoilt. Nevertheless change is being thrust upon it. Many express the fear that the change is sometimes ill-considered and that it takes place piecemeal, without the development of an overall plan. Others fear that despite adequate legislation there is insufficient determination and understanding to enforce it. As a consequence, conservationists are concerned that before long irreversible damage will have taken place and that the Okavango Delta will be changed beyond redemption. Yet there is powerful motivation for change. Botswana has a small but rapidly growing population. As in all developing nations, job creation is of vital importance. The present industrial base is limited to the eastern side of the country, where population density is highest and where such scarce water resources as are currently available are most abundant. Water scarcity is, however, a limit to growth.

The Botswana Government emphasises rural development in its national planning but this too requires water and, as the limits of current resources are approached, speculative eyes are being cast on the Delta itself. If at least 95 per cent of the water evaporates anyway, what harm, it is argued, would it do to remove some of that water? Not only does Botswana need water but so do her neighbours. The Republic of South Africa, for example, a politically and economically powerful force, in the 1980s felt her own national growth retarded by the lack of water when annual rains failed across the country. Namibia and western Zimbabwe, too, could both benefit from Okavango water and, although serious consideration has barely started, it is difficult to see how large-scale utilisation of the Okavango can be avoided in the long term. It is not, however, likely to be easy or inexpensive.

The FAO report gives some very pointed indicators to the future. It says that the project is not presently economical, a conclusion which follows from end-price considerations as well as political and other factors. That it might become so in the future is acknowledged and extraction from a site near the southern end of the Panhandle has been suggested, despite the increased cost this will involve in moving the water, probably by canal, right across or around the Delta. The report correctly points out that extraction on a large scale would engender heavy socio-economic dependence upon the supply, which therefore must be totally reliable.

The distribution mechanism of water flow anywhere in the Delta proper is so erratic and unpredictable that absolutely reliable extraction in that area would be almost impossible. The critical question is how much water can be removed. The United Nations' team recommended withdrawals of the order of 500 to 1 000 million m$^3$, estimating that this would cause a reduction in the area of the Delta of between 5 and 10 per cent and would be unlikely to cause drastic changes in the general ecology.[27] The consultants report that no water manipulation scheme currently proposed would reduce the flooded area by more than 3 per cent, even in the driest year, and in a normal year far less. This is compared to the normal average variation of 14 per cent in the flooded area and a year to year variation of 30 per cent. The controversy, when it comes – as it surely will – will range around whether or not the forecast physical changes are correct and what is an acceptable level of change.

It is not only water extraction that threatens to change the form of the Delta as it is today. Because it is such a unique and fascinating place, as a tourist attraction it is becoming increasingly popular. That tourism is burgeoning is without question. In 1981 there were 28 safari companies of one sort or another in Botswana, most of them centred upon the Okavango region; in 1984 there were 64 operators. Safari lodges had increased from 22 in 1981 to 34 in 1985. In 1984, 37 000 visitors were handled by these companies.[28] These figures may not appear large by some standards but, in terms of their rate of growth, they are considerable and there is no reason to suppose, given Botswana's political stability, that they will not continue to grow. This has meant an increase in traffic of every kind in the Delta – more safari camps, more island hideaways, more airstrips, more domestic staff, aircraft, boats, vehicles and people. As yet the impact is small, but already the 'old hands' are noticing the change and voices speak with concern about 'what is happening to the Delta'.

The Motswana who lives on the fringes of the Delta is equally concerned for the future of his grazing lands. There is some dispute as to the actual number of cattle in Ngamiland (most of which are concentrated along the Delta's shores) and estimates range from 250 000 to 300 000. An ideal stocking rate of one head per 12 ha is recommended, yet at least 70 per cent of the herd is stocked more densely than this. The environmental impact of this heavy stocking rate upon the areas adjacent to the Delta, as well as in the Delta itself, is a matter of grave concern. Some claim that there is no widespread evidence of overgrazing but others disagree, and my own experience tends to the latter view.

The elimination of tsetse fly within the Delta has raised fears as to its future protection from an invasion by cattlemen and their stock. Those sceptics who believe that cattle encroachment will not be prevented, point out that, measured by weight per hectare, the carrying capacity for wild animals is two to three times that of cattle and urge that some way be found to exploit and develop this fact.[29] That this will happen in time seems unlikely for game ranches, after fifteen or twenty years in Southern Africa, are only now beginning to be seen as viable enterprises. No one has tried ranching an area as large or as inaccessible as the Okavango and certainly no government has been involved in game ranching. Researchers from the University of the Witwatersrand have been monitoring vegetation in some areas of the Okavango and they report major vegetation changes.[30] These they attribute to cattle and donkeys grazing in riverine and floodplain zones which, they say, is directly attributable to the successful anti-tsetse spraying which has made these areas accessible.

The Okavango Delta is one of Africa's magic places. With its broad reaches of still, clear water, of tree-studded islands and beautiful lagoons, it offers tranquillity and peace and a glimpse of the 'old Africa', largely unsullied by modern man. For those who love wild places, it can be the greatest escape of all, but it cannot hope to remain untouched by the pressures of development and the demands of men. One can but hope that a balance will be struck so that our children's families and generations to come will not be deprived of the opportunity of sharing this remarkable wilderness.

## REFERENCES

1. Games, I. 'Feeding and Movement Patterns of the Okavango Sitatunga'. In *Botswana Notes and Records,* Vol 16, 1984, pp 131–37
2. United Nations. *Investigation of the Okavango Delta as a Primary Water Resource for Botswana. Vol 1.* United Nations Development Programme, FAO, Gaborone, Botswana, 1977, p 111
3. Graham, A. 'A Crocodile Management Plan for the Okavango River'. Investigation of the Okavango as a Primary Water Resource for Botswana. Technical Note No 10, United Nations, FAO and the Government of the Republic of Botswana, 1976, pp 1–21
4. Pooley, A C. 'The Nile Crocodile, *Crocodilus niloticus'.* In *The Lammergeyer,* Vol 2, No 1, February 1962, pp 1–56
5. Seaman, J. Personal communication, December 1984
6. Wilmot, U. Personal communication, December 1984
7. United Nations. Op cit, pp 135–36
8. Ibid, p 5
9. Ibid, pp 176–79
10. Tomkinson, A J. 'Notes on the Mass-carrying Ability of the African Fish Eagle'. In *The Lammergeyer,* No 22, October 1975, pp 19–22
11. Liversedge, T. 'The Fishing Owl in the Okavango Delta'. In *The Babbler* (newsletter of the Botswana Bird Club, Box 71, Gaborone, Botswana,) Vol 1, No 2, pp 8–12
12. Gunn, M. Personal communication, 1984
13. Cooke, H J. 'The Origin of the Makgadikgadi Pans'. In *Botswana Notes and Records,* Vol 11, 1979, pp 37–42
14. Lister, L A. *The Erosion Surfaces of Rhodesia.* Unpublished PhD. thesis, University of Rhodesia, 1976, p 205
15. Bowmaker, A P, Jackson, P B N and Jubb, R A. 'Freshwater Fishes'. In *Biogeography and Ecology of Southern Africa.* Edited by Werger, M J A. The Hague: Dr W Junk, 1978, p 1197
16. Pike, J G. 'The Development of the Water Resources of the Okavango Delta'. Proceedings of the Conference on Sustained Production from Semi-Arid Areas. In *Botswana Notes and Records, Special Edition No 1,* October 1971, p 37
17. Brind, W G. *The Okavango Delta.* Report on the 1951–1953 Field Surveys. Report to the Botswana Government, Ministry of Water Affairs, p 52
18. Wilson, B H. 'Some Natural and Man-made Changes in the Channels of the Okavango Delta'. In *Botswana Notes and Records,* Vol 5, 1973, p 138
19. Pike, J G. Op cit, p 36
20. Hutchings, D G, Hutton, L G, Hutton, S M, Jones, C R and Leonhert, E P. A Summary of the Geology, Seismicity, Geomorphology and Hydrogeology of the Okavango Delta. Government of Botswana, Geological Survey Department, Bulletin No 7, pp 6–7
21. Ibid, p 6
22. Wilson, B H. Op cit, pp 132–54
23. Potten, D H. 'Aspects of the Recent History of Ngamiland'. In *Botswana Notes and Records,* Vol 8, 1974, p 75
24. McKenzie, L A. Report on the Kalahari Expe-

dition, 1945. Government of South Africa, Department of Irrigation, Pretoria, 1946, pp 1–35

25. Ibid, p 8
26. **United Nations.** Op cit, Vols 1 and 2
27. Ibid, Vol 2, **pp 217-19**
28. **Fowkes, J D.** *The Contribution of the Tourist Industry to the Economy of the Republic of Botswana.* Report to the Kalahari Conservation

Society, Gaborone, Botswana, Feb 1985, **p 20**
29. **Tinley, K L.** *An Ecological Reconnaissance of the Moremi Wildlife Reserve, Botswana.* Johannesburg: Okavango Wildlife Society, 1966, **p 108**
30. **Reavell, P.** 'Further Deterioration of the Swamp Ecosystem in the Boro-Thamalakane Region, Delta, Botswana', In *Botswana Notes and Records,* Vol 15, 1983, **pp 105-06**

# 8. Ngamiland

NGAMILAND extends across the north-western corner of Botswana and includes, at its heart, the Okavango Delta. Adjacent to it, in the north, is Chobe District and these two areas between them contain some of the Kalahari's most remote, varied and inhospitable country. In the south is the mysterious Lake Ngami, and in the north the enigmatic Savuti channel and the great Mababe Depression into which it leads. Dividing the area and carrying away the minimal overflow from the Okavango Delta is the Boteti River, now a faint relic of its former self, when it once led major rivers to the vast super-lake which covered much of this region. Now it takes a much reduced trickle of water far into the Kalahari where it sinks into the thirsty sands or collects in a terminal, man-made reservoir to the south of the great Makgadikgadi Pans. In the centre of this sprawling wilderness lies the busy little town of Maun.

Maun is the tribal capital of the baTawana people, who established it in 1915. Then, as today, it was a frontier town. Straddling the Thamalakane River, it is set at the very gateway to the Delta. It served as a base and port of call for all who wished to explore Ngamiland from earliest days. Thanks, at least partially, to Charles Naus, two bridges link the separated town. One is a modern construction and carries the main traffic from Francistown 480 km away. The other seems to have changed very little from the time when Naus built it. Its origin as a dam with gaps in it is still plain to see and it consists largely of a pile of rubble, stone and clay, precariously held together with tree-trunks which bridge the gaps. Crossing it is a decidedly hair-raising experience!

As an administrative capital, all the usual functions of government are represented in Maun, housed in white-painted, concrete block, corrugated iron-roofed buildings. Maun is also the home of many thousands of baTawana people who live in large traditional villages within the town's boundaries. Their dwellings are of a type that has changed little in millenia: rounded in shape, the mud walls reinforced with straight wooden poles cut from saplings. The conical roof is thatched and reed palisades often surround the living area. There are numerous stores to be found, some very well stocked shops and Maun boasts the busiest airport in Botswana. The pride of the town is the 5 km of tarred road that dominates its centre. Maun is also the home of Ngamiland's tourism and hunting industry and here one may conceivably come across many of the 'characters' of tomorrow's history. These are the people who live in Maun, wresting a living from the wild by their knowledge and experience. They live constantly at the frontier of safety and the unknown, and theirs is a life filled with excitement and danger. This spirit makes Maun, small as it is, a place of warm-hearted, generous people, to whom tragedy and hardship are no strangers, and who are often closely bound in a spirit of friendship and sharing that is less common elsewhere.

Maun has seen more than its fair share of strange happenings, humorous incidents and memorable characters. One such character is Tom Kayes, now in his ninety-second year, who has lived in and about Maun for over 60 years and is still going strong. I saw Tom as recently as 1985 in the workshop of his son's garage, still working productively. A legendary 'bush mechanic', with a vast store of accumulated knowledge, Tom came to Maun from

Ghanzi in the 1920s where he had worked on his father's and other farms. In those early days he made the eight to nine day journey regularly by ox-wagon.

In his life in Ngamiland Tom has done and been many things. With his father he rode 1 000 head of cattle to Angola, a journey that took six or seven months; he has put up houses and worked for locust control, built roads in the District and operated a transport service in the 1930s, driving a 3-tonne lorry through bush tracks from Maun to Livingstone. He remembers the times when petrol was almost impossible to obtain and recalls how people used to convert vehicles from petrol to wood burning. A little vague now about the details, he recalls wood fires being lit and the gas from the smouldering wood being mixed with drops of water. It was just as efficient as petrol, he claims, although it was a lot of bother and maintenance was much higher. The situation must have improved, though, because he remembers AROP petrol – Anglo Russian Oil Products – being sold in Maun in about 1928-9.

Maun now boasts a very smart and modern hotel. It has recently been taken over by a large corporation and given a complete face-lift. In its day it was the epitome of colonial small-town architecture and was not without a great deal of character, set beneath tall trees, on the banks of the Thamalakane River. It was started by the Riley family and was known, appropriately, as Riley's Hotel. In those days liquor licences were hard to get, and in Maun impossible, since by law licences were only available east of the railway line – and that was a long way to the east. Harry Riley inveigled the Resident Commissioner into accepting a place on a hunting party and used all his knowledge and skill to make sure that a fine lion fell to the Commissioner's gun. The celebration that followed later was copiously laced with good spirit and, at an appropriate moment, the question of the liquor licence was raised. The euphoria of sweet success, plus the intoxicating effect of Scotland's finest export must have influenced the Commissioner's decision, and the end result was all Harry could have asked for. He got his liquor licence.[1]

Maun was then (and to a large extent still is today) a place where one had to do things for oneself, to be a jack of all trades, and Harry Riley actually built his own hotel. He was not a qualified builder but the construction stood the test of time, despite one small hitch. The building was already at roof height when friends pointed to the absence of a waterproofing layer just above ground level. With growing dismay, Harry made enquiries as to how essential this was considered, meeting everywhere the same adamant reply: it could not be omitted. Faced with the prospect and the expense of knocking down all his hard work, Harry gave the matter some thought. With the imaginative creativeness typical of those who have learnt to become self-reliant, Harry solved the problem in an ingenious way. With a handful of labourers, he took a metal saw and sawed his way around the entire building, about 30 cm above ground level, inserting in the narrow gap that followed the blade thin sheets of corrugated iron that had been hammered flat. They are still visible in the walls of the building today.

The roads of Ngamiland are among the worst in the Kalahari and are notorious for their deep, clinging sand. There is a tale of one Cornelius de Lange who used to drive the railway's lorry from Maun, around the southern margin of the Delta, to Shakawe on Botswana's western border. The sand on that road was so deep that once a vehicle was in the ruts, there was no need to hold the steering – it would follow the road entirely on its own. One day Cornelius had the misfortune to suffer a fatal heart attack while in the driver's seat. The labourers on the back of the lorry knew nothing about it as the vehicle trundled on, held at top speed by the foot of the dead driver, until at last on a bend it left the tracks and came to a halt in the bush. On discovering the driver's fate, the labourers fled and it was six days before Cornelius was found on the lonely road.[2]

Lionel Palmer, a genial and generous host, as well as an internationally known hunter, who still lives and works in Maun, was once bringing back a young client from a hunting safari. He was having difficulty in controlling the vehicle and the

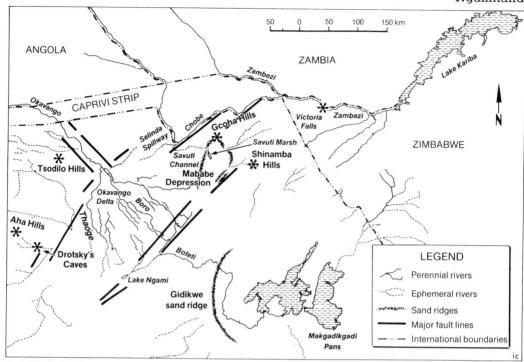

## NGAMILAND

Major, deep-earth fault lines have given shape to the Okavango Delta and the rivers of this area.

The faults clearly show the trough containing the Delta. Their close proximity to the middle Zambezi river, itself part of the Great East African Rift Valley system, suggests a link with this feature. Indeed, the Delta is now considered to be its southernmost extension and still developing.

Also shown is the Mababe Depression and its connecting link to the Chobe river – the Savuti Channel, which has mysteriously opened and closed a number of times in recent history, leading water from the Chobe to flood again the marshes of the Depression. There is no satisfactory explanation as to why this should happen, although it is suggested that there is connection with the high levels of tectonic activity in this area.

The instability of this area may throw some light on the demise of Botswana's former superlake which once may have drawn its waters from the combined flow of the Okavango, Chobe and upper Zambezi rivers. Their possible diversion, due to major faulting, could have cut off these supplies and caused the lake to dry out.

client, who perhaps ought to have known better, grew impatient with Lionel's struggling. 'Why don't you give it to me?' he said, referring to the steering wheel, at which point Lionel did, literally. The deep corrugations of the dirt road had worked the steering wheel loose from its mountings and Lionel was compelled to use friction alone to turn the steering.

One of the least explored and least visited areas of Ngamiland is the region north-east of the Okavango. Largely uninhabited except for the fringes of the Delta itself, it is almost entirely controlled hunting area. Running across it, from the Delta to the abrupt bend in the Chobe River, where it turns north-east, is what is called the Magwagqana or Selinda spillway. This curious feature has been little studied but it seems to be an overflow of the Delta, by means of which excessively high floods escape from the end of the Panhandle and, instead of flowing down into the Delta, turn

along the spillway to the north-east and flow into the Chobe River. Its existence is not controlled by hidden fault-lines and whether it is the channel of a former river or whether it is one of the outermost limits of the Delta when it was much larger in size, has not been established. However, one myth about it, at least, can be laid to rest. Contrary to popular belief, water does not flow both ways. Whilst it may appear at times to do so, water cannot flow from the Chobe to the Okavango, as some people claim it does. The difference in height between the two ends is just over 30 m. Often water from one end or the other backs up for considerable distances, but when a flow takes place it is only from the Okavango.[3]

The Selinda empties into the beautiful Chobe River. This river, like the Okavango, rises in the highlands of Angola and crosses immense distances of Kalahari sand before reaching the northern border of Botswana. As we have already seen, it may once have continued its south-east direction, feeding the super-lake, but today its course has been changed by the fault-lines which are an extension of the Great Rift Valley. No longer visible to the naked eye, the fault runs almost due north-east to south-west and when the river reaches it, it swings through right angles in its course, heading north-east to join the Zambezi. The valley through which it flows is broad and flat so that the river meanders through great beds of reed and papyrus. Large, secret lagoons abound and the slightly raised south bank is characteristically divided between open, grassy floodplains and areas of dense woodland. Here the great sweeping branches of the massive evergreen trees cast deep pools of cool shadow. In the thick undergrowth that shelters beneath these trees the shy and delicate Chobe bushbuck will be found and, in the riverside marshes, the fiercely territorial red lechwe.

Essentially a creature of the shadowy riverine forests, the Chobe bushbuck is very much at home in this area. This is not to say that it is either common or easily seen, for it is a timid and solitary animal. Once it was common along the whole of this river system, along the Chobe itself and the Zambezi, but its habitat has steadily been destroyed, forcing it to venture into less favourable areas, where it is more vulnerable and where its numbers are declining. The Chobe riverine forest may well be the last safe habitat of this beautiful, dainty, flower-eating antelope.[4]

Far less threatened and much more common, even though restricted to an equally tenuous habitat, the red lechwe is often seen in herds of up to 30 or 40 animals. They favour the seasonally flooded grass plains. In the mating season the males 'stake out' small territories to which they try and lure a harem of females. Fiercely aggressive, they will defend their territories stoutly, although research has shown that, despite appearances, actual aggression is very limited. It is replaced with a ritualised display and combat which consists of apparently violent butting and the locking of horns.[5] The males have adopted a curious habit, reported from Chobe, the

Okavango and from areas of Zambia, the observation of which has caused much speculation as to its possible cause. The males have been seen to carry accumulations of dried grass in their horns. One suggestion has been that it is to help keep flies away, but as it only occurs in the breeding season this seems unlikely; that it has sexual connotations is the more probable explanation. Work done by Hans Robbel and others[6] suggests that the collection of grass is not, per se, an intentional act, but results from displacement activity of sexually aroused males. Often, when in this condition, they lower their horns and make sweeping, butting motions, aimed at conspicuous tufts of grass, small bushes or even recumbent females. Such movements are often accompanied by weak pelvic thrusts, erections and, occasionally, spontaneous ejaculation.

There is no evidence of a decline in the population of red lechwe. At the last official count, there were more than 30 000 in the Okavango and 15 000 along the Chobe. Increasingly, however, they are coming into competition with man for use of the open flood plains, their preferred habitat. If this continues, inevitably the animals will slowly disappear and the Kalahari will be minus another species in its once rich faunal population.[7]

A less immediately obvious manifestation of man's misuse of his environment, but one which is no less threatening or serious in its consequences, concerns a water weed, known variously as Kariba weed or salvinia (Salvinia molesta). Salvinia is a free-floating fern, rather like a very small cabbage in shape, indigenous to South America, and it is a curse of many tropical waterways. It multiplies with extraordinary rapidity and forms dense floating mats upon the water's surface which exclude all light and smother life below. Under favourable conditions salvinia can double its numbers every two and a half days and forms stable mats up to half a metre thick. The exclusion of light and the massive death toll that results gives rise to large quantities of decaying matter. The rotting process uses much of the water's oxygen so that the oxygen level in badly infested waters is generally low. The thick vegetative covering slows the normal diffusion of oxygen into the water at the surface so that oxygen levels fall lower still. Eutrophication and subsequent alterations in pH result in marked changes in aquatic life under the weed mats. Plant growth is retarded while animal life and species diversity are considerably reduced. In time, rivers and lagoons can become sterile, lifeless zones. In addition to absorbing nutrients and de-oxygenating water, salvinia's spread can interfere with and seriously affect boating and fishing activities, in addition to threatening the habitat of such animals as the sitatunga.[8]

Salvinia was first recorded in the Chobe River in 1948. It has spread since then throughout the length of that river and down to the Zambezi and Lake Kariba beyond. So far the plant has not invaded the Delta and strenuous efforts are being made to ensure that this does not happen for, should it do so, control would be exceedingly difficult. The plant is curiously adapted to its aquatic existence. On the surface are two small, fleshy leaves. These are covered with a dense layer of very fine hairs which trap air bubbles among them. The air keeps the plant afloat. Below the two leaves and completely submerged beneath the water is a third, highly modified, leaf. This is divided into numerous finely-feathered, root-like parts and is the mechanism by which nutrients from the water are drawn into the plant.[9]

Being an imported, exotic plant, salvinia is subjected to none of the natural controls which limit its spread in its indigenous environment. However, knowledge that natural controls do exist has provided the key to eliminating the pest. Africa is not the only continent blighted with this unwanted weed. Australia, India, Sri Lanka, Fiji and New Guinea have it too, and much of our knowledge of control techniques comes from these countries. There are several species of salvinia, so subtly distinct that differentiation is by no means easy.

At least three invertebrate species attack salvinia: a moth, a grasshopper and a weevil. Botswana's first efforts at biological control took place in 1972-4 with the release of grasshoppers and weevils. The

experiment was not a success; nor was a second attempt in 1975-6. It was found that these creatures are exceptionally species specific and that those which had been introduced had come from Salvinia auriculata, not S. molesta. More appropriate plant predators have since been introduced and early success looks promising. In the meantime, chemical and physical control measures are still being used and relied upon until the biological approach proves sufficiently effective.

Of great interest to students of biology is the fact that the weevil (Cyrtobagous sp.) taken from Salvinia auriculata and known to survive on no other species of the plant appears to have adapted itself to a new host on the Chobe River. Introduced in 1972 and 1975, populations seemed to be dying off and the realisation that S. molesta was not their preferred host plant explained the matter. Scientists were surprised and intrigued, therefore, when weevil populations were recently found to be thriving on the Chobe's S. molesta. Nowhere else in the world has this happened and scientists are left to ponder the possibility that the weevil is more adaptable than was first believed or that it has evolved with great speed.[8]

Leading in an easterly direction from the abrupt bend in the Chobe River lies the Savuti Channel. This remarkable feature is one of the great mysteries of Ngamiland and the Kalahari. In essence, it is a river that winds its way in tortuous meanderings across extremely flat country for a distance of nearly 100 km. Two factors make it extraordinary. Firstly, instead of carrying water to a river, as most tributaries do, it carries it away from a river, pouring it out onto a vast swampland where it soaks into the sand or evaporates in the sun. Secondly, the channel is known to 'switch on and off' in a quite unpredictable fashion. Sometimes it will flow for years at a stretch and then will suddenly cease. There is no certain explanation for this strange phenomenon and it has been the subject of speculation for many years.

I once walked the length of the Savuti with a couple of friends. We started on the Chobe River and followed it upstream to the point where the channel makes its exit.

There is a large lagoon there, surrounded by the inevitable papyrus, and I remember on that occasion seeing an extraordinary number of hippo there. This lagoon was typical of those still ahead of us. Its surface, as we approached, was dotted with the black-rock heads of motionless hippo, only the occasional languid flapping of an ear revealing the presence of life. At that time the channel was drying from its eastern end and as the waters receded so populations of these animals moved further towards the source, crowding the narrow waterway and every available pool.

When it is full along its entire length the channel has a vital role to play. This northern part of the Kalahari's sands, blessed as it is with higher rainfall, provides extensive grazing for the region's herbivores, but it is of no use to them in the dry season unless water is available too. A full channel means a 100 km water-trough and opens up an area of grazing which would otherwise be unavailable at certain times of the year. Game, therefore, is plentiful. Buffalo, lion, lechwe, impala, kudu, wild dog, hyena, giraffe, and elephant exist in great numbers and to walk the area is to have the privilege of sharing wild Africa as it once was, beautiful, untouched and teeming with life.

As the channel nears its eastern end, the flow diminishes. When we walked it, it thinned to less than a metre across in places. Sometimes the banks are high and marked, often as much as 6 m or more in height, giving the impression of a much greater flow in times gone by. The most obvious feature of the channel to the first-time visitor, particularly towards the east, are the gaunt skeletons of once large trees that stand in their hundreds in the channel bed itself. The trees are mostly of the acacia species, a hard, heavy wood that grows slowly. Evidently their seed took root in the moist clay and mud of the channel bed at a time when the water departed. Clearly, it was empty for many years for the trees became established and were able to grow to their full height, nourished perhaps by remaining water deep beneath the ground. In time the water returned in full force, the channel was flooded and the trees, their roots submerged, were drowned. Since then the waters have come and gone sev-

eral times but the hard wood is durable and is made more so by the burning sun which sucks from it every last drop of moisture. Grey and stark, the great trees still stand, stripped of their natural beauty, a striking reminder of the harshness of this environment and the unpredictable vagaries of nature.

A number of people have attempted to trace the curious presence and absence of water in the Savuti Channel during the last 130 years. Part of the difficulty in establishing when the channel flowed and when it did not is caused by the fact that travellers who crossed it often did so midway along its length or close to the western source on the Chobe River. It is known from very recent years that water can lie far into the channel without it necessarily reaching the eastern extremity. In June 1851, David Livingstone, his wife and three children crossed the Savuti by ox-wagon on their way north to the Chobe and Zambezi rivers. Their exact crossing point is not known but at least one researcher is satisfied that it was closer to the Chobe than the Mababe Depression and he believes that, although there was water in the channel, it was not at that time flowing the full way to the Depression.[10]

Chapman was another who passed through the area. In 1853 he crossed further to the west and his map shows his route crossing what he indicated as the dry channel of the Savuti. Several other travellers followed but their observations are no more informative and it was not until the great hunter Frederick Courteney Selous appeared that more reliable information became available. He reported that in 1874 the Savuti was very full and water was flowing into the Mababe marsh. In 1879, when he returned, the water had ceased to flow that far west and had reached little more than halfway.

It is generally agreed that sometime in the 1880s the channel dried. The year 1888 is a commonly quoted date. In 1899 Percy Reid travelled eastwards from the channel's mouth and found that the water had dried after only 8 km. The Savuti remained dry until the 1957-8 rainy season, when it flowed strongly to the Mababe Depression and continued to flow in subsequent years until 1966 when it was dry again. It was probably during the years from 1888 to 1957 that the trees became established, and the inundation which followed caused their deaths. Some attempts have been made to obtain date data from the trees but nothing conclusive has been established so far. Having stopped flowing in 1966, the Savuti, capriciously, flowed again the following year and remained flowing until 1981.[11] It has been dry since then.

What causes this remarkable pattern of flow in the channel? The fall, from one end to the other, is very gradual, less than 20 cm for each kilometre, so that the difference in height between opposite ends is something of the order of 18 m, over a distance of less than 100 km. The most common theory hinges upon the level of flood waters in the Chobe River. It stands to reason, claim its proponents, that as the water level in the Chobe rises, so the 'head' of water available to push down the Savuti increases, and in this way the waters make their way to Mababe. This theory does not, however, stand up to close examination. Despite the remarkably gentle gradient, about 1 in 5 300, the flow of water in the Savuti seems unaffected by flood levels in the Chobe. The year 1925, for example, was a year of exceptional floods, with record levels in all the river systems of the Chobe, Okavango and Zambezi. In that year, however, the Savuti did not flow. The absence of water in the channel in 1925 and in subsequent years leaves only one other explanation: flow is controlled by tectonic rather than hydrological factors.[12]

We already know that the Okavango is an extension of the Rift Valley and that it is tectonically unstable. The Savuti Channel runs directly athwart the system of faultlines which have modified the flow of the Chobe and Zambezi and which reach further south to contain the Delta itself. The regional instability is manifested by the high level of local earthquake activity. As crustal movement seems the only possible explanation, one must conclude that, remarkable as it is, the land at one or other end of the channel is in constant motion, flexing, bending and buckling and that, while we stand upon it and look at it, it is physically moving. At too small a rate,

perhaps, for humans to measure, the movement nevertheless continues.

A detailed study of earthquakes in Ngamiland between September and December 1974 showed that, active as the whole region was, the highest level of activity was in and around the Mababe Depression,[13] a finding which has been confirmed in many such studies. In the short space of 25 years, for example, between 1957 and 1981, the local flexing of the earth's crust has been of sufficient magnitude to reopen the channel after nearly 70 years, close, reopen and close it again. Assuming that the water during the recent 'open' times never receded past halfway, it still means that a crustal rise or fall of 9 m would be necessary somewhere along the channel for it to flow again. If this is true, then it is indeed a remarkable feature. Rarely is one presented with so vivid a demonstration of the dynamic nature of the earth's crust.

Towards the eastern extremity of the Savuti lie several groups of low, rounded, rocky hills. Two of these groups, Gubatsaa and Gcoha, seem to anchor a prominent sandy ridge that swings up in a gentle curve from the south, around to a tight arch in the north. This is the Magwikhwe sand ridge. It is more than 100 km long, 20 m high and more than 180 m wide. There are two gaps in this long ridge. One is created by the Savuti Channel and the other is 24 km further south and is a fossil river valley where water no longer flows.

To the west of the hills and the ridge lies the Mababe Depression. It is flat, almost unbelievably flat, with not a blemish on the horizon nor the slightest trace of a fold, the shape of a long forgotten sand dune or any change in the unrelenting levelness of the ground. For the most part, it is covered with scattered bush and a wide variety of nutritious grasses. A glance at the solid rock of the low 60 m hills shows that the eastern faces are sheer and even undercut, whilst the western side slopes gently away. Suddenly you will realise that what you are looking at is the bed of an ancient sea, and indeed the Mababe was once part of the great super-lake (see map on p. 16). The hills have been worn and scoured to their present shape by pounding seas. If you walk into the lee of their storm-scarred

The Chobe River in reflective mood

▲Baines' baobabs after late rains ▼Vultures roosting at Savuti

cliffs you will find banks of rounded pebbles, worn smooth by constant friction. Now buried beneath the sand, they have at last found peace from the turbulent motion and have passed silent millenia here, undisturbed.

The Savuti Channel is not the only source of water for the Mababe marsh. The Ngwezumba River flows in from the north-east, draining the south side of the watershed that separates Hwange Game Reserve in Zimbabwe from northern Botswana. The Ngwezumba flows only in years of exceptional flood, but when it does vast volumes of water can be delivered. In the flood year of 1925, for example, it burst into life and ran 3 m deep and 20 m wide. Its massive size suggests a far more important role in the past but now, in most years, it collects only local drainage which soon soaks away into the sand and seldom reaches the Depression. Rivers from the Okavango Delta also reach into Mababe but it is more than 50 years since any of these carried water to the southern parts of the Depression.

The Depression hollows imperceptibly. One of its lower levels, though not the lowest, occurs where the Savuti breaks through the sand ridge and terminates in a large marsh. The size and nature of the marsh varies, of course, with the flow of the Savuti. Sometimes it will be deep in water for years on end and at others it may be baked hard and quite moistureless. In the years when there is abundant water, however, the Mababe becomes the greatest game paradise on earth. The flat, fertile plains teem with countless animals. Zebra, tsessebe, hartebeest and impala by the hundred thousand move easily among herds of elephant, buffalo and giraffe. Honey badgers, wild dog and hyena hunt and scavenge, and large prides of lion lie indolently in the shade of trees.

Hundreds of species of birds fill the air, while ducks, herons, waders and other waterbirds by the thousand can be observed all along the channel and across the marsh. Honey-guides, doves of half a dozen varieties, minute waxbills, hornbills, bee-eaters, owls, widow birds, and weavers crowd the perches and flutter, like so many falling leaves, down to the water's edge for

an end of the day drink. Among the most striking of the birds are the rollers. Iridescent blue and pink breasted, their aerial acrobatics are fascinating to watch, for they roll and twist and turn in flight, appearing to do so out of sheer exuberance and unashamed joy in the thrill and mastery of flight. Their eyesight must be extraordinary for I have seen a roller leave its perch and fly directly to a small insect 110 paces away.

Vultures, too, appear to have extraordinary eyesight and in an area like Savuti, with its heavy concentrations of game and predators, the pickings are rich. I have a theory that vultures patrol specific areas of the sky and that each watches its neighbour as zealously as it watches the ground far beneath it. I can recall a lion kill on the banks of the Savuti Channel, which I watched from the shelter of dense bush. I focused my attention on the clear sky and it was only a few minutes before a dark shape materialised, spiralling down from the blue directly above. Within seconds other vultures appeared, higher and further away. They were like faint knots in an invisible hair-net which had been cast across the sky, one of which was being pulled steadily to earth, dragging the others irrevocably with it, funnelling down to the kill.

When the water departs Savuti and Mababe remain rich in game. The diversity of species is not quite as great, nor are the numbers as large, but there remain sufficient still to rival any competition with other localities. The reason for this is the richness of the vegetation and the fact that numerous small pans hold water well into the dry season. Even without the Savuti, therefore, game can survive for long periods on the lush plains. Those animals which need more water than is available can move easily to the Chobe River no more than 40 or 50 km away. The tragedy of Mababe arises for those creatures which are water dependent and which cannot easily move.

Near its end at the edge of the Mababe marsh, the Savuti forms a large pool. When the channel runs dry this pool sometimes remains long after the supply of fresh water has stopped. It gradually shrinks under a succession of hot, cloudless days. Most of the aquatic creatures, sensing the coming change, will have moved westwards, back towards the Chobe; some move in the opposite direction, perhaps hoping that the pool will last the season until fresh water washes in again. Occasionally, it does not. Mudfish, like barbel, hippos and crocodile are gradually forced into closer proximity with one another. Fish eagles and other predatory birds can enjoy a continual feast as they swoop down on dying barbel struggling and flopping through the slimy mud which is all that remains of their river. Crocodiles line the banks, like a forest of fallen tree-trunks, while the hippo are wedged side by side, desperately seeking the shelter of the last cooling mud. A thirsty elephant may wander down, picking its way carefully past listless crocodiles. Squelching into the edge of the deep mud, the tip of its trunk will delicately examine the last drop of muddy, soiled water filling the footprint of a previous caller. Unattracted by the noisome fluid, it backs slowly away and accepts the inevitability of a long trudge to the Chobe. The hippo and crocodile will move too, but not before there is no possibility of reprieve. Some hippo will put off the long walk until the skin on their backs, cracked and broken by the sun into suppurating sores, attended by swarms of flies, finally drives them away. Occasionally, they die on the journey.

It may seem surprising, but crocodiles, too, are capable of undertaking long journeys. Sometimes, though, one will do the unexpected. Not far from the edge of this pool one of the Savuti hills rises from the sand. Near its base, among the broken rocks, there is a narrow, horizontal cleft that stretches back some 2 m into the cool shade of the mother rock. Here, about 400 m from the drying pool, a small, 1,5 m crocodile chose to spend the dry season. In June 1982 it first took up residence, sliding deep into the crevice and lying undisturbed and motionless as the dry months passed. With the coming of the rains, when the pool filled again, it returned to the water but by May the following year it was back in its reptilian retreat. Again it survived the year and in the wet season of 1983–4 it returned to the rain-filled pool. When the pool dried the crocodile slipped back into

its rocky crevice, probably in May or June 1984. By September it was dead. The cause of death is not known. Some suggest that it simply did not get enough food in the wet months to sustain it through the lean times; others say it was because of the constant attention and disturbance it had to endure from those who knew of its presence.[14]

The phenomenon of crocodiles hibernating far from water is not unknown. John Seaman told me of one he found, just under 4 m in length, hiding in an ant-bear hole at Toteng, near the Delta, in November 1983. It had been there since April or May.[15] What intrigues me are the implications of this behaviour. How did the Savuti crocodile find its winter lair? Was it a chance encounter, or was it the result of a deliberate search? If it was a search, was it systematic and what motivated it, since escape to the Chobe is always an alternative? Either way, the crocodile would have been required to memorise the location and the route. The memory clearly persisted, not only from the time of first discovery to first occupation, but through several successive seasons thereafter. In addition, there was an element of judgement involved in the decision whether to chance the walk across dry Kalahari sands to the Chobe River, which other crocodiles had done, or to stay in the immediate vicinity and risk discovery by a predator, or death following the failure of rains. How did the crocodile make those decisions?

In many ways the Mababe Depression is not unlike the Okavango Delta. It is an inland, terminal drainage basin and depositional centre into which several river systems have flowed. Today it has been abandoned by its rivers, but possibly only temporarily so. The Savuti may flow again and a redistribution of water within the Delta, which we have seen is entirely possible, may set its northern distributaries flowing strongly once more so that water will enter Mababe again from the south. The Depression and its marsh are typical of the ephemeral lake features in this part of the Kalahari. Lake Ngami, to the south of the Okavango Delta, is another such feature. Like Mababe, it too was once part of the super-lake and, similarly, was far larger than it is now. It is also a terminal drainage basin and depends for its existence on inflow from several rivers. As with Mababe, some of these no longer flow and, like the Channel, have probably been severed by crustal activity.

Lake Ngami lies at the southernmost corner of the Okavango Delta and at the end of the Thamalakane and Kunyere faultlines. In the south it abuts against the Ghanzi Ridge. The lake is of interest because of its peculiarly ephemeral nature. Many times in the last 130 years since it was described by Livingstone its size has altered dramatically. On some occasions it has been an impressive sheet of water, and on others it has ceased to exist at all. It is also interesting because of the very clear evidence it provides of how the distribution of the water within the Delta has changed in recent times. Livingstone's account of the lake spurred many others to follow in his footsteps and probably gave rise to myths, no longer current, which spoke of a vast inland sea and vaguely hinted at ancient civilisations.

Like Mababe, Ngami was also part of the great super-lake but as it slowly dried and shrank the lake emerged as a separate entity. Exactly when that might have been and what was the history of the lake before the creation of the super-lake has not yet been established, although it is the subject of current research. At least four major rivers have flowed into Lake Ngami at various times (see map on p. 16). Only two of these remain active today. From the south-west, the Groot Laagte brought water from the slopes of the Ghanzi Ridge and from the western Kalahari. It does not flow at all today and its discernible course ceases long before the lake is approached. From the north-west flowed the Thaoge, the largest and, in recent times, the most south-westerly of the Okavango's distributaries. From the north-east comes the only supply of water that remains today, the Thamalakane River.

We have seen how the Okavango is abruptly truncated by a parallel pair of fault-lines running north-east to south-west. Between them, the Thamalakane acts like a drain that cuts at right angles across the base of the Delta, collecting all its overflow and carrying it away. Some 25 km downstream from Maun the Thamalakane splits into two. One part turns due east and becomes the Boteti River and the other continues in the original direction and is called the Lake River. This junction is a perfectly natural, if unusual, feature, although it has been modified by man to alter the volumes of water that flow in the two directions.

Originally, the proportion of flow between the Boteti and Lake rivers was 2 : 1. A structure was created that was intended to alter this to 7 : 3, but in fact the ratio has been closer to 5:1.[16] The purpose of this manipulation is to divert water away from Lake Ngami, down the Boteti where, after a journey of 240 km, it enters Mopipi Pan. Mopipi has been bunded so as to increase its storage capacity and it serves now as a reservoir from which the Orapa diamond mine can draw water.

The Boteti is practically a relic river. It never dries today, although the flow can become almost imperceptible. Very probably, it once carried the entire flow of the Okavango River before the Delta came into existence. Whether in those days any of its water was diverted to Lake Ngami would be pure speculation, but it certainly carried huge volumes in times past. It is also possible that somewhere along its present course the original Chobe River, and perhaps even the Upper Zambezi, entered it, although where and when is not known (see Chapter 2). That it was once a very much larger river is evident from its physical characteristics today. Often the bed of the river is more than 250 m wide and there are many places along its length where riverside calcrete cliffs tower more than 20 m from the water.

Downstream from the Boteti junction, the much reduced flow of the Lake River continues towards distant Lake Ngami. After 64 km it reaches the village of Toteng and is here joined by the Kunyere River. From Toteng the winding course of the Lake River reaches Ngami after about 25 km. The Kunyere and the Lake rivers are the only two waterways that empty into Lake Ngami now. Neither necessarily flows all the year round; sometimes neither flows at all although, in years of high floods or good rains, Lake Ngami fills again.

When Livingstone first saw Lake Ngami on 1 August 1849 he described it as a 'fine looking sheet of water' and estimated the circumference as approximately 120 km. In the next five years Oswell, McCabe and Andersson followed, and their estimates were similar, or larger. At that time the Thaoge River was flowing strongly into the lake from the north-west. McCabe crossed it in 1852, not far from where it entered the lake, and noted that the river was nearly 1 m deep and 3 km wide. Andersson sailed up it for 110 km and only in a few places did he find the water less than 1,5 m deep. However, just 24 years later, in September 1877, McKiernan planned to sail up this same river and found only 10 cm of water, just over a kilometre from the lake.[16] In that short space of time the Thoage had dried up completely and had been transformed from a major river of very significant proportions, to nothing more than a dry and dusty area of Kalahari sand.

Research has indicated that the flow of the Thaoge began diminishing as early as the 1850s and had ceased altogether by the 1880s. Interestingly, the evidence is that the Thaoge stopped flowing when the lake was at a fairly high level, for today there is a long distance between the visible river bed which marks the end of the Thaoge's flow and the present edge of the lake. The event was a mystery at the time and in the decades that followed, but it is now clear that its occurrence is attributable to major shifts in the distribution patterns of the Okavango's waters. Some consider this change in flow to have been caused by blockages of papyrus reeds in the Thaoge itself, others believe that it was brought about by tectonic forces which are reshaping the earth's surface in this region.

Many of the travellers in the nineteenth century, noting the high water levels of the lake, observed how they backed up along the Lake River, towards the Boteti. There was some speculation as to whether the water was flowing in, or out, of Ngami, along the Lake River. Many came to the conclusion that, depending on the relative water height and flood level, the water could flow either way. There is no record of anyone actually witnessing the reverse flow of the Lake River but it has probably done so.

The lowest level of Lake Ngami is to be found at a series of pools where the Lake River flows in. This point is 919,5 m above mean sea level. In recent times, the highest level of Lake Ngami was recorded after the 1925 floods when it rose to 923,7 m a.m.s.l., giving a surface area of 250 km² and a circumference of about 80 km. There are, however, a great many relic shorelines about the lake, showing clearly that it has in the past stood at very much higher levels. The highest is between 940 and 943 m but there are many shorelines at 936, 934, and between 932 and 929,5 m. The last mentioned level would enclose a lake of some 810 km², with a circumference approaching 170 km. Dr Paul Shaw, who has carried out much research in this area, believes that Ngami probably stood at or close to this level when Livingstone first arrived. At that time, then, the Lake River would indeed have been backed up for a very considerable distance and may even have closely approached, if not exceeded, the critical level of 929,9 m a.m.s.l., which would allow it to have reversed its flow and carried water from Lake Ngami down into the Boteti.

It is easy to see how the extinction of the Thaoge River has caused Ngami to reduce so much in size. That the contribution of this river was highly significant can be illustrated as follows: to maintain Ngami at a level between 929,9 m a.m.s.l., so that the Lake River would flow in a reverse direction and allow Lake Ngami water to move down the Boteti, the Thaoge would have to deliver a volume of water equivalent to 11 per cent of the entire flow of the Okavango.[17] Clearly, within the last hundred years, it did so. Today it is completely dry.

The phenomenon of the disappearing lake is not new and the fact that its surface area has changed dramatically over the ages is quite certain. One report, in about 1750, denies that there was any lake at all, claiming that the Lake River flowed through a heavily wooded plain.[18] Evidence of the older and higher shorelines shows that Ngami, at the 940–943 m level, was certainly part of the super-lake and its surface area would have been between 2 100 and 1 800 km². As the levels fell to

936 and 934 m, it would probably have emerged as a separate entity, existing in its own right quite separately from the shrinking giant lake. Its area then would have been somewhere in the vicinity of 810 km².

In the last hundred years, and more particularly since the Thaoge ceased to flow, Lake Ngami has been completely dry for two or more consecutive years on at least five and possibly seven occasions. It has also filled six or seven times during that period, mostly during years of exceptional flood, although it has never exceeded the 923,5 m level; until the Okavango is flexed again and new flow channels are established, it is unlikely to do so.

As a source of water in the Kalahari, the lake has played an important role in the development of the area and it is now the centre of a traditional cattle ranching industry. It has several advantages which make it particularly suited to this purpose. Its extensive flat floor, quickly inundated when the water does come, is rich in accumulated clay and loam and offers excellent grazing when the waters have receded. The cattle population in its vicinity is estimated in excess of 30 000.[19] The availability of water is out of sequence with local conditions as inflow originates in Angola and only arrives from the Delta in May or June, some months after the local rains have ceased. Much of it evaporates or sinks into the ground but the presence of the lake does guarantee surface water for far longer periods than elsewhere. Interestingly, the system of fault-lines in the Okavango region and around Lake Ngami is such that it effectively blocks the wide distribution of groundwater. Outflow to the western and southern fringes of the Delta does not take place.[20] Thus it is that wells around Lake Ngami, despite its close proximity to the Delta, do not draw Okavango water but tap into water that is older and of different origins, which is not always easy to find and is neither copious nor reliable.

Being at best a shallow and ephemeral lake, great banks of reeds grow prolifically in Ngami. When I first saw it, in December 1983, there was no water in it at all and there was nothing to see but a disappointing vista of dried and uninteresting reeds. As the years pass, new reed growth sprouts upon remains of the old and great thicknesses of rotting vegetation slowly accumulate. Sometimes the local people deliberately fire the reeds – often to flush out wild animals which may be sheltering there – and despite extinguishing itself on the surface, the fire may continue to smoulder for many months, deep beneath the ground. This the locals attribute to the anger of a god, Lengongoro. It is also possible that spontaneous combustion may account for some of the fires. In 1922 an enquiry, emanating from Jan Smuts, then Prime Minister of the Union of South Africa, demanded to know why Lake Ngami was burning.[21] It usually takes the next rains or the new flood-waters to extinguish the fire completely. When the water returns and the lake is flooded it becomes a temporary home for some of the greatest concentrations of bird-life in this part of Africa.

The shallow water, warmed by the hot sun, and lying as it does on layers of decomposing vegetation, quickly turns into a highly nutritious feeding ground. Aquatic plants grow at an incredible rate and algae flourish in ideal conditions. Every kind of bird is drawn to the lake and its shores. Many, like the sandgrouse and doves, rely upon it and in good times, when there is water through a number of years, their populations grow to fantastic numbers. Several bird-hunting safaris are organised in this area and I've heard hunters say that nowhere in the world are game birds so prolific.

It is for water-fowl, however, that Ngami is really famous. Ducks by the million crowd the shores, white-faced whistling ducks being the most common, but pochards, white-backed ducks, yellow-billed ducks and several varieties of teal are also there. The knob-billed duck, shovellers and shelducks are present in their thousands and on the shore patrol the sentinels, the Egyptian and spur-wing geese. Wading the waters are the long-legged flamingos, both greater and lesser, pelicans, marabou storks, white-bellied storks and ibis. The number and variety of birds is too great to describe but it is an extraordinary experience to stand among them and watch countless millions swirling, turning, soaring, landing and taking off and, above all, feeding from the bountiful waters of Lake Ngami.

In terms of the variety it offers, Ngamiland is one of the most exciting areas of the Kalahari. Blessed with great expanses of standing water, it contains the largest concentrations of birds and animals. It offers the intrigue of the super-lake and capricious waterways, lakes that appear and disappear, rivers that flow and cease to flow, great dune fields and ancient shorelines. There are still the excitement and adventure of the unknown, for large areas remain to be explored. Despite the development that has taken place, those who venture into the remoter regions soon discover that they have left civilisation behind – they are indeed penetrating a last frontier.

## REFERENCES

1. **Seaman, J.** Personal communication, December 1984
2. Ibid
3. **Brind, W. G.** *The Okavango Delta.* Report on the 1951–1953 Field Surveys to the Government of Bechuanaland, Dept of Water Affairs, Gaborone, Botswana, **pp 6-7**
4. **Simpson, C D.** 'Food Studies on the Chobe Bushbuck, *Tragelaphus scriptus ornatus Pocock 1900'.* In *Arnoldia*, Vol 6, No 32, 28 June 1974, **pp 1-9**
5. **Joubert, E.** 'A Note on the Challenge Rituals of Territorial Male Lechwe'. In *Madoqua*, Series I, No 5, 1972, **pp 63-7**
6. **Child, G and Robbel, H.** 'The Possible Significance of "Grass Horning" by Male Lechwe'. In *Mammalia*, Vol 39, No 4, 1975, **pp 709-11**
7. **Williamson, D T.** 'The Status of Red Lechwe in the Linyanti Swamp'. In *Botswana Notes and Records*, Vol 13, 1981, **pp 101-5**
8. **Procter, D L C.** 'Biological Control of the Aquatic Weed *Salvinia molesta*. D.S. Mitchell in Botswana using the weevils *Cyrtobagous singularis* and *Cyrtobagus* sp. nov.' In *Botswana Notes and Records*, Vol 15, 1983, **pp 99-101**
9. **Mitchell, D S.** A Survey of *Salvinia auriculata* in the Chobe River System – March, 1967. Unpublished paper, Dept of Botany, University of Zimbabwe, **pp 1-7**
10. **Smith, P.** A History of the Savuti Channel. Unpublished paper, 1974. Dept of Water Affairs, P O Box 107, Maun, Botswana
11. **Campbell, A C.** 'Notes on Some Rock Paintings at Savuti.' In *Botswana Notes and Records*, Vol 2, 1969, **p 22**
12. **Shaw, P.** 'A Historical Note on the Outflows of the Okavango Delta System.' In *Botswana Notes and Records*, Vol 16, 1984, **p 128**
13. **Scholz, C H.** Seismicity, Tectonics and Seismic Hazard of the Okavango Delta. Investigation of the Okavango Delta as a Primary Water Resource for Botswana. UNDP/FAO, Gaborone, Botswana. BOT/71/506, April 1975, **p 13**
14. **Cantle, H.** Personal communication, January 1985
15. **Seaman, J.** Personal communication, December 1984
16. United Nations. Investigation of the Okavango Delta as a Primary Water Resource for Botswana. UNDP/FAO, Gaborone, Botswana, AG: DP/BOT/71/506, Technical report, Vol II, 1977, **p 199**
17. **Shaw, P.** 'The Desiccation of Lake Ngami: A Historical Perspective.' In *The Geographical Journal*, Vol 151, No 3
18. **Stigand, A G.** 'Ngamiland.' In *The Geographical Journal*, Vol 62, No 6, December 1923, **p 405**
19. United Nations. Op cit, **p 283**
20. Ibid, Vol I, **p 72**
21. **Mamashela, L D.** 'Magical Desert Lake.' In *Botswana*, Vol 2, No 3, no date. Ministry of Information, Botswana Government, Gaborone, **pp 6-7**

# Part 4
# Living Creatures of the Sands

# 9. Big Beasts . . .

THOSE who are unfamiliar with the Kalahari do not often associate it with larger mammals. In fact, the Kalahari is far more likely to conjure up images of Bushmen or desert than vast herds of game. Yet the area of Kalahari sands, encompassing as it does such a wide variety of soils, vegetation and climatic variations, provides habitats for an extraordinary range of life. There are forty-six different species of mammals larger than the size of a jackal. More remarkable still, perhaps, is the amazing range of adaptations which have evolved, allowing for the exploitation of the most minute ecological niche.

The single most important element necessary for the preservation and continuance of life is water. Standing water is the one thing, with a few notable exceptions, that the Kalahari lacks. Most of the adaptations seen in animals are aimed at overcoming this formidable obstacle and the success achieved is, as we shall see, a tribute to nature's incredible ingenuity.

It is evening in Savuti. The brazen sun has set. The stark branches of the Channel's dead trees stand out in sharp silhouette against the mauve night, aftermath of the day's demise. The first nocturnal zephyrs stir, bringing to your nostrils the strange, dew-dampened smells of Africa's night. There is a brief interval of silence. Those who call by day have gone to rest, while those whose domain is the night have yet to stir. It is an ethereal time, a time of transition, of beauty and quiet calm, in which a stranger to this land will feel an uncomfortable vulnerability, as if in response to some age-old animal instinct that demands alertness and caution. It is then that the hyena calls.

Nothing quite compares with the refined horror contained in this natural call. It seems to echo from the empty sky, is picked up here and there, repeated again and again as successive creatures announce their presence and a plan is concocted for the night.

Hyenas should perhaps be numbered among the most misunderstood and maligned of creatures. Two species are found in the Kalahari – the brown and the spotted hyena – but they occur throughout most of Africa as well. The family *Hyaenidae* is related to the *Viveridae* which includes the civets, genets and mongooses. Thus, some claim, although this is controversial, hyenas are more closely related to cats than to dogs.[1] The subject of myth and object of hatred, they have been much researched in recent decades, yet still some questions remain unanswered. Research of this nature really requires a lifetime's dedication and so far it would appear that not enough in-depth work has been done. Perhaps other fields of research offer greater attraction and reward. It also appears that what may be true for a group of animals living in one part of Africa may not necessarily be true for a group living elsewhere. Often, significant behavioural variations between groups are revealed, the product, perhaps, of subtle environmental differences. In these circumstances, generalisations are not reliable.

When I was a child I grew up believing that hyenas were hermaphrodites. Today we know this is not so but it is easy to understand how the myth arose. The sexual organs of the young male and female are so similar that it is almost impossible, in the field, to differentiate between them.[2] Females have a pseudoscrotum and a large clitoris which can be erected. When erect, it points directly downwards, exactly as the penis of the male. In the non-parous adult female the similarities persist and even an experienced person can have difficulty in telling the sexes apart. It is only in the case of a female carrying young that differentiation is straightforward. Some say that the female is larger and can be distinguished from the male by her larger nipples. This, one imagines, depends rather on the age of the animal and experience of the observer. Scientists having reached the conclusion that hyenas are not hermaphroditic, along comes a report from Mr Carr Hartley, Chairman of the Kenya Trappers' Association.[3] He reported having two spotted hyenas in captivity, each of which had been both male and female at different times. One had fathered three litters of cubs and itself produced five!

Whatever else, the hyena is a survivor. He is a hunter, a scavenger, opportunistic, incredibly tough and wiley. In Serengeti the discovery was first made that spotted hyenas hunted and killed in packs. Now the phenomenon is well known and throughout the national parks of Southern Africa reports of this behaviour are common. In Botswana there have been incidents of hyena not only combining to hunt in packs in their natural habitat, but doing so to hunt down the locals' sheep and goats.[4]

Perhaps it is opportunism that most characterises this extraordinary creature. Alec Campbell, then of Botswana's Department of Wildlife and National Parks, was once travelling through the Savuti in April 1972.[5] A gathering of vultures led him to where a large python was in the process of swallowing a young female impala. The impala was being engorged head first, coils thrown around the body to hold it, crush it and force it towards the mouth. The python secreted great quantities of saliva to lubricate the swallowing process. When Alec arrived on the scene the head and neck had already been consumed. Fifty minutes later the entire carcass had been swallowed. Knowing that the python would move little during the night because of its heavy meal, Alec and his companions decided to revisit the scene the following morning. They had, however, reckoned without the hungry hyena and we can piece together the events of the night without too much difficulty.

The python, bloated and lethargic, hid as best it could and waited for its meal to digest when it could regain its freedom of movement. Away from its normal sleeping area, it was at its most vulnerable. At some time during the night it might have heard the snuffling, shuffling approach of a spotted hyena, footsteps deadened by the soft sand. It might have seen a black shape, moving against a background of frozen stars – and looked Nemesis in the face. The evidence of daylight told the rest of the tale. There were no signs of a struggle. The python's spine had been broken with a single powerful bite and, although the snake was not dead, its life was slowly ebbing into the red-stained sand on which it lay. Its belly had been ripped open and the carcass removed. Alec followed the hyena's spoor. It led into the waters of the Savuti marsh, which was flooded at the time. With no trail to follow, Alec walked on until the water was above his knees and he could go no further. At that moment, he came face to face with the hyena coming out of a dense bank of reeds. Unable to investigate further, he could only conclude that the creature had hidden its grisly meal among the reeds, intending to return to it later.

Hyenas seem to like water. If it is abundant within their range, they can often be found standing or lying in it during the heat of the day. Dr Graham Child, while making observations in Botswana's Moremi Game Reserve, four times saw a single hyena chasing groups of lechwe into the water.[6] Three times the animal succeeded in catching and drowning its prey. There is some evidence that hyenas may conceal food in water. From the Kalahari Gemsbok National Park staff report that hyenas placing food in the water troughs maintained by the park have, at times, created a serious problem. Jessie Neil, a visitor to Savuti, saw a spotted hyena carry a haunch of meat out into the flooded Mababe Depression. The animal seemed to 'bury' the meat in the water, some distance from the shore, and returned to retrieve it later the same day. Harry Cantle, another well-known man of the bush, has witnessed hyenas carrying old, dried-up hides to water where they've been left to soak for as long as two days before being chewed and swallowed.

That hyenas do scavenge is well known. What is perhaps less appreciated is the range of items they will include in their diet. Dr G L Smuts, working in South Africa's Kruger National Park, discovered in the stomach of one spotted hyena pieces of leather and sole from at least three different shoes.[7] In addition, he found sticks, leaves, pebbles, bits of cloth, plastic, rubber, silver paper, beer can tops and old newspaper! Apparently the animal had been unable to resist the lure of the park's dustbins.

In a sample of 100 animals, Dr Smuts also found included in the diet impala, wildebeest, zebra, civet cat, lions, hyena, eagles, starlings and finches. Harry Cantle once watched a pride of eighteen lions kill a buffalo. Before they could get down to the meal, they were chased off the kill by over forty hyenas. Later, a second and larger pack of hyenas chased off the first. The lions presumably went elsewhere for their evening meal. There is a report from Zambia of six spotted hyenas killing an old and sickly black rhino.

For toughness and resourcefulness, the hyena has few competitors. One has only to speak to those who operate tented camps in the wilds of Africa to receive confirmation. Practically nothing can match the hyena's ingenuity for getting into fridges, meat safes and deep-freezes. I once saw an upright refrigerator which had been favoured by the nocturnal attentions of a hungry hyena. The door was secured by two metal clasps but the hyena, using its jaws as a lever, had bent up the lower portion of the door, tearing the metal as it did so, and raided the fridge of its contents. Short of killing the raiders, no one has so far found a successful way of deterring them.

From the Kruger National Park comes a tale of a spotted hyena which for three months wandered the park with a wire snare around its neck.[8] Eventually, the animal was shot and upon examination it was found that the wire had jammed between its teeth. This prevented the noose, though tight around the neck, from actually throttling the animal. A loose end of the wire had worn a hole in the side of its tongue. The tightly stretched metal had cut deeply through the cheek and lay in an open channel. The wire was embedded in the muscles of the neck but the wound had healed over completely. Apparently the hyena experienced little more than mild discomfort. A post mortem revealed that its stomach was full and it was in good physical condition.

Hyenas live in burrows and apparently are not always keen on going to the trouble of making their own, as they are inclined to take over dens made by other animals. There does not seem much formality for this process – it is just a question of moving in whenever the opportunity arises. It follows, of course, that the owner of the den may not know that his home has been usurped and this can be the cause of some embarrassment. The warthog is a case in point. At best he is irascible, short-tempered and highly suspicious, knowing that as a packaged dinner he is a very desirable size. It is never his intention to so far lower his defences as to present a chubby and tempting posterior to would-be-diners. Therefore, as he enters his burrow in the earth, he does so in reverse. Should it happen that during his absence a hyena has installed itself, a brief, startling and painful confrontation occurs. You will find a large number of warthogs, trotting the plains of Africa, minus their tails![9]

The brown hyena is a more solitary creature than the spotted, although strong bonded pairs are formed. They travel widely and in certain circumstances will hunt in packs. This animal occurs throughout the Kalahari and appears to be more resilient than its spotted cousin, often being found where the latter cannot survive. Reports of its presence come from as far afield as the suburbs of Johannesburg and the desolate shores of Namibia.[10] Dr Gus Mills and Mark and Delia Owen have published a large amount of material about these animals. The ritual combat, establishment of an ordered hierarchy, scent marking and pasting, and the communal dens have all been described and make fascinating reading. But it is the stealing of eggs that most intrigues me.[11]

In its endless wanderings across the sand wastes of the Kalahari, the brown hyena from time to time encounters a nest of ostrich eggs from which the parents, for some reason, are temporarily absent. There may be anything from 15 to 30 eggs in a clutch and each is large, equivalent to about 22 chicken eggs. Presented with such a bonanza, the brown hyena's dilemma is easy to imagine. It cannot eat them all, nor can it hope to return time and time again. Either the parents will be there or another predator will have finished the job. The solution is a remarkable illustration of adaptive behaviour and low animal cunning. One by one, the eggs are lifted and carried away from the nest, to be secreted at various points within the vicinity, between 200 m and 600 m away. Some might be eaten at the site but the others will be consumed, a few at a time, in the nights that follow.

Hyenas have long figured in the myths of this continent. Their strange maniacal call and weird laughter are so evocative of the spirit of night in Africa that it is hardly surprising that they should be frequently associated with fear and superstition. The Zulus believe that witches ride about at night upon the backs of hyenas and everywhere they are considered animals of doom and misfortune. In Ngamiland it is commonly believed by most locals that witchdoctors, the traditional medicine men, use hyenas as horses. In fact there are at least three records in the villages of the Okavango where prominent sorcerers have actually taken people to the Chief's court and accused them of killing their 'horses'. Inevitably, the tribal equivalent of 'not proven' is returned since the whole episode is but a figment of the complainant's imagination and designed, perhaps, to earn him a little free publicity. But try telling the villagers that!

The lion is the Kalahari's biggest predator. Its occurrence is widespread throughout the area but pressure upon lion populations is mounting constantly and numbers are probably diminishing. As the cattle ranchers expand their operations remorselessly into the sandveld, man once again comes into conflict with the animal inhabitants of these wilderness tracts. A lion may be shot without a licence in defence of one's stock and many lions die this way.

There are two areas within the Kalahari where lions have been or are being studied. One is in the south, in the Kalahari Gemsbok National Park, the other is on the Mababe Depression and Savuti Channel. Further work has been done on lion populations in other areas too and, because they are so different, sweeping generalisations are not advisable.

It is in the south that conditions seem most extreme and despite the many papers that have already been written, much remains to be discovered. One of the unresolved questions concerns how lions survive without water. Given an adequate kill rate, their water needs are surprisingly low. Lions are found in areas of the Kalahari where there is no surface water and therefore, it seems, they must be able to go without water for months at a time. Dr Mills, writing of carnivores in the Kalahari, claims that they are all independent of water but the larger ones will drink if it is available.[12] In one study, a pride of lions was followed at close quarters for ten days. For seven consecutive days, they did not drink at all but in that time they killed an ostrich, a porcupine and two gemsbok. A lioness with cubs will have a much greater need for water than at other times. Water conservation is a key survival mechanism, and the apparently lazy lion life is not entirely without function therefore. Lying in the shade of trees during the heat of the day is a way of reducing evaporative water loss and of keeping body temperatures low. A lion will not exert itself unnecessarily, and air temperatures in the Kalahari during the summer months can exceed 41 °C and, on the surface of the sand itself, may be more than 70 °C.

These are difficult conditions for young cubs and the mortality rate in the Gemsbok Park is high. In one study a pride was monitored for three years.[13] In that time eleven cubs were born but only one survived past the age of eighteen months. One observer, watching a pride closely, noted that an eight-week-old cub walked a total of 68 km in nine days, in one night alone walking 13 km.[14] There are cases of cubs dying of rickets, or being abandoned by parents. One lioness left her young family of three for a total of five nights. When she returned two of the cubs were dead from starvation. The third temporarily recovered, but its ultimate fate is unknown.

Mortality rates vary throughout Africa, but those of the Kalahari are highest. A general figure for cub mortality in Southern Africa is about 50 per cent deaths, although 60 per cent is reported for Etosha and 67 per cent for Serengeti. Kruger National Park at 29 per cent and Nairobi Park at a reported 15 per cent are by far the best performers. The causes of cub deaths are legion. Bone disorders and starvation are only two. Lion cubs are dependent upon their mothers for up to eighteen months, thus the untimely death of a mother critically affects her cub's chances of survival. Snakes and scorpions are believed to take their toll, although very little research has been done in this area, while cannibalism, mostly by males, has also been recorded. Porcupines are a favourite delicacy of lions, yet the risk factor seems high, judging from the numerous cases on record of lions having died as a result of injuries received in the encounter.

Through the very good offices of Pietri Viljoen, who was studying lions at Mababe Depression, and Rodney Fuhr, who was supporting the research, I had the opportunity of watching a film sequence they had made. The cast included three young lionesses who thought to enjoy a porcupine for dinner. The setting was a small clearing among tall trees. The ground was bare. It was night. Without question the porcupine was an elderly matron. Her quills bustled and clattered, fully erect. Clearly she was not about to oblige this hungry young trio and certainly had no intention of making it easy for them. The lions took up positions surrounding her; she had no route of escape.

The most amazing aspect of the whole episode was the apparent absence of any panic in the porcupine. Every move seemed calculated, almost as if she knew that she could not lose, providing she kept her head. And keep it she did. In turn, each of the lions would approach her with caution, suggesting that, on another occasion perhaps, they had already acquired respect for this small but forbidding opponent. At each approach, with neat, mincing steps

the indomitable lady would scornfully turn her back, presenting an impenetrable barrier of sharp barbs. At no time did two lions attack simultaneously. For over twenty minutes this macabre dance continued. Eventually, as if bored with the game, the lions moved away. The porcupine put her head in the air and strutted away. Although she had put on a very brave face, I have no doubt that inside she was quivering with fear. She'd had a lucky escape.

An example of the variations found among lion populations can be seen in the different feeding patterns of those in the south and those in the north of the Kalahari. In the south the environment is more arid and this impacts upon the distribution, diversity and density of prey species. In the Kalahari Gemsbok Park, for example, small mammals and young animals make up more than 50 per cent of known lion kills, while in the Kruger National Park and in Serengeti less than 1 per cent of kills falls into this category. At Mababe it is different again. Here, with a greater diversity of vegetation, higher rainfall and, sometimes, perennial water, game is much more varied and plentiful. According to Chris McBride, nearly 90 per cent of prey were as large or larger than an impala.[15] Only 7 per cent were classified as small animals – and this included one bullfrog and six springhares. The preponderance of young animals remains high, at 42 per cent, but this is probably due as much to ease of killing as availability alone. Young buffalo accounted for 78 per cent of all the large animals, under one year old, that were selected for prey.

Elephants once widely roamed the Kalahari, far more so than they do today. Now their range and numbers have diminished and they are largely confined to the wetter regions of Kalahari sand, along the major rivers and in the Chobe and Okavango. There are still one or two adventurous individuals however. Quite recently, a young bull appeared in the southern part of Botswana's Kalahari. Its progress could be followed down from the north by a series of startled reports and complaints of crop damage. Regrettably, it had to be shot. Another, no less intrepid traveller, in 1977, visited Ghanzi, a well-known elephant haunt of long ago. Fortunately, it had the good sense to stay out of sight, leaving only its spoor and more obvious visiting cards before returning from whence it came.

Ian Parker, in his excellent work *Ivory Crisis*, makes some very pertinent points about the number of elephants in Africa and the sometimes erroneous conclusions that are drawn from unreliable data. A 1975 elephant count in the Chobe Game Reserve estimated between 5 000 and 6 000 animals. A second estimate in 1981–2 found a population of 25 000. In September 1983 this was estimated again at 21 000. Part of the explanation for the surprising variation in these figures may depend on the time of the year the elephants are counted – they spend a great deal of time outside the National Park in certain seasons.

Ivory has always been a controversial issue and the hunting of elephant in the Kalahari is a sensitive area. There is evidence that the ivory trade may have started as long ago as the ninth century, when Arab traders, exerting their influence from the coast, exchanged trade goods for this valuable commodity.[16] Certainly ivory was worked extensively at Schroda in the ninth century and at the nearby K2 site in the tenth. Both are archaeological sites, close to the famous Mapungubwe, in the extreme north-west of the Transvaal, on the banks of the Limpopo River and within hunting reach of the Kalahari. Clearly, the exporting of ivory from the Kalahari has been going on, with considerable success, for more than a thousand years.

The modern commercial ivory manufacturing trade in Botswana is a comparatively new development, having started in 1975. In its short life it has suffered many vicissitudes. Today it appears in a healthy state but its supply of raw material is somewhat erratic. Much to their credit, the Botswana Government, being uncertain of its elephant resources, banned all hunting of them. This is currently being reviewed and the ivory supply may increase once more. In 1983 Botswana's Department of Wildlife sold by tender 2,2 tonnes of ivory, confiscated, found or acquired from control work.

The average weight of each tusk was 8 kg. It has been estimated that, with a minimum of 20 000 elephants, Botswana could expect, at a natural growth rate of 5 per cent, to remove 1 000 animals each year and have, annually, something in the region of 15 tonnes of ivory to sell, at a sustainable yield level.[17] However, there are other factors to consider. Poaching is increasing significantly. In 1982 an elephant was worth $1 500 and today no doubt the figure is higher. The demand for licences, when they are available, is high. When last issued in 1980, David Peacock, then a game warden, had the task of allocating 100 licences among 10 000 applicants!

Thankfully, elephants are not all ivory and money. They are gentle, oddly beautiful and thrilling creatures. It is from the herds with mothers and young that you can expect trouble. The older bulls, who spend much time on their own, are remarkably tolerant. People who have visited Savuti, which is famous for its big bull elephants, never forget the experience of a close encounter with these softly padding leviathans. They move imperturbably between the guy ropes of tents or search inquisitively with their long sensitive trunks for elusive oranges among the handful of parked vehicles at the public camp site. Harry and Betty Cantle have lived at Savuti for many years. It is said that Harry has forgotten more about the wild than many people ever knew, and indeed he has spent his life in the wild. His own experience of elephant speaks eloquently of their gentle, harmless nature.

A plover had the misfortune to choose for its nesting site a location right in the centre of a trail habitually used by elephant. These giants are creatures of habit and will use the same path indefinitely to move from one place to another. It was some time before an elephant used the track the plover had selected and when it happened the plover was well ensconced. The nest was complete, eggs had been laid and incubation begun. One afternoon a full five tonnes of male elephant came ambling slowly down the path. It was a warm, sunny afternoon and the season of plentiful food. The large male was abruptly halted in mid-stride by the repeated screechings and frenetic wing displays of a small black and white bird, no more than 20 cm high, which stood defiantly in front of him, barring the way. For a moment there was an impasse. Would a fight result? A sudden silence descended, and the world seemed to hold its breath. Perhaps the elephant understood the need to live and let live for with only a moment's hesitation and not the slightest show of irritation, he carefully stepped around the nest and continued on his way. For months afterwards the elephant path had an unaccountable kink in it but, for all we know, there is a plover family, somewhere, which believes that that is just how things should be.

Such sanctity of life is not uncommon in the wild and there are numerous examples of it. Even so, accidental deaths do occur, and I know of one incident which illustrates the point. An elephant was browsing in a leisurely way on the seed pods of a tall acacia. He was not the first to have been at the tree and the remaining fruits were high and difficult to reach. Near the base of the tree was a large fallen branch and if his browsing was to continue, the elephant would have had to step over it. Carefully, but with a touch of absent-mindedness perhaps, he did so. The massive leg rose into the air, passed over the branch and was lowered to the ground, followed by most of the elephant's not inconsiderable weight, an unfortunate moment for the small tortoise who had chosen that precise spot for an afternoon snooze. It is unlikely that he ever woke up, which is a blessing.

Wild dogs somehow catch the imagination of visitors.[18] They have a reputation for ruthlessness, ferocity and great cruelty that is unrivalled by other carnivores. They are known as savage killers. Except in the large tracts of uninhabited Kalahari where game still exists, wild dogs are not often found outside of national parks. They are medium-sized predators, weighing from 27 to 36 kg and seldom measure more than 75 cm at the shoulder. There is a disadvantage in being relatively short, especially in the wet season when the grass is high. Often, however, you will see them pausing in their tracks and standing tall on two back legs, surveying the scene from this greater height before resuming their journey. They usually hunt in the early morning or late evening, although they have been known to hunt on moonlit nights. When they hunt, they do so in complete silence, relying less upon speed than sheer endurance. They ultimately wear their quarry down and only sprint for the kill itself.

I once stood on the banks of the Savuti Channel at a time when it still retained some water, and it was a haven in the otherwise desolate, arid southern Chobe. It was towards sunset. Suddenly, from my left, I saw a young impala sprinting for its life. Within metres were six wild dogs and in seconds the kill was made, less than 20 m from where I stood. It happened so quickly it was not possible to say quite how it was done, but the animal was down and all six dogs threw themselves at it in an explosive fury of biting, snarling, jaw-snapping and growling. There was no time for a camera but I did think to start a stopwatch. In precisely four and a half minutes, the carcass was all but gone. Only the head and one shoulder remained. I do not imagine that that would have taken very long to finish, but nature intervened. A lioness leapt from the channel's bank, bounded through the shallow water and, ignoring the wild dogs, took the remains of their kill and raced away with it. They made no effort to prevent the theft or to recover their meal. They were probably satiated. I estimated that it would have taken the six killers less than six minutes to demolish the 40 kg impala completely. It is impossible to say at precisely which moment, during the four and a half minutes that I observed, the impala actually died.

The question of animals dying in pain has several interesting aspects. I once watched a pride of lions hunting a buffalo. At the death were three large lions. One had its forepaws on the buffalo's back, a second was biting deep into its gut and the third had its claws embedded in the animal's face and neck. To my amazement the buffalo simply stood there, and this was only the first onslaught. It certainly could have run or, one might imagine, have fought back. It did neither, however, but merely stood stock still. Why?

How much pain did the impala have to suffer? How long did it take to die? It has been suggested by some researchers, from studies done on mice, that in circumstances of severe shock or pain, a hormone is released that has the effect, through a chemical reaction, of closing down all pain receptors and motor activity. The animal literally freezes in its tracks. Similar experiences have been recorded in people too. Is what happens in mice a reflection of reactions of bigger animals in similar circumstances? Is there a point in such traumatic occurrences where the body simply decides 'enough', and then closes down?

Surprisingly little work has been done on the wild dog and there remains a great deal about certain aspects of their biology and ecology still to be researched. It is said that no two animals have the same coat and colour patterns. It is also claimed that in each pack only the dominant male and female mate and, furthermore, that it is always the same female who is mated.[19] Why this should be so is a mystery.

Baboons are, at first sight, unlikely candidates for a book about life on Kalahari sands. Yet in the Okavango, where the sands may lie deepest of all, baboons abound, inhabiting many of the Delta's islands. They occur elsewhere, too, of course, but this one particular group is of special interest. Scientists have been researching and living among them for many years and their findings are being reported continually.[20] The object of the research project is to study how baboon communities live, with a view to obtaining some understanding of how man might have lived before he came down from the trees. Behaviour of special interest concerns the baboons' response to the raids made upon them by both lion and leopard. Lion apparently prefer to hunt baboons by day and the technique most frequently used is that of ambush, the lion lying in wait behind a termite mound or hiding in dense vegetation. The success rate in obviously planned attacks was about 24 per cent, but there were many encounters which seemed coincidental. It may well be that attacks on baboons by lion are purely opportunistic. Those made by leopard are clearly not.

At night a baboon troop will roost in a favourite tree. On Chief's Island the great,

tall acacias, with high canopies and spreading branches, make ideal roosts. They are also fairly easy for a leopard to climb. Attacks are made late at night or in the early morning. The method is simple. The leopard climbs the tree and, disregarding the alarm calls of the unfortunate baboons, edges out along a particular branch towards a chosen quarry. Surprise does not appear to be important. A hunt in a single roost may last several hours, and occasionally the whole night. The ability to stay aloft longest determines the outcome. Although many kills have been made, none has actually been witnessed and exactly how a kill is effected remains, for the moment, a mystery. It may be, however, that a gruesome game is played. The leopard has the disadvantage of being heavier, but he can see more clearly in the dark and, once he gets a baboon down to the ground, all the odds are in his favour. The baboon, on the other hand, is lighter and more suited to life in the trees, but he is probably terrified. If the baboon is lucky he can edge out furthest along a branch, keeping beyond the leopard's reach. He has the option of changing branches but in the dark this may not be easy to do. He has little alternative but to sit it out, keeping his head and hoping that he has chosen the right branch to sleep on.

The dassie, or rock rabbit, is another unlikely Kalahari resident. Indeed, it is not found within the Kalahari itself, but is certainly abundant among the rocks and hills that surround it. Dassies are unusual and interesting for two reasons. Firstly, it is said that they are more closely related to elephants than to any other animal, although neither they nor the elephants seem to have benefited by this rather strange example of scientific classification. Dassies like to spend a great deal of their time basking in the sun on top of exposed rocks. They are known to be somewhat thermolabile and it is apparently necessary for them to sunbask as a means of raising their body temperature.

One of the dassie's most persistent predators is the black eagle. Knowing his prey well, part of the black eagle's hunting technique is to make continuous, low-level passes, just above the rocks. In this way, appearing with extreme suddenness, he can hope to catch the dassie by surprise. The latter makes this more difficult by choosing a rock with a good view, or by wedging himself into a small, sunny nook, upon which a surprise attack is unlikely. The eagle's response is to attack out of the sun, hoping that the dassie will be blinded as he searches the sky for his enemy. To counter this tactic, the dassie has developed a most remarkable adaptation. When it looks into the sun a dark, spade-shaped shield, called the umbraculum, is extended across the pupil of its eye, dividing it into two smaller portions, enabling the animal to gaze at the sun without loss of vision. Apparently camels, goats and llamas have a similar, though smaller, mechanism and vestigial traces of the same thing are also found in horses. However, the only expansible umbracula comparable to those in the dassie are found in non-vertebrate fish which live in shallow water and are exposed to light of high intensity.[21]

A second, rather unusual adaptation shown by this interesting creature is the presence of sweat glands on the pads of their feet. These allow the build-up of moisture so that when the foot is slapped onto rock, a tiny vacuum is formed which strengthens the dassie's grip and helps it achieve its remarkable climbing ability.[22]

Two of Southern Africa's most attractive antelope are the impala and the springbok. Interestingly, one seldom finds both in the same area. Impala are water dependent and are seldom far from it; springbok can apparently do entirely without it and are more commonly found, therefore, in arid parts like the Kalahari. Springbok are astonishing creatures and their fecundity is legendary. In good years they can lamb twice and their numbers can increase, over time, at an astronomical rate. Tales of the famous springbok migrations or treks come down to us from within living memory but these are now probably a phenomenon of the past. During the last century, in Southern Africa, they were still very much in evidence.[23] The treks have been described as seasonal migrations and involved literally millions of animals. One of the earliest records comes from 1840 and they seem to have continued at fairly regular intervals

until 1896, when the rinderpest presumably had its devastating effect upon springbok populations. The migrations occurred sporadically and at first were thought to be seasonal; this has since been disproved. In the Prieska district of the northern Cape, for example, only four significant treks passed through between 1887 and 1896, and the direction they followed was not always the same.

The migrating springbok moved at a steady walk, the animals seeming in some way mesmerised, so that often thousands were killed by the press of those behind when some obstacle temporarily slowed the leaders. There was a noticeable absence of fear. The vast herds were deterred by little and passed without hesitation through the towns and villages in their path, where thousands would be clubbed to death in the streets. Horses and wagons could barely pass through the herds and herdsmen caught within them were sometimes trampled to death. Sheep and other animals such as kudu, hartebeest, wildebeest, zebra and eland were sometimes caught up in the throng and carried along to areas where they had become extinct.

Most witnesses have hesitated to attach numbers to the migrations but it is beyond doubt that the numbers were vast, sometimes unimaginable. One estimate, by people accustomed to counting sheep, was 50 000 animals; another was 100 million, the witness having driven 75 km through the throng. There are reports of thousands being shot in a trek in 1896, without any noticeable effect on the numbers. At one time the combined springbok population of South Africa's Great Karoo and the Kalahari regions was estimated at more than 500 million, so these migration numbers are probably not exaggerated.[24] In 1888 a Dr Gibbons and companion tried to count one of these passing animal armies in the Prieska district. They calculated that they saw 20 000 springbok to each hectare and estimated that 4 000 ha were densely covered. Within their sight, therefore, were 80 million animals. In one case a herd stretched for over 210 km on a front 22 km wide. A Mr W C Scully, magistrate at Okiep in Namibia, reported millions of springbok trudging in solid phalanxes down to the

Atlantic Ocean. There the animals drank seawater and died by the million. It is said that their bodies lined the shore for a solid 50 km.

The springbok treks caused havoc. Grazing that was not eaten by the passing hordes was trampled underfoot. They destroyed fences, killed stock and did great damage to the land. Many a farmer faced ruin as a result of a migration passing through his lands. Little pity was spared for the animals and indeed they were almost regarded as vermin and were hunted ruthlessly in the hope of keeping their numbers down or eliminating them completely. To a large extent, man has succeeded. Fences, organised farming and development have generally fragmented the springboks' former range. Today they have been driven back beyond the frontier rivers that mark the boundaries of the Kalahari. There, in that arid environment, they continue to thrive but they will never reach those stupendous numbers again. That is not to say that migrations will not take place. Two migrations out of the Kalahari this century have been recorded, one in 1946 and the other in 1950. The first involved about 20 000 animals. They came down the Nossob River and headed south towards Upington. Many were shot on the way by farmers anxious to protect their grazing. Some reached Upington and dispersed. The second trek began as early as July or August 1950. Herds of springbok were seen accumulating in southern Botswana and exhibited a restlessness that was uncharacteristic. By November the trek began to move. It crossed the Molopo River on 320 km front, down into the very south of the Kalahari and on to Gordonia and the districts of the Northern Cape. There is no estimate of the numbers in this herd.

There has been much speculation as to the cause of these migrations. Generally, however, it is agreed that they are dispersal mechanisms. At first the role of the social hierarchy was stressed and it was suggested that the dominant animals in times of need would force those subordinate to them to find pastures new. Analysis of trek participants, however, did not support this view. General dispersal following population increases is popularly accepted.

Of all Africa's game, perhaps even more so than the elephant, the plight of the rhinoceros must surely be the most tragic. Sought after for its horn, it has been pursued throughout its range in Africa, almost to the point of extinction. Regrettably, it seems that as the numbers diminish the carnage, far from slowing down, accelerates as the ever more efficient poaching systems hurry to take the remaining horns before they are lost to competitors. The horns, which are nothing more than modified and compacted hair, very similar to human fingernails, are used to make handles for daggers and as a medicine in the Far East. Claims of the aphrodisiac properties of powdered rhino horn are without foundation but there are other, mystical, properties attributed to it, too, and the demand continues. Because of the rich rewards, poaching is an ongoing problem, and is particularly rife in countries whose economies are weak and incentive schemes poor. This makes the task of conservationists almost impossible. An example from Zambia illustrates the point.

Rhino horn today is worth about US $10 000 a kilogram. A good animal in this part of Africa may yield between 5 and 10 kg of horn. For 5 kg, therefore, the poacher can expect to earn in excess of $50 000. But it does not stop there. There is a flourishing black market in foreign currency in Zambia, as there is in many African countries. The rate fluctuates but in mid-1986 it stood between 8 and 10 Zambian kwacha to the US dollar. The poacher could conceivably convert his earnings into K 500 000, a sum far beyond anything he could expect to earn by more honest means and one that could offer him a most acceptable standard of living for the rest of his life.

Of course it is not as simple and straightforward as this would suggest. A sophisticated poaching network exists and all involved must take their share. In addition, there are certain costs to be taken into account and the inevitable bribes, all of which reduce the profit. Nevertheless, the potential earnings are enormous and the attraction to the unemployed is irresistible. The sorry fact is that rhinos are fast disappearing and, although vast sums may be expended in trying to protect them, poaching is still on the increase and daily becomes more organised. Since it is only the animal's horn which is sought one wonders why so little has been made of the apparently simple suggestion to dart the animals and remove their horns. The horns will grow again, although not as well, and the rhinos will survive.

Today, the rhino of the Kalahari are mostly confined to national parks or remote and uninhabited areas.[25] The species was once widespread throughout the sands and was probably only absent from the very arid central and south-western areas. The present reduction in range can be almost wholly attributed to hunting and to large-scale habitat changes caused by man's expansion into increasingly marginal areas. In Botswana's Kalahari the rhino, of which there are two species, has been almost completely eliminated. The white rhino inhabited the northern regions, including Lake Ngami, and was found as far south as Ghanzi. The last one was shot in about 1890. There has been the occasional contact with white rhinos since then but it is thought that these animals had wandered across the border from Zimbabwe's Hwange National Park, to which they had been transported from the national parks near Kariba.

The status of the black rhino is less certain. An estimate in 1971 suggested that there were at least twenty animals, with the possibility of many more. It is thought that they are confined to the Okavango Delta, the Kwando River and the north-western part of Chobe National Park. The last black rhino known to have been killed was shot by a poacher in 1936, in north-western Botswana.

With admirable courage and forethought, Botswana's Game Department set about reintroducing the white rhino. In 1967 two males and two females from Zululand were donated to Chobe National Park. In 1971 a calf was born to this group. A further fifty-two animals were introduced in 1976, to Moremi Game Reserve and to Chobe. So far as is known, these populations are flourishing,[26] although it is reported that they are again being hunted and have already disappeared from the Chobe river-

front where once, after reintroduction, they were not uncommon.[27]

In the west of the Kalahari there is a remarkable ridge that can be traced from the south-eastern side of Lake Ngami, south-west to Ghanzi, and from there westwards to Gobabis and, eventually, to the foothills above which stands the city of Windhoek. The ridge is comprised of very ancient sandstone, quartzite and schist of Damara age, something to the order of 900 million years. Most of the ridge is covered with Kalahari sands, supporting grass and trees. It is considered to be excellent cattle country and is now intensively ranched, both in Botswana and Namibia. The sandstone below the Kalahari covering provides a good aquifer and water is not difficult to find. Although most game species have been shot out, some in fact have flourished. Notable among these are the greater kudu. Their explosion in numbers has led to a rather unusual problem, an energetic investigation and a most amusing conclusion.[28]

To 'South Westers' the presence of game on their roads has always been a hazard. It was mentioned as early as 1932, and in recent years the problem has intensified. With the building of more highways and the increased traffic using them, the number of accidents has increased and, perhaps because of higher speeds, consequences are often tragic. 'Animal-related accidents' have become something of a feature in the press, with the greater kudu identified as the principal offender.

The most notorious section of road at one time for this type of accident was a 50 km stretch on the Gobabis-Windhoek road, which followed the top of the ridge. Pressure from the public mounted and eventually the Nature Conservation Department of the South West African Administration was forced to investigate. Mike Griffin and a colleague set to work, their task being to come to grips with the problem and find a way to reduce kudu accidents.

The population increase among eastern Namibia's kudu is the result of many factors. Intensive ranching has provided more watering points and bad land management practices have encouraged bush encroachment, which favours the kudu. Decreased predator pressure and the absence of any rabies epizootics from 1933 until the early 1980s have allowed the numbers to increase almost without constraint. Legislated private ownership of huntable game has led farmers to encourage the increase in wild game on their lands.

As might perhaps have been expected, when the results of the investigation were available the picture was very different from that suggested by the pressures which had initiated the investigation in the first place. Of all the accidents in the entire country between 1977 and 1980, only 8 per cent had involved wild animals. Of those only half involved kudu. The cost to the country of all 'animal-related accidents' was calculated to be in the region of R2 million. If death and carnage on the roads was what the issue was all about, the researchers may be forgiven for feeling that theirs was a futile exercise. It did not affect their work, however, and page after page of facts were produced, all checked and cross-checked and presented in a manner which would surely have pleased the heart of any professor. One hundred and fifty-four pages of report, supported by 138 pages of appendices, all added up to over a year of work and thousands of rands in expenses. And what was the final recommendation?

The investigators may have been influenced by the knowledge that alcohol is believed to be a contributing factor in well over 50 per cent of all motor accidents. Or perhaps they had been thinking about the vehemence of the public outcry in relation to the size of the actual problem. Whatever the case, the final recommendation, to me, is a model of common sense and succinct philosophy which holds a far wider application than the sense in which it was applied. It said: 'In modern democratic society man is displaying an alarming attitude in refusing to personally accept responsibility for his own fate. Natural dangers are no longer considered natural and somebody (anybody but the individual) must be responsible and liable . . . we suggest that the burden of adapting and avoidance must rest with the individual motorist . . . what we are suggesting here is . . . especially in the case of the kudu, not to capture them

but to avoid them as the natural hazards which they are.'[29]

Compared with some other places in Africa, the more remote parts of the Kalahari are extremely inhospitable to animal life. Surface water exists for only a few months of the year and rains are unreliable. In the south-western Kalahari the average rainfall is 150 mm a year but the range is plus or minus 70 per cent. This means one can expect, on average, anything between 255 mm and 45 mm. Some years there may be no rain whatsoever and in others it may all fall in one or two stupendous storms. The temperature range is equally great and will easily extend from below 0 °C to 41 °C or more. The hottest time of the year is in the months before the rains break, i.e. from September, after the cool, dry winter, to December or January. During this time the Kalahari is at its worst.

Branches are bare so that evaporation is reduced. The grass has long since dried and crumbled, to be blown away by the wind. Promise for the future lies stored in tubers beneath the ground or dormant in countless millions of tiny seeds that nestle between the grains of sands, waiting. The sand is bare and throws back the heat of the sun like a solar reflector. The sky is blue and cloudless; there is no shade. The distance dances in shimmering waves of light and the world reverberates with the call of cicadas whose strident tones seem to pierce the brain. On a really hot day one can collapse and die of heatstroke. Clouds herald the approach of the rainy season, appearing at first in twos and threes, then in greater numbers. Soon towering giants tempt the senses with the promise of rain but it may yet be months away. Life must wait.

In the intense heat and absence of water, the animals have had to evolve some remarkable adaptations in order to survive.

We think of camels and goats as being well adapted to survival in arid lands, and indeed they are. Both can withstand a loss of up to 30 per cent of their body weight in water. For most other animals, between 12 and 14 per cent is the critical level. We all know to slake a severe thirst with small quantities of water, for consuming a large quantity is to run the risk of what is known as osmotic shock. Other animals are as much at risk here as humans. Only the ruminants have an extra stomach which acts as an osmotic barrier and prevents osmotic shock to the tissues following rapid rehydration.[30] Thus the goat can replenish its lost water with little danger to its system. Watching the tribesmen of the Kalahari watering their goats and cattle, you will appreciate more readily the advantage this confers on domestic stock, which are allowed but a moment or two at a hand-filled water trough.

The eland and the oryx are fascinating examples of heat tolerance and adaptation. Both are large animals, the eland, being the larger of the two, weighing up to 1 000 kg. The oryx, or gemsbok as it is known in the Kalahari, is somewhat lighter between 700 and 900 kg. Both are common in and favour the drier regions.

Humans require a steady body temperature. One of the ways to prevent rising body temperature is to cool the body by evaporating water. This works very well if plenty of water is available. If there is not, an alternative method is to allow the body's temperature to fluctuate. There are certain risks inherent in this approach but it is used successfully by a number of animals, among which camels, eland and gemsbok are outstanding examples.

Dr C R Taylor, in a series of elegant experiments, came to some interesting conclusions as far as desert ungulates are concerned.[31] Firstly, he found that for all such creatures, when they have access to sufficient water, a steady temperature of about 39 °C is maintained by evaporative cooling, just as in humans. It is when water is restricted or unavailable that curious differences emerge. A camel, being a large animal with a relatively small surface area per unit mass ratio, starts a desert day with a very low body temperature, when it is dehydrated. Because of its large mass, its temperature rises slowly during the day, by as much as 7 °C, and seldom reaches a level where sweating is necessary. During the night the camel cools and is thus ready to face the next day.

Much the same process was found in dehydrated eland and gemsbok. Their morning temperatures would start as low as 33,9 °C and then rise during the day by more than 7 °C to 41,2 °C (a little lower in the gemsbok). Dr Taylor calculated that for a 1 000 kg eland a 7 °C rise in temperature would store some 6 000 kilojoules of heat. Dissipating this heat by evaporating water would need about 10 litres. In other words, by allowing the body temperature to fluctuate in this way, the eland 'saves' up to 10 litres a day. The animal 'stores' heat rather than spends water to maintain its steady body temperature.

Taylor's experiments were carried out in a maximum temperature of 40 °C. Being aware that desert temperatures often exceed this level, he then repeated them, using dehydrated animals and a maximum of 45 °C. With or without water the eland managed to keep its temperature at about 5 °C below the new air temperature. Not so the gemsbok when it was dehydrated. Its response was quite amazing. The gemsbok's body temperature soared and rose above the experimental 45 °C temperature where it remained for hours without apparent harm to the animal. This is all the more remarkable as 42 °C is usually lethal for most mammals. In simple terms, strange as it may sound, the gemsbok's body was hotter than the surrounding air and accordingly shed metabolic heat, by conduction and radiation, into the atmosphere. How is it that vital organs in the body can survive these high temperatures? The most critically exposed area is the brain and to protect it a number of ungulates have developed an extraordinarily useful mechanism known as the carotid rete, in the cavernous sinus region below the brain.

The carotid rete is known to have developed in certain gazelles, the gemsbok, and in sheep. It consists of a network of blood-vessels and forms a kind of heat exchange unit. Blood destined for the brain and coming direct from the heart is at a high temperature. It passes through this fine network and in the process is cooled by venous blood returning to the heart from the nasal sinuses. This venous blood has been cooled because, although the gemsbok at these high ambient temperatures is not sweating, the animal continues to pant and so the returning blood from the nasal passages is several degrees cooler than hot arterial blood from the heart. This difference in temperature has been measured and can amount to as much as 2,9 °C, sufficient, if the heat exchange is effective, to reduce the temperature of blood entering the brain to an acceptable 42 °C.

Drs Gideon Lowe and Mary Seely, in their fascinating book *Ecology of Desert Organisms*,[32] take this a step further and, while suggesting the need for more research, point out that an enlarged nasal sinus area will have adaptive value for many animals. They propose that the grotesquely enlarged nasal region of the Mongolian saiga antelope has some function which may be related to temperature and also suggest that the carotid rete may not be limited to desert-adapted animals. As its major function appears to be in cooling the brain, it may also be found in sprinting predators and prey animals whose body temperatures rise dramatically during exercise.

Tolerating extremely high temperatures without sweating is one way of reducing water loss. Another method is to reduce the metabolic rate. Three animals, the zebu, gemsbok and Grant's gazelle, do this and show a reduction in this rate about twice that found in other animals.[33] Slowing the metabolism reduces faecal water loss, urinary water loss and respiratory evaporation. Taylor found that this method is used when food and water are scarce and when animals are dehydrated.

Despite all these intriguing adaptations, animals still need water. It is the basic fuel for their existence and simply by living they are using it up. How then, in these waterless areas, is it replaced? Again we turn to Dr Taylor's work. He observed that eland, in the heat of the day, sought shelter under acacia thorn trees and browsed upon the small dry leaves. Dry as they were at the time, analysis showed that they contained 59 per cent water and that the eland could eat, in a single day, sufficient leaves to yield the 5 litres of water it needed to survive without drinking. The gemsbok, however, does not necessarily seek the shade of trees at midday and often stands out in the baking sun; nor does it eat the leaves of acacia trees. What it does eat,

however, are dried grasses and shrubs which, in the middle of the day, contain as little as 1 per cent moisture and are so dry that they fall apart at the touch.

As long ago as 1930 a Dr Buxton had observed that dried grass is hygroscopic and that it absorbs moisture from the air, even when there is no dew. This provided Dr Taylor with the clue he needed. He took some of the dried plants, exposed them to the equivalent desert airs and found that after ten hours they contained 42 per cent water. He concluded that, by eating at night, the gemsbok could obtain all the water it needed to be independent of other sources. The implications of this discovery must seem significant to cattle ranchers in the Kalahari, yet to my knowledge few, if any, take advantage of it, as cattle are always enclosed after dusk.

These examples of adaptations are of course not the only ways in which animals can avoid the massive heat loads to which they are subjected. Many seek shade or arrange their working hours to take advantage of the cooler periods.

The delightful ground squirrel, which is widely found in the Kalahari, has its own built-in solution in the shape of a large bushy tail. Whenever it stops, the tail flicks up and is held in a gentle arc over the squirrel's body, shading it from the sun. The tortoise has an unusual way of dealing with overheating. Some have very large bladders and spray urine on their legs to keep cool by evaporation. If you watch the springbok carefully you will notice that it takes great care with regard to the position of its body in relation to the sun. When the animal is grazing and temperatures rise it will either turn to face directly into the sun, or present its rump to the sun's rays. By this means, the animal reduces the profile presented to the sun and by as much as 50 per cent the heat load to which its body is subjected.

Fascinating as they are, these adaptations are not the exclusive preserve of large mammals. Smaller animals, plants and insects all show similar responses to the environment. Some of them, as we shall see in following chapters, are even more miraculous.

## REFERENCES

1. **Cohen, M.** 'Notes on the Spotted Hyaena'. In *Custos*, Vol 5, No 1, December 1975, **p 8**
2. **Deane, N N.** 'The Spotted Hyaena'. In *The Lammergeyer*, Vol 2. No 2, June 1962, **pp 26-44**
3. Ibid, **p 40**
4. **Campbell, A C.** Personal communication, March 1986
5. **Campbell, A C.** 'A Big Meal'. In *African Wildlife*, Vol 27, 1973, **p 24**
6. **Child, D and Robbel, H.** 'Drowning of Lechwe by Spotted Hyaena'. In *Mammalia*, Vol 39, No 4, 1975
7. **Verhoef, J.** 'The Hyaena's Diet'. In *Custos*, Vol 5, No 2, Jan 1976
8. **De Vos, V.** 'An Unusual Case of Snaring in a Free Living Spotted Hyaena . . .' In *Koedoe*, Vol 24, 1981, **pp 205-07**
9. **Deane, N N.** Op cit, **p 35**
10. **Campbell, A C.** Personal communication, March 1986
11. **Mills, M G L.** *Ecology and Behaviour of the Brown Hyaena in the Kalahari.* Proceedings of a Symposium on Endangered Wildlife in Southern Africa. Endangered Wildlife Trust, Johannesburg, South Africa, July 1976, **p 38**
12. **Eloff, F C.** 'Water Use by the Kalahari Lion'. In *Koedoe.* Vol 16, 1973, **pp 149-54**
13. **Eloff, F.C.** 'Cub Mortality in the Kalahari Lion'. In *Koedoe*, Vol 23, 1980, **pp 163-70**
14. Ibid
15. **McBride, C J.** 'Age and Size Categories of Lion Prey in Chobe National Park, Botswana'. In *Botswana Notes and Records.* Vol 16, 1984, **p 139**
16. **Voigt, E A.** 'Ivory in the Early Iron Age of South Africa'. In *Transvaal Museum Bulletin*, No 18, Nov 1982, **p 17**
17. **Martin, E B.** 'The Ivory Industry in Botswana'. In *African Elephant and Rhino Group Newsletter*, No 3, June 1984, **pp 5-7**
18. **Fourie, P F.** 'How Cruel is the Cape Wild Dog?' In *Custos*, Vol 3, No 8, August 1974, **p 17**
19. **Reich, A.** 'Hunting Dogs, Facts and Fiction'. In *Custos*, Vol 6, No 7, June 1977, **p 41**
20. **Busse, C.** 'Leopard and Lion Predation upon Chacma Baboons Living in Moremi Wildlife Reserve'. In *Botswana Notes and Records*, Vol 12, 1980, **pp 15-21**
21. **Millar, R P.** 'An Unusual Light-Shielding Structure in the Eye of the Dassie'. In the Annals of the Transvaal Museum. Vol 28, No 11, August 1973, **pp 203-205**
22. **Campbell, A C.** Personal communication, March 1986
23. **Child, G and Le Riche, J D.** 'Recent Springbok Treks (Mass Movements) in South Western Botswana'. In *Mammalia*, Vol 33, 1969, **pp 499-504**
24. **Barrow, B.** *Song of a Dry River.* Cape Town: Purnell & Sons (Pty) Ltd, 1975, **pp 83-6**
25. **Von Richter, W.** 'Black and Square-lipped Rhinoceros in Botswana'. In *Biological Conservation*, Vol 5, 1973, **pp 59-60**
26. **Von Richter, W and Passineau, J.** 'Endangered Wildlife Species in Botswana'. In *Botswana Notes and Records*, Vol 11, 1979, **pp 121-5**
27. **Campbell, A C.** Personal communication, March 1986
28. **Griffin, M and Lensing, J E.** *The Road Accident Problem in SWA with Special Reference to Kudu and Other Animals.* Govt of SWA, Dept of Agriculture and Nature Conservation, Windhoek, Namibia (undated)
29. Ibid, **p 154**
30. **Lowe, G and Seely, M.** *Ecology of Desert Organisms.* New York: Longman, 1982, **p 60**
31. **Taylor, C R.** 'The Eland and the Oryx'. In *Scientific American*, Vol 220, No 1, January 1969, **pp 89-95**
32. **Lowe, G and Seely, M.** Op cit
33. **Taylor, C R.** 'Ranching Arid Areas: Physiology of Wild and Domestic Ungulates in the Desert'. In *Botswana Notes and Records.* Special Edition No 1, October 1971, **pp 167-78**

# 10. ... Have Little Beasts ...

TO many people living in Africa and to most of the people who visit the continent, the focus of attention, when it comes to wildlife, seems always to fall on the bigger animals. This is understandable. There is the undeniable thrill of watching massed herds of buffalo or wildebeest covering the plains, of watching lion, blood-stained at their kill, or spending hours observing a herd of elephant and being privy to their almost human intimacy. Larger animals are also easier to see; there is no doubt that skill in 'spotting' game improves with practice and visitors don't usually spend long enough in the game parks to develop this skill. As a result of these factors, the realm of the smaller animals and insects is often passed by in complete ignorance. That such a large part of nature's wonders is overlooked in this way is a great pity, and this would be confirmed by those who have become familiar with this side of wildlife.

Even in areas where it is most concentrated, game is not always to be found exactly where and when you want it. Harry Cantle, taking a party of five clients through Savuti, had such a morning once. However, crossing the road in front of him he saw a dung beetle, which was obliviously rolling its ball of dung along the road, looking for a likely nest site. For the next hour and a half three Americans and two Australians, aided and abetted by Harry, spent most of the time on their hands and knees, following with absorbed fascination the activities of this remarkable creature, as they listened, engrossed, to Harry's explanations. Not one of them would have missed the experience, they all said afterwards.

Throughout most of the Kalahari, and in some cases having an even wider distribution, there occur the four Southern African species of sandgrouse. These pigeon-sized birds have evolved an interesting adaptation which has allowed them to occupy in their millions an ecological niche which would otherwise have been completely denied them. For the most part, they live in very arid areas. Dr Gordon Maclean, who has made a comprehensive study of them, was among the first to publish certain information about the Namaqua and the spotted Sandgrouse.[1]

These birds are seed-eaters; so far as is known, they eat nothing but seeds. The moisture content of a dry seed which might have been lying on the baking sands of the Kalahari for a year or more, is very low, usually less than 10 per cent. Whilst adult birds may cope with this, their young most certainly can not – it is essential that they have water. The very youngest birds are also exclusively seed-eaters – in the crop of a week-old sandgrouse were found 1 400 tiny, hard seeds and nothing else. How then, do these young birds get the water they need, when their nest may be a great distance from the nearest supply?

It has long been known that doves carry water to their young in the crop, and regurgitate it to the nestlings. It was presumed that sandgrouse did the same but upon investigation this was found not to be the case. In fact the male bird physically carries water to his young. He does this by soaking his belly feathers in water and flying back to the nest, where the young actually drink from his saturated feathers. It is generally only the male who performs this task and his lower breast feathers are uniquely adapted to carry water.[2] In his abscence, the female can also carry water, but not as efficiently. The barbules on the male's abdominal feathers react to immersion in water so that a helically coiled portion unfolds and, with other barbules, creates a feather meshwork that holds water effectively. As much as 20-40 ml water can be held in this way which, for comparison, is more efficient than a nylon sponge![3] Chicks have been found with as much as 3 ml water in their crops – an amount almost equal to 30 per cent of their body weight, itself a remarkable phenomenon. The great advantage of this mechanism is that it allows the sandgrouse to extend its range significantly, living much further away from water than it would otherwise have been able to do. Maclean suggests that these birds may travel up to 160 km a day on a round trip to water.

Sandgrouse are remarkable for a number of other reasons. The Namaqua and the spotted sandgrouse both occur in great numbers but never in the same habitat, although both often inhabit the same area. The former is found almost exclusively on limited calcrete outcrops, the stony appearance of which blends perfectly with its plumage. The spotted sandgrouse, on the other hand, with its rich salmon-pink colour, blends perfectly with the red Kalahari sand, so perfectly in fact that, during a nineteen-month study period, Dr Maclean was able to find only one nest of the species, despite the fact that the birds occupied the area in vast numbers and were certainly nesting. Larks, in the Kalahari, share this colour pattern. Red larks are found extensively in the red sand dunes; grey ones inhabit the restricted areas of grey calcrete outcrops.[4]

Since sandgrouse nest during the hottest part of the year and as their nests are always on open ground, unprotected by any form of shade, the birds absorb a tremendous amount of heat. A bird may sit for eight continuous hours in the full sun. They have several methods of coping with the heat. They can raise their dorsal feathers, creating more air spaces between them, thereby, as air is a good insulant, improving their thermal insulation. Times of peak activity are restricted to the cooler parts of the day and, incredibly, the birds seem to have some way of knowing how hot the day is going to be and adjust their water intake accordingly. This behaviour, which is not yet fully understood, can be shown experimentally. From recordings taken in the field on days that subsequently turn out to be unusually hot, it is found that more birds will have been drinking during the early morning. How the sandgrouse anticipate these conditions is simply not known.[5]

Perhaps most remarkable of all is how it is that returning birds find their nests. A sandgrouse nest occupies a space no larger than a champagne glass and consists of little more than a shallow scrape in the ground. The eggs are coloured so as to deceive the eye of a predator. The female, if she is sitting, is just as cryptically coloured. What subtle mechanisms lead the male unerringly back to such a tiny target in so featureless a landscape after a journey of possibly 80 km? We simply do not know.

Ostriches are at the other end of the scale in size from the small sandgrouse but, like so many arid-zone birds, they have evolved special adaptations which allow them to thrive in this most harsh of environments.

It is generally believed that the male ostrich, which is much darker than the female, incubates the eggs at night, and the female attends to this duty during the day. In fact, this is not necessarily so and the birds are flexible in how the task is apportioned. Heat is the biggest enemy of successful incubation. Researchers from Cape Town University, implanting thermistor probes inside the air spaces of incubating eggs, made some interesting discoveries.[6] Firstly, despite the enormous variations in day and night temperatures, the temperature of the eggs remained remarkably constant. Although the male did tend to sit more at night, there were many occasions when his mate became heat-stressed during the long, hot days, at which point he would take over, reversing their day-night roles. Heat stress occurred on one occasion when the air temperature rose above 49 °C. Under these circumstances, it is not keeping the eggs warm which is important, but rather preventing the flow of heat from the environment into the eggs. It is this fact that compels the birds to remain sitting, in close protection of the eggs, at times when it is least comfortable to do so.

Where there is no surface water available ostriches, like so many other desert-adapted creatures, gather sufficient water for

their needs by consuming dew- and mois-
ture-laden vegetation. It is believed that
the male's practice of taking over incubation in the early mornings allows the female, who often has to face the unrelenting
heat of the day, the opportunity to graze at
a time when the vegetation is at its most
moist. Interestingly, these birds can withstand a loss of 25 per cent of their body
weight in water during dehydration.[7] Ostriches control their temperature by relying
on convection cooling. They achieve this
by fully erecting their feathers and by
drooping or raising their wings, both
methods allowing a circulation of cooling
air. Often this enlarged area of shade will
be taken advantage of by hatched chicks,
grateful for a portable sunshade. At night,
when the temperature falls, ostriches will
be found with their feathers tightly clamped
to their bodies, entrapping air and keeping
them warm. Water being as precious as it
is, only as a last resort do these birds
increase evaporative cooling by breathing
more rapidly.

Those who have travelled in the Kalahari, particularly in the more southerly and
westerly regions, will have come across
the enormous communal nests of the social
weavers. These nests are made solely from
straws, taken by the birds from the ground
and carefully laid in an interlocking pattern until a structure, roughly 10 m x 2 or
3 m, is completed. It is punctuated throughout with small tunnels which lead into the
separate nesting chambers of paired birds.
Many hundreds of birds will inhabit a
single communal nest, in the building of
which they have cooperated. Deeply thatched, the nest provides an ideal refuge from
excessively high temperatures.

These weavers are particularly interesting because, unusual for many Kalahari
birds, studies have been made of them and
we know a fair amount about them. They
do not, for example, normally drink in the
wild and, like so many creatures in the
Kalahari, they depend on the ubiquitous
termite as a major source of food. In fact, in
the southern Kalahari termites represent
34 per cent of the total weight of food eaten
by these birds. In the early mornings, especially after rain, weavers will seek out
the small fresh cones of newly turned soil

which indicate a termite home. The birds
get at the insects by flicking the cones open
with their beaks and when the supply is
exhausted move on to the next cone. This
somewhat unusual behaviour has been observed in a number of other avian species,
including plovers, hornbills, rollers and
larks.[8]

As far as I am concerned, the social
weavers are engaged in a fascinating battle
with mankind. It may well be that most
people are not aware of this, but I am certain that I share the secret at least with a
number of post office officials.

It seems that social weavers are quite
unable to make their nests any differently.
The nests have a great many advantages –
they are warm, comfortable, waterproof
and, if properly maintained, will last for
well over a hundred years. However, they
have one or two major drawbacks. Firstly,
they need a large tree or similar structure
to support them. There are a lot of trees in
the Kalahari but the further one is to the
west, and the drier the climate, the fewer
trees are to be found. Another disadvantage
is that in a drenching Kalahari thunder-
storm the nest will absorb a vast amount of
water, the weight of which is sometimes so
great that the branches collapse, the nest is
thrown to the ground and a new home has
to be found. Man, with his advance into the
Kalahari, has been instrumental in removing quite a few of the trees himself, the
net result being that the birds are on occasion hard pressed to find suitable sites in
which to build their nests. Their cunning
and imagination should not be underestimated, however.

All over Namibia, in particular, you will
see, sprouting from beneath the cross-trees
on innumerable telephone poles, the beginnings of social weaver nests. The Post
Office takes a dim view of the weavers
'moving in', and so the battle lines are
drawn. Somewhere in Namibia, I imagine,
there is a small, dedicated band of men,
whose sole job it is to rake down from the
telegraph poles the daily crop of new nests.
Elsewhere in Namibia there are many millions of homeless weavers, equally determined, trying to put them up again. On my
last visit there I thought I saw a gleam of
hope for bringing this conflict to an end –

but I can't be certain. On a number of telegraph poles, about a third of the way to the top, I noticed a peculiar, obviously man-made platform structure, and occasionally on one of these could be seen the makings of a weaver's nest, well clear of the wires ...

Perhaps we give too little credit to animals for anything other than purely physiological adaptations. There seems much less evidence of behavioural adaptation, although when it is reported it is usually startling. One thinks immediately of reports from the Galapagos Islands of finches using lengths of grass as tools, but there are many little-known reports of this nature from Africa as well.

In 1867 came the first account of Egyptian vultures in Namaqualand, Cape Province, using stones to break open ostrich eggs.[9] Since then similar reports have been made from all over Africa.[10] In some the birds are described as 'bombing' the nest with stones carried aloft; in others, stones are used as a hammer. A third technique involves throwing stones at the eggs from a standing position beside them. The Egyptian vulture, once common in Southern Africa, is now very rare indeed and we are unlikely to hear reports of this behaviour today – at least, not from the Kalahari. However, it is of interest that several other birds, among them the apparently intelligent crow, have also learnt to do this, although the behaviour does not seem, yet, to be widespread.

The Cape vulture has been the subject of much public attention during recent years in Southern Africa. The bird's range is vast and, although it does not breed in the Kalahari, it is a common visitor there. Various studies[11] have been undertaken on its biology with specific reference to mortality rates, which are, some claim, devastatingly high. In 1976 and again in 1981 Dr P J Mundy published a report based on his work at a number of the very large breeding colonies in Southern Africa. He claimed the future of the bird was threatened owing to a high infant mortality rate, attributable to a lack of calcium in the diet. He estimated a death rate, due to a nutritional bone disease, at something in the order of 20 per cent of all Cape vulture chicks born. The cause was believed to be the decline in the hyena bone-crunching population, which in turn deprived the vultures of a supply of bone fragments and the necessary source of calcium for their chicks.

Their plight attracted the attention of the media and vultures were given a good deal of press coverage. All over the southern continent 'vulture restaurants' sprang up. At these sites, usually remote, volunteer groups spread out on the ground meat and bone for the stricken birds to eat.

In 1984 two more researchers got to work and their results, not yet formally accepted, were very different. Far from confirming the 20 per cent rate, Drs Joan Dobbs and Patrick Benson found, at one colony, a bone abnormality rate of only 3,5 per cent. Their growth studies showed that calcium requirements for vulture nestlings are, in fact, abnormally low compared to other animals, and that there is no evidence that a significant number, as had been suggested, were receiving less than they needed. They concluded that bone abnormalities in growing Cape Vulture chicks was *not* caused by an inadequate calcium intake.[12] They also discovered that the Cape vulture characteristically displays extremely rapid wing growth as a chick and, as the bone calcifies relatively slowly, the wing is vulnerable and fragile for most of the nestling period. They believe that there is a natural mortality factor arising from this fact.

There are other factors that can adversely affect the breeding rate in vulture colonies. Apart from bone abnormalities and natural predators were factors such as poisoning, human climbing activities, man-made structures, such as high-tension cables and stays for radio and television masts, and, not least of all, interference by teams of willing and enthusiastic ornithologists intent on studying the birds to find out why they were dying!

Bad weather is an interesting cause of death among young vultures. Mist and heavy cloud keeps the parents away from the cliff sites commonly chosen by breeding colonies, and during this time young chicks are deprived of regular feeding. In consequence they often resort to a behaviour known as 'pica', in which they consume large quantities of nesting material within their reach. Often, their crops and stomachs are filled with this material, sometimes to the point of impaction, presumably with occasionally fatal results.[13] Another curious feeding habit of vultures – and other carnivores too – is known as 'rangle', a word that refers to the swallowing of stones. Nobody is quite certain why this behaviour is followed except that it is thought to be a possible aid to digestion.

The Kalahari, lacking as it does suitable rocky outcrops of the type preferred by the Cape vulture, has no breeding sites. However, there are two sites in Botswana which are practically within sight of the Kalahari, and between them there are approximately 250 nests. One of the colonies is at Otse, just south of Gaborone, and the other is in the Tswapong Hills, further to the north. Populations at both colonies fluctuate and at present they appear to be in a decline. One explanation for the decline is the current drought which, although causing the death of many thousands of animals, leaves their carcasses so emaciated that even carrion eaters can find little to consume. It has also been suggested that the flesh of animals which have died in this way is unpalatable, so that the scavengers too face stress due to starvation.[14] The Cape vulture ranges widely in the southern Kalahari and also over the Kalahari sands in west Zimbabwe. It is not, however, seen in Botswana's northern game reserves and this is something of a mystery. Its absence may be due to a lack of accurate reporting, or indeed any reporting at all.

There are few creatures in this world who need their image improved more than does the unfortunate snake. The villain of a thousand horror tales, cartoons and movies, the hero's role has remained for the snake an elusive one. This is a great pity as there is much of interest to learn about snakes, which have been wonderfully successful in adapting to their various, and sometimes unusual, life styles. Perhaps if their interest in us was less fatal, we might get along better together.

In point of fact, of the hundreds of species of snakes found in Africa, relatively few are sufficiently poisonous to be dangerous to man and nearly all of those are as keen to avoid an encounter as we are. Many of the very poisonous snakes are back-fanged,

that is the poison fangs are set back far in the mouth. Often the mouths of these snakes are so small that it is difficult for them to strike a human effectively. In a lifetime of wandering on foot through various parts of Africa, covering many thousands of kilometres, I doubt if I have seen more than twenty or thirty of these creatures. By and large they keep out of our way. Sometimes, if they are caught unawares and feel threatened or cornered, and particularly if they are defending a mate or young, they will show aggression.

Probably the most highly feared of the African snakes is the puff-adder, which is found throughout the continent, except in the Sahara and rain-forest areas. It is a very sluggish snake and relies on its cryptic colouring to escape notice. More than with any other snake, therefore, there is an ever-present danger of stepping on it and more domestic stock lose their lives to the puff-adder than to all the other snakes put together. When it is disturbed, the puff-adder inflates itself with air – hence the name – and hisses or puffs a warning that it is about to strike.

The speed of a puff-adder's strike is legendary and has in fact given rise to the erroneous but widespread belief that the snake can strike backwards. It strikes either forward or sideways, recoiling so quickly to its original position that the impression of an ability to strike backwards is given. As it strikes, its mouth is wide open and two long, curved fangs are automatically raised to an upright position. These will penetrate deep into the flesh of its victim, the bite being thus more of a stabbing action. The snake quickly withdraws and prepares to strike again.

For some reason not fully understood, the puff-adder appears to use its poisonous bite only on warm-blooded creatures. Cold-blooded prey are simply caught and swallowed, head-first, while still alive. There are records of toads being removed from a puff-adder's stomach immediately after ingestion and emerging quite unaffected by the ordeal.

Puff-adder young develop in eggs, inside the mother's body. When they are ready to hatch the eggs are laid and the young emerge within a few minutes. Occasionally they may break out of the egg while still inside the mother, and this has given rise to another myth about this snake – that the young eat their way out of the mother! The young snakes are immediately active and venomous and can live for up to three months without eating. An average of 20 – 40 are born at any one time, although there are records of well over a hundred eggs hatching.

I find the egg-eating snakes, which occur widely in the Kalahari, the most fascinating. They live exclusively on eggs and are specially adapted to do so. They live in trees, raiding birds' nests. I was once sleeping beneath a tree in which some weaver birds were nesting. A weaver's nest is a delicate basket of woven grass that hangs, in an attempt to escape the attentions of snakes, from the very outermost tips of the branches. It was early evening and my attention was drawn to a disturbance in the branches above. Three masked weavers were flitting from branch to branch in a great state of agitation. Steadily progressing along one of the branches towards a hanging nest was an egg-eating snake. The birds chattered frantically and attempted to mob the snake, which ignored them completely. Its passage along the branch was slow but inexorable. Coiled firmly around the branch above, the front third of its length hung down and, with rapidly flicking tongue, it explored the nest's entrance with slow deliberation and evident interest. The bird's concern mounted but I had the feeling they knew it was futile. There was nothing they could really do and the snake ignored them totally. Not only concerned by the horror of this silent invasion of their home, they might have been disorientated by the darkness and the confusion of dancing shadows cast by my dying fire. The snake's head and neck curled slowly into a 'U' shape and disappeared into the nest. It was there for some minutes before the body uncurled and sinuously unwound the anchoring knots that held it, retracing its route back into the bulk of the tree.

The special skeletal adaptations that this snake has evolved are a series of 'gular' or 'vertebral teeth', which are projections of its spinal column into the gullet, in the region of the neck. There are between 24 and 30 of these 'teeth' which commence just behind the neck and extend towards the tail for 6 or 7 cm. The last few, which are the longest, project forward and are pointed. There are no teeth in the mouth itself, but there are thick folds of gum tissue so that the whole mouth is pleated like an accordian. This allows the jaws to open to great width and permits the snake to swallow eggs much larger than the diameter of its head. In cases where the egg is particularly large, the snake will seem to 'measure' it by curving its head and neck along the outside of the intended meal. If it does try to swallow too large an egg, it sometimes dies in the process.

To swallow an egg, the snake pushes it against some firm barrier and, in a series of slow, deliberate gulps, eases its mouth around and over the shell. When the egg is in position below the gular teeth it moves its head backwards and forwards, allowing the spines to pierce the shell and rip it apart. A special set of muscles in the throat closes during this operation to prevent the liquid contents from spilling out. Later, the egg shell is regurgitated.

The olfactory organs of this snake must be extremely sensitive as it will seldom take any but fresh eggs and can apparently distinguish between those that are addled or hard-set. It is believed that they use this well-developed sense of smell to locate nests in the first place, since many would be difficult to find by sight alone.

Pythons occur in the Kalahari, usually where there is permanent water, but also in places where none is found at all.[15] They tend therefore to be limited to the more northerly regions in the area of the Boteti River, Chobe and Okavango. Pythons often lie along overhanging branches and, as the more exotic stories will have it, unfortunately do sometimes drop upon their unsuspecting prey. There is little danger of man falling victim to one of these ambushes, nor, so far as I am aware, has there ever been a record of such an incident. We are too large and they are too small. A python's bite is not poisonous and they have no fangs, but a wound can quickly become infected because of the foulness of the snake's mouth. They are mostly nocturnal reptiles and find their warm-blooded prey by using heat receptors which are embedded in special pits that line the upper lip.

There has been much exaggeration about what these snakes will swallow. A large, 4 m snake can consume prey up to about 25 kg in weight, whilst an exceptionally large python of perhaps 6 m could manage something in the order of 50 kg. They generally confine themselves to warm-blooded creatures but there are records of them consuming fish. Amongst their prey species are hares, dassies, cane-rats, rodents, small antelope up to the size of impala and, remarkably, porcupines! A great deal of saliva is produced during the act of swallowing and this is thought to lubricate the process. It is not true that the prey is covered with saliva before swallowing begins.

An occupational hazard of being a python is the possibility of antelope horns or porcupine quills lodging in, or piercing through, the stomach wall and skin. However, their digestive juices are exceptionally strong and bone and horn are dissolved very rapidly. Any extruding piece simply falls off and the wound heals up without any apparent ill-effect.

Although pythons are not agressive, if cornered they will attack and will aim to bite. They can, and do, constrict and a large python would be a formidable opponent for a human being. It is a fallacy that they need to anchor their tails when constricting, although they usually do so because it allows for greater leverage.

Pythons can last without food for as long as two and a half years but they cannot generally do without water, except during the colder times of the year, when they hibernate. Then they can last for two to four months without it.

Unusual for snakes, pythons incubate their eggs. A nest containing approximately 30 to 50 eggs is made and the female coils herself around them. Her body temperature then rises by about as much as 6,5 °C, which heat is transferred to the eggs and aids incubation. The female will visit water almost daily during this time but apart from these brief respites she remains in protection of her clutch of eggs for about two months. The young use a temporary 'egg-tooth' to break out of the tough, lea-

thery shells, and are immediately able to cope for themselves.

The cobra is another of Africa's snakes with a fearsome reputation and yet, as is so commonly the case, it is not entirely deserved. Like most snakes it chooses to avoid humans and is only aggressive in defence or in the face of extreme provocation. Cobras have a reputation for 'spitting' and some are adapted to eject a thin stream of venom from their fangs, which breaks up into a fine spray with a maximum range of about 2 m. Usually the venom is aimed at the eyes. In the event of it hitting its target, if the eyes are washed out immediately, either with a weak solution of anti-venom or something bland like milk, serious eye damage or blindness can be avoided.

Less common than the puff-adder but even more feared, is the black mamba, and horrific tales are told about this snake, many with some justification. The venom of the black mamba is not as potent as that of the yellow cobra, for example, but the mamba is more feared because of the speed with which it attacks, its formidable size and the bigger reserves of venom it holds, which allow it to make repeated attacks. The black mamba is not necessarily black. It is more usually dark brown, olive brown or gunmetal in colour and only becomes very dark in old age. This mamba is of uncertain temper and shows great readiness to attack if it is suddenly disturbed or molested. It is particularly aggressive during the mating season, that is in spring and early summer.

The lightning speed of the black mamba is well known but most stories about it are exaggerated. According to Dr Broadley, the maximum speed of a mamba is not likely to exceed 15 km an hour. A sprinting man is capable of much higher speeds than this, although of course it is not often, in a mamba/man confrontation, that the man gets the chance to run. The snake is the attacker and man's speed is of no benefit to him at all. The chances of recovery from a mamba bite are slim, unless anti-venom is immediately available. The poison is a neurotoxin, essentially causing paralysis of the nervous system. Involuntary control over the heart and lungs is lost. Once bitten, the victim's breathing becomes increasingly la-

boured and shallow and finally death results after a terrible struggle for breath. In
the meantime, the heart beats wildly and
rapidly and often continues beating after
breathing has ceased. It is possible, therefore, to keep a victim alive by artificial respiration, until it has been possible to administer anti-venom serum.

Certain snakes are particularly well adapted for their lifestyles. One is the shield
snake, which has a specially shaped scale
that curves down over the nose like a shield.
It is especially common in loose sand and
its prey are rodents and lizards. Much of
the time it is actually pushing through the
sand and this special adaptation, rather
like a shovel blade, allows it to do so with
greater ease. The vine snake is another arboreal species, which is exceptionally fast,
the reason being, apparently, because the
pupil of the eye extends very much further
forward than in other snakes, allowing it
unimpeded binocular vision. This gives it
improved depth perception and distance
judgement, hence the snake's markedly
increased speed and agility. Its coloration
is particularly successful, being a mixture
of greens, browns, greys and pinks, and it
is very difficult indeed to see the snake.

Vine snakes have the curious habit of
laying their body along a branch with the
front third hanging, unsupported, out into
space. It is said that the brightly coloured
tongue, another unusual feature, flicking
in and out, is a lure to various types of prey
which allows the snake to get within striking range before the victim is aware of any
threat. The venom is highly potent but bites
often have no effect at all and few fatalities
have been recorded.

The sense of smell in snakes does not
operate in quite the same way as our own.
They literally smell with their tongues. As
it flicks in and out, the tongue picks up
pheromones (chemical messengers of
smell) from the air and transfers these to a
site in the roof of its mouth known as Jacob-
son's organ; it is there that an interpretation
is put onto the chemical traces received.

For most of us it is difficult to be objective
about snakes. We are taught from childhood to dislike and fear them and this is
reinforced in later life when we hear
horrifying and exaggerated accounts of

confrontations, designed to impress, as well
as unfortunate but equally unpleasant true
reports. The fact is that most snakes are
harmless and wish to avoid us as much as
we do them. For the rest, however, it pays
to be extremely cautious for the price of
carelessness may be very high indeed.

The rodents of the Kalahari must be
among the least studied of their kind anywhere in the world. This is frustrating because they are singularly abundant and,
whilst they may still enjoy the privacy denied other animals, it does make it difficult
to find out anything about them.

One of the objectives in establishing and
maintaining a national park is to provide
the opportunity and facilities for research.
The Kalahari Gemsbok National Park, in
the southern Kalahari, is one of the few
parks on Kalahari sands where such research has been taking place. Some of it
has been devoted to rodents and, in particular, the black-tailed tree rat.

As its name implies, this rodent is a tree-
dweller. It is mostly nocturnal but can often
be seen in the late afternoon and early
evening. It lives on seeds, berries, gum,
insects, roots and leaflets but seldom ventures far from the safety of its tree. A very
good clue to its presence in any particular
tree is its nest, which can hardly escape
attention. If you can imagine someone
gathering up all the twigs that have fallen
from a tree, tying them into a rather loose
and untidy bundle and dumping them on
some convenient branch, you would have
a very good idea of the tree rat's nest. In
fact it is not a nest at all in the true sense of
the word, but is used as a playground for
the young and for taking shelter in at night.
The real nest is a collection of sticks and
grass in some convenient hollow or hole in
the tree trunk.[16]

I once camped under a tree which I shared with a colony of these creatures. The
tree had one long, heavy bough which leaned out quite close to the ground, and I
thought it a useful place to hang shirts,
dishcloths and a metal grill containing
meat for my supper. The rats saw it as a
four-lane commuter highway. It did not
take long for their curiosity to overcome
their caution and soon their whiskered
faces were peering curiously down at me

from the safety of the branch above. I was not surprised that my shirt should attract attention – it had been worn for several days – but I did not think it would cause quite such a stir.

First one bewhiskered busybody inched cautiously up to it, then scuttled back whence it came, evidently to make a report. Shortly afterwards it returned with two companions and, just as hesitantly, they approached this strange but fascinating object. Soon curiosity prevailed, caution was thrown to the wind and the rats embarked on a thorough investigation. Long forgotten gravy spots, dried blood and human salt kept them engrossed for several minutes. The dishcloth received scant attention but the meat-laden grill held them fixed with longing, desire – and frustration. The thin metal handles frustrated every attempt to explore its appealing contents more closely. Eventually boredom set in, but not for long. Joined by several others, the rats began a racing game, the object of which seemed to be to cover the length of the branch in the shortest possible time. They seemed quite oblivious of my presence and threw themselves into their new occupation with such enthusiasm and abandon that I was soon showered with loose fragments of bark knocked from the branch by their scampering pink feet.

Tree rats have long tails, much longer, in proportion to the length of their bodies, than terrestial species. This is believed to be a special adaptation for climbing, at which they are particularly adept, as it assists in balancing. The tail is covered with fine, short hairs and, although this has not been investigated, it is thought that it also serves as a tactile organ. Like that of some monkeys, the tail is prehensile and is actually used as a fifth hand, curling round and gripping thin branches, to help support the animal.[17]

There is some evidence, again uncertain, that the long-tailed tree rat may 'scent-mark' its territory from a special gland on the cheek, which it rubs against the bark after gnawing at it. This could be an aid to finding its way during its nocturnal travels. It has also been claimed that the young attach themselves to the mother's nipples and are carried in this way when she is running or climbing, but there are few eye-witness reports of this behaviour.

A very small animal, such as a rodent, will heat up quickly in the full Kalahari sun. Unlike the larger animals which have the benefit of great bulk and can absorb this heat, the smaller creatures have to take avoiding action.[18] Most arid-zone rodents live in burrows or are nocturnal. Those which are diurnal are compelled either to seek shade or, periodically, to return to their burrows. They use their burrows, which are deep in the lower sands, as a heat sink, where they can shed their excess heat and cool down before returning to the open. There are several physiological adaptations which assist in overcoming the problems of too great a heat load. Interestingly, rodents that live in hotter, more arid areas tend within the same species to have slightly larger bodies than their kin elsewhere (giving a more favourable volume to surface ratio), and also to have longer tails as these too aid in heat dissipation. Some diurnal rodents have average body temperatures which are a little lower than their nocturnal counterparts. This slight difference allows them to absorb more heat, and therefore to operate for longer periods of time before being compelled to employ behavioural, heat-avoiding strategies.

The gerbil is a nocturnal rodent about which little is known beyond the fact that it is a vector for plague in wild rodents (see Chapter 19). Gerbils live in colonies and may be among the most numerous and widespread of the Kalahari's rodents. In terms of numbers alone, they are undoubtedly an important source of food for many other creatures. Despite this, the sum of our knowledge about them is small; there is even disagreement as to what species may actually exist. Their communal homes consist of great systems of interlinking burrows.[19]

The blind mole-rat is another of the Kalahari's unknowns, in this case perhaps because of its fossorial or burrowing nature. The development of the eyes is suppressed and it is, effectively, blind. Like the traditional mole it so closely resembles, it is characteristically 'short-tempered'. Also like the mole, the incisors are used for digging and the front feet to clear away the

▲Stapelia flowers, Ngamiland

▲Flower, Nata Delta

▲Day-flying moth

▲Moth caterpillar, Tsodilo Hills

▲Baobab flower and fruit ▼Acacia blossom

▲Corps de ballet, Tsodilo Hills ▼Dung beetle, Ngamiland

▲The Chobe at twilight ▼Mekoro terminal at a busy crossing point on the Okavango River at Shakawe

soil. It seldom, if ever, comes to the surface.

Mole-rats construct extensive systems of tunnels (19 m was measured in one case[20]), have excellent hearing and a highly developed sense of touch. They communicate with high-pitched squeals. Like almost all of the Kalahari rodents, they show little or no interest in water, which it is thought they obtain from the deeply rooted tubers to which they tunnel and eat. The snout and the cornea of the eye are extremely sensitive to air currents and researchers believe that it is this faculty which enables the blind mole-rat to detect, so readily, perforations in its system of burrows and nests.

Night-time in the Kalahari belongs to the geckos, charming, delicate, lizard-like creatures. Most are nocturnal and stealthily stalk the undergrowth in patient search of beetles, moths and termites. Many are burrowers and you will seldom see them during the day when they hide, safe from the incinerating sun, deep in the earth, under rocks and stone or in the fissures of tree bark. Possibly one of the most evocative sounds of a Kalahari evening is the summertime chorus of the barking geckos. With a splendid sense of occasion, these small creatures respond to the glories of the desert dusk and fill the air with their incessant chatter which seems to reflect the excitement of what is, for them, the beginning of a new day.

Just before sunset and until eight or nine in the evening these fiercely territorial creatures emerge from their burrows to hurl vocal abuse and defiance at their nearest neighbours, at the same time, no doubt, extolling their prowess as lovers and providers. The call, a sharp sound with few musical qualities, is a series of clicks and ticks or chirps, sounding rather like 'chick chick', repeated rapidly in couplets. Some say it sounds like a box of matches being shaken. Wulf Haacke, of Pretoria's Transvaal Museum, is probably one of Southern Africa's foremost authorities on these fascinating members of the lizard family and has spent many years studying them and their intriguing call.[21]

The geckos are the only members of the lizard family with true vocal cords. The call is only uttered by the male and is probably associated with territorial defence and with attracting females. Occasionally, the calling will go on through the entire night but this occurs only in summer and is never heard in winter. Even in summer there may be several weeks of silence, but why this should be so is not known, nor do we know the reason for the great variation in calls among different species and even within the same species. Moreover, the calls are affected by fluctuations in humidity and temperature, but how and why we cannot say.

The barking gecko excavates for itself a deep burrow in the sand, leaving a funnel-shaped entrance. This may act as an amplifier because the call can often be heard for a surprising distance, several hundred metres in fact. The funnel-shape may also add ventriloquistic properties to the gecko's challenge because it is extremely difficult to locate the burrow by homing-in on the sound.

There are numerous species of gecko in the Kalahari. Most are under-studied and many completely unknown. One of the larger species is the large ground gecko. It is a stout, heavily built creature, which may explain its rather predatory attitude towards smaller relations, notably the barking gecko, which it consumes in large quantities. The ground gecko has a very slow and deliberate gait and, in many ways, particularly when it is hunting at night, resembles a chameleon. It will hiss and attack when confronted, will lunge at its aggressor and even leap into the air, uttering a squeaking sound. Its bite can draw blood from a finger. Understandably, this small creature, barely 15 cm from head to tip of tail, has earned a reputation among local inhabitants quite unrelated to its diminutive size. Its bite is considered to be deadly, whereas in fact it is perfectly harmless. Females are known to carry eggs but where these are laid is not known.[22]

On as many of my 'safaris' as schooling will allow, my children always accompany me. After supper, with Gypsey keeping watch, it has become a routine for the three of us to take torches and search the surrounding bush for whatever might be of interest. One night my son Andrew caught a ground gecko. We put it in an open-sided box in order to study it and take photographs. In the scuffle of its capture, we suspect some sand got into its eye because, once it had settled down, it treated us to a most remarkable sight. Peering through the close-up lens of a camera, at a head that completely filled the screen, I watched a long, bright pink tongue slowly emerge from a cavernous mouth. With deliberation, the tongue reached up, above the eye, and pressing firmly on the eye-ball, swept gently across it, presumably removing the irritating sand. Several times this obliging gecko repeated the performance, and we used up may rolls of film. There are immutable laws designed for situations such as this, and one of them states: if a camera is going to succumb to months of exposure to the cloying sand and dust of the Kalahari, it will pick the most inopportune time to do so. To our utter dismay, this was the time! Of course the discovery was only made much later – nevertheless it was a most unusual and rewarding experience.

The southern Kalahari boasts many species of lizards. While working there, Eric Pinaka identified 23, of which 7 were nocturnal, 14 diurnal and 2 fossorial.[23] No doubt many more remain to be discovered and studied.

One of the most startling behaviour patterns is to be found in a lizard rejoicing in the singularly unromantic name of *Agama makarikarika*. This reptile, which is found throughout the Kalahari from Etosha Pan to Botswana, has been dubbed 'the sand-shuttling, eye-popping lizard'.[24] Its name requires some explanation.

The sand-ducking behaviour is probably protective and involves the lizard in a kind of shuffling, scuttling movement, by which means it can immerse its body in the sand so that it is partially submerged. The process of 'eye-popping' begins when the lizard appears to 'screw up' its eyes. The eyelids are almost closed and the eye-ball is gradually protruded, taking the eyelids with it, so that the whole effect is as if the eyes are, literally, standing out on stalks. Both eyes protrude simultaneously. It is not yet known why this takes place. It may afford the animal better vision when it is submerged in the sand or it may be a display device to threaten enemies by making it look larger than life. It could also be an

eye-cleaning mechanism or perhaps, because the eyeball can be withdrawn independently of the eyelid, thus creating a 'lens hood' effect, it is a way of protecting the eyes from the glare of white pan surfaces. Whatever the reason, it is a most peculiar experience to watch these creatures as they stand, four-square, defiantly 'popping' their eyes at you.

The fossorial lizards are extraordinary creatures. They have no legs, having long ago relinquished these appendages in favour of the doubtful advantages of spending a life almost wholly under the sand. There are two species that are known of in the Kalahari and both depend almost entirely upon the termite for their food. They travel under the sand, mostly at night. Occasionally they will travel, like a snake, for short distances above the surface, but as a rule they follow a sinuous lateral path just beneath it. Their bodies are well adapted for this kind of life for, in addition to being without legs, they have a shovel-shaped head and nasal plugs that prevent them from suffocating. Interestingly, these sand-swimming skinks give birth to live young and the embryo, rather than curling up as it does in most animals, lies parallel to the body axis of the mother. This reduces the swelling of pregnancy and maintains the beautiful streamlining of its body.[25]

Lizards, no less than other inhabitants of the Kalahari, must find ways of coping with the heat. Some methods are quite obvious; some are intriguing. The diurnal lizards usually alternate between a middle-of-the-day foraging time in winter to a bi-modal strategy in summer, when they use the early morning and the late evening to search for food. Of course, refuge can always be taken in underground burrows and another alternative, used particularly by arboreal species, is to vary their height above the ground, according to the ambient temperature. There are other, less well-known strategies which have been thoroughly researched elsewhere, but to what extent they apply in the Kalahari is not yet certain.[26] One of these involves the lizard in adapting to having higher body temperatures. The risks in doing this are high, because the safety margin is lower and the consequence of error is greater. On the other hand, because the creature starts the day at a low temperature, having cooled off during the night, it takes longer to reach its thermal ceiling. This additional time can be devoted to foraging. Panting, of course, can reduce heat gain, but as this involves a considerable loss of water, it is usually only employed as a last resort.

Many desert lizards can change colour, turning darker during the cooler periods to absorb solar radiation and hasten heat gain, and lighter during the hottest part of the day to increase reflectivity and reduce heat gain. An interesting possibility, which has not so far been recorded from the Kalahari, but which is most likely to occur there, is the altering of body shape as a heat control mechanism. Lizards elsewhere achieve this by pulling the ribs backwards; this makes the animal deeper and slimmer and reduces the surface area which is exposed to the direct rays of a directly overhead sun. Longer limbs lift the body away from the aching heat of the surface sand and even a short distance can have quite significant results. A 1 cm rise from the surface of hot sand, at approximately 70 °C, will result in a 15 °C drop in temperature. For this reason we might expect to find that arid area species would have slightly longer legs than the same species in a cooler environment, but this has yet to be verified. One study shows that, despite the wide variety of body sizes, shapes and proportions within the lizard families, there are remarkable similarities with regard to sprinting ability. Maximum speed, stride and acceleration all increase with age, demonstrating perhaps the complexity of adaptations and compromises that every animal has to make.[27]

In addition to solving the problems of heat, making optimum use of resources can present other challenges. Two species of sand lizards have adopted what appears to be a most unusual approach. They are widespread in Southern Africa north of the Orange River and are also found in the Kalahari. The two species often occur together, but when they do one is invariably represented by adults and the other only by juveniles or sub-adults. Both species have a very short lifecycle, probably less than a year. Each can survive in egg form for three or four months, and this ensures that there is no overlap between generations. In this way the two species, because they are at different age levels and are of different sizes, are segregated by the differing size of prey they hunt and there is no competition between them for scarce food resources.[28]

In one of the most absorbing scientific papers I have ever read, Eric Pinaka, with a refreshing sense of humour, describes the remarkable consequences of the foraging mode adopted by lizards.[29] Lizards, of course, are predators, and Dr Pinaka divides them into two general groups, based upon the method they employ to obtain their food.

The first of these groups comprises those which are very active, which cover a large area and are constantly on the move. He calls them 'widely foraging'. The second group is much more sedentary and they tend to sit in ambush. These he calls the 'sit-and-wait' group. Of the seven species that were studied, five fell in the first category and two in the second. Once these two divisions are recognised, a number of fascinating consequences follow. For example, the foraging mode that is adopted is largely a function of the type of prey consumed. Thus, widely foraging lizards tend to eat prey that itself is not widely foraging. Such prey is usually sedentary, large in size or is 'clumped', like groups of termites. In contrast, the sit-and-waits tend to eat prey which is more active and which could be described as widely foraging. Thus the sit-and-wait tends to eat more mobile prey but its catch is low, as is the energy it expends to get it. It tends to have a stocky body and shorter tail. It has limited endurance and depends primarily on eyesight. The sit-and-waits are, however, vulnerable to encounters with widely foraging predators. On the other hand, the widely foraging lizards eat sedentary or clumped or unpredictable prey, with a high energy cost but also with a high return on their investment. They are vulnerable to both sit-and-wait and widely foraging predators. They have a higher endurance capacity and rely on both vision and smell to detect their prey. Lizards employing either foraging mode rely on camouflage or speed for escape.

It has been estimated that the widely foraging lizard will expend about 1,3 - 1,5 times
more energy than those which sit-and-wait,
but then the gross food gains are 1,3 - 2,1
times greater.

Just as there is what could be described
as a 'cross-over' between lizard and prey,
so, logically, there is a similar cross-over
between predator and lizard. Thus, as one
might expect, sit-and-wait lizards are predominantly preyed upon by predators
which habitually forage widely. Widely foraging lizards, on the other hand, are the
victims of predators who tend to sit-and-wait,
a prime example of which is the Kalahari's
horned adder. This snake, which buries
itself in the sand until it is barely visible, is
the archetypal sit-and-wait predator. With
their strange horns and well camouflaged
eyes protruding above the sand, horned
adders sit, with endless patience, ready to
strike with lightning speed. And, indeed, it
is the widely foraging lizard which is dominant among its prey.

The whole system appears to be one of
carefully intermeshed checks and balances
and, like any system, offers rewards to those
who stay within it, but carries high penal-
ties for those who transgress its boundaries.
An example is the little barking gecko.

The barking gecko is a sit-and-waiter.
His time is completely taken up in conserving his energy for the evening's territorial
defence and he chooses rather to allow his
meals 'to deliver themselves to his door-
step'. Like many of us, however, he has a
fatal weakness – his is an abiding passion
for termites.

As the rains begin to fall, when that magical, uniquely African smell fills the air, termites leave their nests in hundreds of thousands. Many fall immediately to the ground,
to mate and scurry for shelter, there to start
a new nest. It is a time of abundant food for
everybody and the termites are plucked
from the air and off the ground almost as
fast as they emerge. In the feeding frenzy
that follows, caution is forgotten. Predators
know this too and, though some do not eat
termites, many will gather in the trees and
on the ground, waiting their turn, knowing
that a tasty morsel may well present itself.

Imagine the gecko's dilemma: on the one

hand, a sumptuous meal, on the other the
possibly fatal consequences of becoming
for a short time a 'widely foraging' animal.
The temptation proves too much and, in a
flash, he is gone, searching the sands for
termites he knows are there, anticipating a
succulent meal. One of the risks in switching hunting mode, of course, is that the
creature lacks experience and is highly vulnerable.

Blind to the risks, the gecko races to the
termite mound and falls upon the writhing,
fluttering mass of creatures, snapping them
up as quickly as he can. He does not see
the fiscal shrike that drops like a stone out
of the sky, and may not even feel the fatal
clutch of claws nor the piercing blow with
heavy beak. Eric Pinaka, with a telling
touch of irony, ends his paper with a photo-
graph of a barking gecko pierced through
and hanging by its neck from a thorn –
mute evidence of the consequence of error.
The gecko had, indeed, been killed by a
shrike, whose habit it is to so suspend his
food until such time as he is ready to eat it.

At certain times of the year in the Kalahari, when the rains have fallen and the
pans, and perhaps even the rivers, are full,
frogs and toads will be found in abundance.
Their sudden presence immediately raises
the question of how they survived the long
dry spell, for some of them live much longer
than a year. Generally speaking, there are
three groups of anurans, as they are called:
those which require an aquatic environment; the fossorial anurans, which dig their
own burrows or live in spaces under rocks;
and, finally, the arboreal anurans which
are adapted for life in trees. Each has its
own way of dealing with the dry times.

The aquatic anurans tend to be largely
dependent upon perennial open water and
are usually concentrated near it. If a water
source dries up, some will migrate to another source, but how they know in which
direction to go, no one can tell. An alternative strategy is to burrow in the mud at the
bottom of a pool or stream.

The fossorial anurans are not necessarily
associated with permanent water and so
have a well-tried and ready routine for the
inevitable drying up. They burrow and go
into a state somewhat akin to suspended
animation. One of the best-known examples

of this is the African bullfrog (*Pyxicephalus adspersus*). The bullfrog is a well-known sight all over Southern Africa and even in the cities it is not uncommon. I can well remember a road in Harare which crosses an area of marshy land. Attracted by the warmth of the tarmac road or the insects drawn to the lights of passing cars, the bullfrogs can sometimes be observed there in their hundreds. They can weigh up to a kilogram and are the size of a large dinner plate. These bullfrogs epitomise our caricature of some frog-like qualities: gross, ugly, squatting immovably, greedily gobbling up anything within reach. Nevertheless, the fact that they appear, fully grown, at the beginning of the wet season is a tribute to their uncanny ability to survive the dry.

They do this by burrowing into wet clay soil which subsequently dries out around them. In one experiment, a bullfrog weighing 961 g was allowed to bury itself.[30] After 229 days it was taken out and found to have lost only 45 g, less than 5 per cent of its body weight! Some of these bullfrogs, found in the wild, have shown evidence of having made a cocoon about them, but it is not certain whether this is common practice, and indeed very little is known about it. Generally speaking, burrowers have large bladders which possibly serve to store water during this period of dormancy but exactly how this is achieved, in African frogs, has not been determined.

The mechanisms by which Southern African arboreal frogs survive desiccation is a mystery. They have been observed to remain exposed in direct sunlight and dry air for long periods of time and yet do not appear to suffer from dehydration. There is some suggestion that there may be a seasonal change in the permeability of the skin, whereby it increases during the breeding and rainy seasons, and reduces during the dry season, but much research remains to be done in this area.

From a brief survey of the animals in the Kalahari, one is struck not so much by what we know, but by what we don't know. It is an inaccessible place and a difficult environment in which to work. This in itself is part of the attraction for me. Because it is so unknown, there is so much more waiting to be discovered and there is every promise that those discoveries will be interesting and exciting.

## REFERENCES

1. Maclean, G L. 'Field Studies on the Sandgrouse of the Kalahari Desert'. In *The Living Bird*, Seventh Annual, 1968. Edited by Pettingill, O S. and Lancaster, D A. Laboratory of Ornithology, Cornell University, New York, 1968, pp 209-33

2. Joubert, C S W and Maclean, G L. 'The Structure of the Water-Holding Feathers of the Namaqua Sandgrouse'. In *Zoologica Africana*. 8(2): 141-152 (1973)

3. Louw, G and Seely, M. *Ecology of Desert Organisms*. New York: Longman, 1982, p 15

4. Maclean, G L. 'Arid-Zone Adaptations in Southern African Birds'. In *Cimbebesia*. Series A, Vol 2, No 15, March 1974, pp 163-76

5. Thomas, D H and Robin, A P. 'Comparative Studies of Thermoregulatory and Osmoregulatory Behaviour and Physiology of Five Species of Sandgrouse'. In *Journal Zool.*, Lond. 1977, No 183, pp 229-49

6. Siegfried, W R and Frost, P G H. 'Egg Temperature and Incubation Behaviour of the Ostrich'. In *Madoqua*, Series 1, No 8, March 1974, pp 63-6

7. Lowe, G H, Belonje, P C and Coetzee, H J. 'Renal Function, Respiration, Heart Rate and Thermoregulation in the Ostrich'. Scientific Papers. Namib Desert Research Station. No 42, pp 43-54

8. Maclean, G L. 'The Sociable Weaver, Part 5: Food, Feeding and General behaviour'. In *Ostrich*, Vol 44, Nos 3 and 4, Sept/December 1973, pp 254-61

9. Brooke, R K. 'Tool-using by the Egyptian Vulture to the Detriment of the Ostrich'. In *Ostrich*, Vol 50, No 2, June 1979, pp 119-20

10. Brooke, R K. 'Predation on Ostrich Eggs by Tool-using Crows and Egyptian Vultures'. In *Ostrich*, Vol 50, No 4, Dec 1979, pp 257-8

11. Mundy, P J and Ledger, J A. 'Griffon Vulture, Carnivores and Bones'. In *SA Journal of Science*, Vol 72, 1976, pp 106-10; also Mundy, P J. 'The Comparative Biology of Southern African Vultures'. Ph.D. Thesis, University of Rhodesia, 1981; and Richardson, P R K, Mundy, P J and Plug, I. 'Bone Crushing Carnivores and their Significance to Osteodystrophy in Griffon Vulture Chicks'. In *Journal of the Zoological Society of London*, Vol 210, 1986, pp 23-43

12. Dobbs, J and Benson, P C. 'Calcium Requirements and Bone Abnormalities in the Cape

Vulture'. Proceedings of the 2nd Symposium, African Predatory Birds, Natal Bird Club, Durban, 1984. Edited by Mendlesohn, J M and Sapsford, C W

13. **Dobbs, J and Benson, P C.** 'Causes of Cape Vulture Mortality at the Kransberg Colony'. Proceedings of the 2nd Symposium on African Predatory Birds, Natal Bird Club, Aug 23-25, 1983

14. **Campbell, A C.** Personal communication, March 1986

15. **Ibid**

16. **De Graaff, G.** 'Notes on the Southern African Black-tailed Tree Rat (*Thallomys Paedulcus*) and its Occurrence in the Kalahari Gemsbok National Park'. In *Koedoe*, Vol 21, 1978, pp 181-90

17. **Earl, Z and Nel, J A J.** 'Climbing Behaviour in Three African Rodents Species'. In *Zoologica Africana.* Vol 11 (1), 1976, pp 183-92

18. **Nel, J A J and Rautenbach, I L.** 'Body Temperatures of Some Kalahari Rodents'. In *Annals of the Transvaal Museum*, Vol 30, No 17, August 1977, pp 207-10

19. **Schlitter, D A and Rautenbach, I L.** 'The Brush-tailed Gerbille (*Gerbillurus Vallinus*) in the Kalahari Gemsbok National Park'. In *Koedoe*, Vol 20, 1977, pp 189-91

20. **De Graaff, G.** 'On the Mole Rat (*Cryptomys Hottentotus Damarensis) (Rodentia)* in the Kalahari Gemsbok National Park'. In *Koedoe*, Vol 15, 1972, pp 25-35

21. **Haacke, W D.** 'The Call of the Barking Geckos'. Scientific Paper of the Namib Desert Research Station, No 46, Vol 4, 1969, pp 83-93

22. **Haacke, W D.** 'The Burrowing Geckos of Southern Africa, 4'. In *Annals of the Transvaal Museum*, Vol 30, No 5, June 1976, pp 53-69

23. **Pinaka, E R.** 'Lizard Species Density in the Kalahari Desert'. In *Ecology.* Vol 52, No 6, pp 1024-9

24. **Steyn, W and Steyn, S.** New Data on a Sand-shuttling, Eye-popping Lizard. Madoqua 2, 1970, pp 39-44

25. **Huey, R B, Pinaka, E R, Egan, M E and Coons, L W.** 'Ecological Shifts in Sympatry: Kalahari Fossorial Lizards (*Typhlosaurus*). In *Ecology.* Vol 55, 1974, pp 304-16

26. **Avery, R A.** *Lizards - a study in Thermoregulation.* The Institute of Biology's Studies in Biology, No 109. London: Edward Arnold, 1979, pp 31-9

27. **Huey, R B.** 'Phylogenetic and Ontogenetic Determinants of Sprint Performance in Some Diurnal Kalahari Lizards'. In *Koedoe*, No 25, 1982, pp 43-8

28. **Broadley, D G.** 'The Life Cycle of Two Sympatric Species of Ichnotropis (*Sauria: Lacertidae)'.* In *Zoologica Africana*, Vol 3, No 1, December 1967, pp 1-2

29. **Pinaka, E R.** 'Ecological Consequences of Foraging Mode'. In *Ecology*, Vol 62 (4), 1981, pp 991-9

30. **Loveridge, J P.** 'Strategies of Water Conservation in Southern African Frogs'. In *Zoologica Africana* 11 (2), 1976, pp 319-33

# 11. ... Upon Their Backs to Bite Them

PART of the attraction of the Kalahari is the silence. It is never complete silence, however, although it may sound so to the unaccustomed ear. If you listen carefully, there is always some background noise – birds, the musical tone of a cow-bell, the shrill scream of cicadas or the creak of wood and branch as trees pay homage to a light breeze which whispers on its way. One of the most common yet least recognisable sounds is the incessant rustling from the undergrowth and in the leaf litter on the ground. It is caused by hordes of innumerable termites. Harmless to us, unless we annoy them, these tiny creatures, just over half a centimetre in length, are part of the chain that breaks down dead vegetable matter, reconstituting it so that it can be used in other ways and by other creatures.

Theirs is a vital role and they are members of a hugely successful family of which there are many species, more than 400 in fact. Their task is unending for the waste of dead material – leaves and plants and grass – is unending. Not only do termites make this otherwise waste matter available for alternative uses, but they also play an important part in the regeneration of grass. Grass seeds are part of their diet and these are carried deep beneath the ground. As we have already seen, termites themselves are a vital food source for countless animals, from hyena and jackal to foxes, civet cats, birds, lizards, geckos and many others. It is claimed that termites are the most important single source of insect food for numerous vertebrate species in the Kalahari. The Kalahari termites have not attracted the attention that has been given their relations elsewhere in the world and are therefore relatively little studied.

Termites are an ancient species and may have evolved little from when dinosaurs walked the earth one hundred million years ago. They live in huge colonies, with sometimes as many as two or even three million members. Their homes are the grey, brown or red mounds that dot the African landscape, some barely visible in the grass, others extruding as great towering structures 6, 7 or 8 m in height. The nest is a labyrinth of narrow tunnels and chambers and can sometimes reach as far as 40 m down into the earth, searching always for moisture. Termites do not like the sun and prefer to avoid exposure to direct sunlight for long periods of time. It is for this reason that much of the dead wood one finds in the bush is covered with a thin sandy layer. This is a protective barrier, erected by the termites while they work within.

At least fourteen genera of termite are to be found in the Kalahari.[1] All have different modes of foraging, favour different vegetable matter and have different capacities for enduring sunlight. All in one way or another gather dead cellulose material and take it underground. The rate at which vegetable litter, like leaves, wood and grass, is broken down, is an important regulator of overall plant production. In more tropical areas it has been estimated that termites may well account for about one third of the annual production of greenery and wood.[2] In desert areas it is less, between 25 and 12 per cent.

Part of the explanation for the remarkable success of termites as a species can be found in the extraordinary way in which they overcome the problems posed by the type of food upon which they exist. The food consumed by termites is totally unsuitable for any creature and yet termites consume it and thrive. How does this happen?

Nitrogen-containing lignin is one of the key components of wood and insect enzymes cannot break it down. In addition, lignin combines with valuable proteins which are thus also denied the termite. The largest component of plant cell walls, also part of the termite's diet, is cellulose. Cellulose contains energy, but again the termite is not equipped with the necessary enzymes to break it down, thus rendering it quite useless to the termite. Finally, all creatures need nitrogen, which is an important part of protein. As leaf litter contains very little nitrogen, presumably termites would suffer from a nitrogen deficiency. All these apparently insuperable problems, however, are solved at a single stroke by a simple and ingenious method. Termites employ a fungus called termitomyces to do the work for them, to prepare the food so that they can eat it.

The presence of this fungus in termite mounds was first recognised as early as 1779 by a German naturalist. It takes the form of 'gardens' or 'combs' within the termite nest. There has been much controversy concerning the material that comprises these combs but it is now generally agreed that it is of termite origin, and is faecal in composition, and not chewed food, as was first believed. The fungus, which belongs to the same group as that which includes the mushroom, lives in a symbiotic relationship with termites; it is only found in termite nests and it lives on termite faeces. By digesting that material the fungus alters the comb's chemistry, making it palatable for reconsumption by the termites. In doing this, they break down lignin and, by consuming the material themselves, increase the nitrogen content by three or four times. Termitomyces can also digest cellulose. It does this both on the comb and in the termite's mid-gut when the comb is ingested and where the fungus persists. The termites build up the comb from the outside and after five to eight weeks begin consuming it from the inside.

It is a most remarkable system and a classic example of symbiosis in which neither of the contributors can exist without the other. The question that intrigues me is, how did it get started in the first place?

The relationship between termites and their fungus has other consequences. The heat generated through the fungus's respiration is about six times that produced by the termites themselves; it needs to be dissipated but, at the same time, a comfortable operating temperature has to be maintained. The fungus also requires a great deal of space. A highly complex nest structure or termitarium has evolved to meet these requirements, and it is believed to be the most advanced nest built by any animal in the world. The permutations of design are infinite, yet all seek to achieve and maintain 100 per cent humidity and an ambient temperature between 29 °C and 31°C, which suits both the fungus and the termite. Some nests are totally enclosed, some are beneath the ground, while others have soaring turrets and yet others chimneys. All are ventilated and air currents are generated by convection. Every nest is, effectively, a perfectly air-conditioned unit.

There is one final twist to this amazing story. Every year termite colonies raise reproductive flying termites, whose function it is to colonise or recolonise new areas. Not one of those alates, as they are called, leaves the home nest without a supply of the vital fungus. Each one carries in its fore-gut the spore of the precious termitomyces. How the availability of spore is coordinated to coincide with the departure of the alates is unclear.

Eugène Marais, in his *Soul of the White Ant*, touched upon the complexities of this strange creature. Now, many years after his death, when we have learnt so much more, our increased knowledge presents us with more mysteries, not fewer. A termite, like a bee, cannot survive for very long on its own. This fact has given rise to the question of whether the single bee or the whole hive (or the single termite or the whole nest) is the living animal. The more one learns about termites, the more difficult it is to decide which is the case. Drs D S Wilson and A B Clark offer some fascinating suggestions resulting from their study of the defensive strategies in harvester termites.[3] Harvester termites are a species that forage widely on the ground in the vicinity of their nest. Unprotected by tunnels, sheltering only beneath the litter, they

are exposed and highly vulnerable to predators, and indeed predation upon them is
extremely high. Consequently, harvester
termites appear to have developed sophisticated defensive strategies, as this example
of a predatory spider will illustrate.

*Ammoxenus psammodromus* is a spider
which specialises in hunting termites. Like
most of its genus, it has an ability to bury
itself in soft sand and may spend much of
its non-hunting time concealed in this way.
It hunts by travelling quickly over relatively
large areas, searching for prey. It will not
kill the first termite encountered but appears to prefer to wait until it is among
large numbers of them. When this happens,
the spider moves freely among them, often
running over their backs. The spider's presence elicits no response from the termites
at all.

When a victim is chosen, the spider delivers a bite directly behind the head cap-
sule, immediately paralysing the termite.
This paralysis is important. If the termite is
not killed in this precise way, it will release
an alarm pheromone which warns other
termites of danger. Killed in the right way,
a termite, placed at the entrance to a foraging hole, will elicit no response from
other, passing termites. Incorrectly killed,
or injured, it can give out its warning signal
and frenetic escape behaviour will ensue.
After killing its victim *Ammoxenus* then
buries itself upside down in the sand, the
termite remaining on the surface. The
spider then feeds on the termite from below.

In investigating this behaviour, the researchers began studying the timing of termite activity. At first it appeared that there
was no nocturnal foraging but it quickly
became evident that foraging in fact took
place at all times of the day and night in
random, unpredictable bursts of activity.
They discovered that *Ammoxenus*, who
was otherwise not in evidence, was frequently encountered in the pitfall traps that
were set at those times. These observations
suggest that the spider is in some way able
to detect and respond to termite activity at
any time of day or night, although just how
this is done is not understood. Faced with
such a sophisticated predator, what can
the termite do? In fact it adopts a number
of extraordinary strategies.

One would suppose that in the absence
of predators, termites would forage in all
areas within their territory simultaneously.
A study of the foraging behaviour, however, shows it to be characterised by a noticeable spatial patchiness. The pattern of
activity changes constantly. A small area
will have no termites in it for a long time, it
will then become active for a few days and
then quiescent again. Judging by the results of certain experiments, it would appear that this random pattern of activity
does reduce predation on termites, but the
reason remains obscure.

It may be that underground processing
requires a cessation of above ground activity; it may be more efficient to 'work' a
small area intensively and then return to it
at a later date. It may also be a deliberate
strategy to defeat the predator. If this were
the case it would be effective in three ways.
Firstly, termites would no longer be a reliable food source for stationary predators
such as ant-lions. Secondly, wandering predators, such as *Ammoxenus*, would need to
spend much time and energy searching
large areas in order to locate the concentration of prey. When high concentrations of
predators built up the termites could
abruptly switch their area of activity, compelling the predators to embark upon a
random search of another, large area to
relocate the prey, an exercise which might
take several days. Thirdly, by concentrating
all their resources in a small area, the termites could, by sacrificing some of their
number, saturate the predators.

The termite faces a wide array of predators and each have differing characteristics. Birds, for example, will eat many termites in rapid succession, whilst an insect
predator will take a long time to consume
one, and is therefore less of a threat. On the
other hand, termites are not the only prey
of birds, nor are birds active all the time.
Spatial patchiness is not likely to be an
effective strategy against birds but sacrifi-
cial saturation may well be. Alternatively,
carefully chosen times could be effective –
termites can forage during a bird's inactive
period. If individual termites can withstand
the heat and low humidity of midday, even
for a few minutes, then, working in relays,
they can continue to forage at a time when

it is very stressful for most other predators.

These intriguing suggestions put forward by Wilson and Clark imply an intelligence which we may find difficult to understand and accept. Such sophisticated use of carefully devised defence strategies demands some kind of long-term 'colony' memory. It would necessitate registering a full spectrum of predators, their activity times and characteristics, and retaining some awareness of how these changed with season, time, temperature and humidity. In addition, it would be necessary to retain knowledge of certain predation events and to use these as indicators in deciding present and future foraging strategies. Is this possible, or is the whole defence system nothing more than the random workings of chance?

Man is also a predator of termites. In many rural or poverty-stricken areas protein is sometimes hard to come by. As the rainy season approaches and swarms of termite alates take to the air on their nuptial flight, the local people descend upon the termite mounds, collecting up the small flying creatures. Cunning traps are often devised and vast quantities of the alates are caught. The bodies and wings of termites have a very high percentage of fat and it is for this reason that they are valued. When a pot is filled with termites, a little water is added and the catch is 'blanched' by heating the pot over a fire for a short while. The termites are then taken out and dried. Once dry, the bodies are rubbed between the hands and the wings fall away. These are collected and sometimes ground to a fine edible powder, which can be stored for an indefinite period. The wingless bodies are also used in the diet in various ways.[4]

At about that time of the year when young termites are taking to wing, there emerges onto the sands of the Kalahari an exotic jewelled insect of breathtaking beauty. It has many common names but is widely known as the red velvet mite. These mites range in size from a match-head to a pea and their most obvious feature is the dazzling bright red of their velvet coats. The entire animal is covered with densely packed, soft, short hair, which feels and looks exactly like velvet. You will find them in sandy areas in the early mornings, usually after a shower of rain, crawling about in great numbers. By ten o'clock they are gone. It is only at the beginning of the rains that you see them. They appear to be quite harmless and can be picked up very easily. The purpose of their brief appearance is hard to fathom. There is no obvious pairing, mating or feeding. At some appropriate place a mite will suddenly up-end itself and, with slow, scraping movements, will work its way down into the earth.

Practically nothing is known about these creatures in Africa. Their scientific name is *Dinothrombium tinctorium* and close relatives occur in western United States and in Mexico. A report from the latter country describes how, in 1943, an emergence of these creatures was first sighted from the air.[5] So vast was the accumulation that it was first thought to be an unusual flowering of lichens, but on closer inspection they were found to be giant red velvet mites, between three and five million individuals packed into a single hectare at a rate of some 400 to 1 m². Such occurrences are rare, though, and I know of none similar in Africa. The Mexicans call these mites 'little angels' or 'angelitos' and there are at least five species of them in America and Mexico. Worldwide there are thought to be between 25 and 30 species, but how many occur in Africa I do not know. I suspect there may be more than one because I have found, and photographed, different varieties, some with small white patches on their flanks. What little is known about them suggests that the adults may be predators on subterranean termites and that the larvae parasitise grasshoppers and other insects.

According to Professor Erik Holm, head of the Entomology Department at the University of Pretoria, in Africa the larvae of this mite are known to be parasites, acting, in much the same way as ticks, on scorpions, reptiles and almost every major group of vertebrates.[6] It is believed that they pass through five larval stages, during the first two of which they have six legs and in the remainder, eight. The larva drops off its host to pupate in the ground and the adult becomes a free-living creature. It is thought that, like scorpions, they conduct a complicated mating dance and that actual copulation does not take place. Instead, a silken thread, to which the sperm adheres, is deposited by the male and taken in by the female. This may all be somewhat speculative, however, because so little research has been done on these creatures, and there is much detail of their biology and ecology that is not yet known. One question which remains is why, if the red velvet mite spends so much time underground, is it such a vivid colour? Red is often a warning colour, but what predator is being warned and how is the warning reinforced? Sadly we do not have the answers.

Yet another creature which spends much of its life beneath the ground is the cicada. Unless you look very carefully, you will seldom see it, for it is a shy, secretive insect; but you cannot fail to hear it. Not more than 2 to 3 cm long and most cryptically coloured, cicadas crouch on the branches of trees and shrubs and fill the summer air with their high-pitched stridulations. It is one of the characteristic sounds of Africa and evokes images of searing days and aching heat, of stark black shadows and wilting vegetation. Soaring mercury numbs the senses while the whole world seems to quiver in a shimmering haze that echoes the undulating rhythm of this penetrating, strident screech.

Very little work has been carried out specifically on cicadas in Southern Africa. Such as is known about them is generalised from studies elsewhere. Cicadas, it appears, are root feeders and they spend many years of their lives underground. As a diet, roots are not high in protein and so this long period is not considered surprising. Studies of their life cycles indicate that one species spends thirteen years as a subterranean dweller and at the end of that time emerges for a brief two weeks, during which a female is found and mating takes place. After eggs have been laid the insects die. Other cicadas, of the same species, appear to have a seventeen-year life cycle. Why this should be so and what the biological significance of it is, is not known.

It is the males which are responsible for the cicada's shrill call. They have a special sound-generating diaphragm which they vibrate and which begins to oscillate, moving faster than it could by muscle power alone. The whole body acts as an amplifier and many hundreds of these insects within range of a dominant male, will time their pulsing call with his. According to Prof Holm, if you can produce artificially a louder noise in the correct frequency range, the other cicadas will abandon the 'lead voice' and follow the new rhythm.

One of the less appealing of the Kalahari residents is a creature which has earned itself a most unwelcome reputation and it is one that most people would happily do without. The sand tampan, or tampan tick, looks like a tick and is in fact related to the tick family. However, it is also a highly specialised creature. Most ticks will attach themselves to a passing animal, leaving chance to decide at which point they will be returned to the ground. Not so the tampan. They cannot tolerate exposure to sun or sand temperatures above 55 °C and so they select a suitably shady site, there to wait in ambush below the sand for a suitable victim. They emerge in hordes and fall upon the luckless animal, drinking rapaciously, but immediately releasing their hold if their prey should show signs of leaving. Falling back onto the sand, they return to their cool abodes beneath it. Their saliva contains a mild neurotoxin which, if released in sufficient quantities, will paralyse a young, aged or sickly animal. One Kalahari farmer reported collecting over 13 litres of engorged tampans beside the bodies of three dead cows which had been killed by exsanguination or the draining of blood.[7]

We are not certain about the origins of the tampan. They may have come into Africa from the East, with camels, or they may have originated in the continent's arid regions.[8] Today they occur throughout Africa's sandy areas where rainfall is below 500 mm. Tampans are well adapted for life in sandy deserts. They have flat bodies and long legs which facilitate movement through the sand. Their skin is covered with a waxy layer which protects them against dehydration. They avoid the sun and live in large colonies around the base of trees offering dense shade. By burrowing down to more than 20 cm below the surface, tampans can establish for themselves an equitable environment, the temperature and humidity of which changes little with the time of day and seasons.

For many years it remained obscure how the ticks knew that a victim was in the offing. Vibrations caused by movement was the obvious method but this is only part of the answer. The tampan has built-in carbon dioxide receptors. As soon as sand movements tell of approaching prey, the tampans move to the surface and, using their dectors, home in on the animal by following the trail of $CO_2$ molecules which are exhaled or exude from its skin.[9] Tampans can feed very quickly; within ten to twenty minutes they can be fully engorged. In addition to containing the paralysing neurotoxin, tampan saliva also contains a remarkably strong anti-coagulant. Under experimental conditions this substance has prevented blood from clotting for thirty days - longer than any other similar agent known to science.[10] Humans are sometimes allergic to the tampan bite, which can lead to swelling and, in extreme cases, unconciousness.

Tampans can survive for surprisingly long periods without food, first-stage nymphs for six months to a year or even two, and adults from two to five, or even eight years.[11] Buried deep beneath the sand in a stable environment, tampans are immune to fires and appear to have few natural predators. They are therefore extremely difficult to eradicate. In Mogadishu the residents throw seawater onto infected areas, but whether this is effective because of the salt or the water is not known. Tampans have benefited from the rapid spread of the ranching industry and today pose a serious economic threat.

There is a tale from Khartoum which vividly describes the horror of these small creatures. At a certain quarantine station cattle were tied to a post in the full sunlight, while a few yards away, separated only by a strip of hot morning sun and helplessly confined to the shade of a row of acacia trees, were thousands of tampans. As the day progressed the cattle were forgotten and it was only at seven o'clock the next morning that a grim report was made: '... those tampans under the trees are all blood-bloated and resting comfortably in the sand, others are dragging back from their hosts across the now non-existent barrier, and the legs of the cattle are beaded with yet other podshaped ticks taking their fill of blood, in a regular line just above the hoof.'[12]

In my journey across the Kalahari I was determined to obtain photographs of the tampan and yet wherever I went the story was always the same. 'Sorry, it's the wrong time of day' or 'We've just sprayed, there aren't any'. I began to doubt what I'd read. Helpful people would make a special effort to find some for me, but the creatures they collected were always too small and not what I wanted. Eventually I did find my tampans but it was not an experience I like to repeat.

My dog Gypsey and I once found ourselves in the area of Lake Ngami. We were on foot; I had two rucksacks, one for living out of and the other containing my camera equipment. I had been walking for most of the morning and was exhausted and probably dehydrated. Lake Ngami is good cattle country, but over-grazing and the drought have sent them elsewhere. The soil is deep and rich and stands of great acacia thorn trees are abundant. I came to a grove of them and, selecting a particularly pleasing tree, I sank down gratefully in its deep shade, put the rucksacks aside and settled comfortably onto my back with my head resting against a convenient root. The relief was immense, as I lay and relaxed. I had a cigarette and may even have dozed off.

At first it was just a minor irritation. Absentmindedly I reached behind my head and scratched. Then I rubbed my elbow, then scratched my side, reached down to my thigh ... With slowly dawning horror, I realised that something was wrong. I leapt up and saw a shower of small dark shapes cascading from my body to the sand where they threw up powdery spouts of white as they thudded onto its surface and scuttled deep into its shelter. Tampans. Hundreds of them. Even now the memory of it makes me recoil and shivers of revulsion crawl across my flesh. Unerringly, like an animal, I had chosen an inviting tree, not knowing that under its cool sands starving tampans were waiting patiently in hungry, silent ambush. Within seconds they were all gone – all, that is, except the eight fat specimens that I frantically clawed from the sand and which finished the journey with me in a sealed plastic container. I obtained my photographs!

Insects are the biggest animal group in the world and beetles comprise the largest division within it. According to Mary-Louise Penrith of the Transvaal Museum, one of the most successful of the beetle species are the tenebrionids.[13] They inhabit the highest mountains, the coldest antarctic wastes and, of course, the deserts. There are many unidentified beetle species. In the Carpathian Basin of south-eastern Europe, over 12 000 species are known. Mary-Louise believes that there are twice that number in Southern Africa and at least a few thousand unidentified beetles in the Kalahari.

It is a strange but interesting fact that desert beetles are predominantly wingless and slightly larger than their kith and kin in cooler climes. It appears that this is so because of a physiological advantage.[14] Beetles respire through a series of small holes in their sides. These are called spiracles and open into the space beneath the wing casing. When the insect flies the wing-cases open and during flight air flows directly over the spiracles and accelerates the loss of water by evaporation. For desert species, this could be a serious and irreplaceable loss.

We do not know if beetles actually drink water. As we have seen, many other arid-adapted creatures do not, but their prey usually contains a high moisture content. Beetles are plant and detritus eaters – an important reprocessing link in the food chain – and it is difficult to estimate what moisture they would get from this source. As their skin is practically impermeable to water, it is also difficult to estimate their water requirements.

Faced with a choice of conserving water or losing the power of flight, some beetles appear to have opted for the former. Many of the desert species have retained their wing covers but no longer have the wings themselves. The spiracles still open into the same space but, protected from direct exposure to the outside air, much more moisture is conserved. Beetles in extreme desert conditions tend to exhibit several other interesting modifications of structure. Wing muscles, no longer needed, are done away with. Eyesight, necessarily acute for visual orientation during aerial dispersal, is depended upon less in those which do not fly. Desert beetles tend, therefore, to have reduced visual acuity but, in compensation, other senses are often more developed.

The tenebrionids can be divided broadly into two categories – diurnal and nocturnal. Generally speaking, there is an easy way to tell the difference. The nocturnal species have short legs and their daytime cousins have long legs. The reason is simple. The nocturnal tenebrionid is less exposed to predators and the sand is warm whilst the night can be cool. He therefore moves fairly slowly and is short-legged. During the day the reverse is the case and the diurnal species is very fast moving and has long legs. A 15 °C drop in temperature is recorded 1 cm above the ground and for a heat-conscious, water-conserving beetle, that centimetre can be a matter of life or death.[15]

A well-known tenebrionid in Southern Africa is the toktokkie beetle. This amusing character, frustrated no doubt by the silence of the beetle world, has developed a novel way of announcing its presence. Frequently pausing in its travels, it will be seen knocking its abdomen on the ground. Apparently the pattern of sound is species specific and is used for identification within the group.

All tenebrionids have defensive glands which secrete a fluid which is then spread by movements of the legs all over the beetle's body. It is a deterrent to predators. Dr J A Brits describes persistently confronting one beetle until it paused for a few seconds, lowered its head and pointed its abdomen in the air. A flow of its defensive fluid coursed along the sides of its upper surface, the edges of which are skirted by a gutter-like structure. Suitably doused, the beetle then folded its legs and 'sat' down, awaiting developments, apparently feigning death. On further handling, it used its legs to spread the fluid all over its own body and Dr Brits's fingers.[16] It seems a very effective system!

In some of the tenebrionids this defensive fluid is poisonous. The compounds which comprise the poison are highly toxic and that such potent poisons can be produced and stored in high concentrations in living tissue is scientifically most interesting.

The study of insects is fascinating. Insects impact on almost everything man does and an understanding of their roles and how they affect us and our activities is vital to our long-term survival on this ever-shrinking planet. One has only to think of agriculture and the countless millions that are spent in understanding and combating one insect pest or another. One illustration of the benefits to be gained from well-directed research can be found in what I call the remarkable dung beetle story. Apart from the interesting aspects of the story itself, the dung beetle story must be a rare illustration of an insect-led, national export drive.

When the first English colonists arrived in Australia in 1788 they had with them five cows, two bulls, seven horses and forty-four sheep and the makings of a national disaster – although it took a long time to manifest itself.[17] The Australian grassland ecosystems were to be much disturbed by the consequences of this event. Animal dung is not something to which we normally give a great deal of thought, 'out of sight, out of mind' probably being one reason. However, except in urban areas where there aren't all that many animals anyway, 'out of sight' is only the case because there are a host of beetles which are specialised dung removers. In one form or another they occur universally, mostly adapted to a particular environment and sometimes specialising in a particular kind of dung.

Like everywhere else, Australia had its dung beetles, but they were adapted to dealing with the dung of Australia's principal herbivores, the marsupials, which was coarse-textured and pellet-like. The Australian dung beetles were not at all attracted to the large, moist and quite unpalatable products of these new, exotic animals. So the cowpats were ignored. As long as the animals were few, and spread over a large area, the problem remained unnoticed but, as populations increased, its nature was revealed. Grass does not grow under cowpats

or, if it does, it is of a kind that is not palatable to cattle.

An adult cow drops, on average, 12 dung pats a day. In 1974 it was estimated that there were 30 million cattle in Australia and something in the region of 350 to 450 million pats were daily making their appearance. Each one that was not removed rendered useless for about a year the patch of ground beneath and around it. More than 2 million ha of pasture lands were being lost to production each year. It was an economic and ecological crisis of monster proportions.

It did not stop there, however. Huge quantities of nitrogen, vital to the ecosystem, were being lost. In the course of one summer, it was calculated, a steer excretes about 13,6 kg of nitrogen. If the dung remains unburied, only about 2,7 kg of this nitrogen is returned to the soil.[18] This means an appalling loss of fertilising potential. Unburied cattle dung was the source of a further two serious problems. It provided a breeding site for two species of flies, the populations of which, in Australia, reached almost epidemic proportions. One was the bush fly and the other the blood-sucking buffalo fly. In addition, other pests bred in the dung and were vectors for several diseases that affected cattle. Millions of dollars were spent each year in trying to control these pests, amid a deteriorating situation. Finally Australia decided to import dung beetles and research projects in a number of tropical countries began, including Southern Africa.

The dung beetle is the sacred scarab of the ancient Egyptians who revered it as symbolising their sun-god, Ra, rolling the sun across the sky. The thirty segments in the beetle's tarsus represented the days of the month. The dung beetle buries its ball of dung in the ground and, about a month later, as the Egyptians noted, the young beetle emerges and flies away. Thinking that it was the original creature, the dung beetle came to symbolise the immortal soul.[19]

There are some 4 000 recognised species of dung beetle in the world, most of which occur in Africa, India and South-East Asia. Africa has approximately 2 000 known species, of which 780 occur in Southern

Africa. The volume of dung these beetles are able to remove is quite amazing. In the Kruger National Park 7 000 beetles have been recorded at a single pile of elephant dung, whilst in Kenya's Tsavo National Park, 22 746 beetles were collected from a 7 kg pile of elephant dung in the course of twelve hours.

Dung beetles vary in shape and size. Some are only 2 mm long while others are relative giants measuring 60 mm in length. Sometimes the males have horns, which are purely ornamental, while the females are generally less gaudy. In favourable conditions in Africa dung beetles can be so numerous and efficient that they can remove a cowpat in less than an hour. It is not always so, however. Perfect conditions seldom prevail and performance is affected by the type of soil, the climate and the time of year. In most cases, a pat is likely to be removed and buried within thirty hours.

Those who live in Africa owe much to the dung beetle. Not only does it remove and bury dung, but fly species are controlled, the eggs of internal parasites are destroyed and the spread of disease by bacteria is prevented. Plant growth is also stimulated, natural fertiliser is widely distributed, soil porosity is improved, and seeds which may be included in the dung are carefully picked out by the beetles and are left on the soil surface, where they have a better chance to germinate. Experiments in South Africa showed that over 90 per cent of faecal nitrogen was returned to the soil. In a survey carried out some time ago in India, it was calculated that some 40 to 50 tonnes of human excrement were removed by dung beetles each day.

Dung beetles in Africa do not escape predation. The beetles are eaten by moles, mongooses and jackals which, in winter, will often violate the nests, crack open the huge brood-balls and eat the larvae. Hornbills, owls, guineafowl, lizards and toads will also eat the beetles.

The Australians were concerned about predators, or the lack of them, and understandably so after their experience with the cane toad. This delightfully cunning creature was itself an import to Australia, having been brought in from South America via Hawaii in the 1930s to deal with beetles which were infesting the roots of sugarcane in North Queensland. Predictably perhaps, the cane toad population multiplied and never achieved what was expected of it. It became a predator on beneficial as well as noxious beetles and, with the first introduction of exotic dung beetles, quickly learnt to include them in its diet. At least it did so with style. Noting that dung beetles congregated on cowpats, this intelligent toad adopted the practice of positioning itself on top of freshly deposited pats and there it waited for its next meal to deliver itself. Apart from the discomfort of slightly messy feet, it did very well. One toad, sacrificed in the cause of science, was shown to have eighty beetles inside it!

There are three basic categories of dung beetle: those which bury the brood-ball beneath the dungpat, those which bury it within the dung and those which roll a ball of dung away and bury it at some more distant point. The strength of these creatures is phenomenal. The wings are extremely powerful and operate on a sophisticated system of hydraulics. They are 'pumped' into position by a combination of blood and air pressure which is released after flight so that they fall back into place as a result of their own elasticity. The movement of the wings is incredibly rapid, moving up and down between 40 and 90 times a second (the humming-bird moves its wings 30 to 50 times a second). Large dung beetles are difficult to hold within a clenched fist, so powerful are they. The ball they roll is often as much as 40 times their own mass and it is believed that they may use the sun to guide them in rolling it in a straight line. In most species each female produces 50 to 60 brood-balls, each one containing a single egg, within her lifetime, which is roughly four years. Some species only produce one brood-ball a year. As might be expected, dung beetles have an exceptionally well developed sense of smell.

Eventually, after many years of research, the first imported dung beetles were released in Australia on a large scale in 1968. There were six original release points and the population exploded so rapidly that the gaps were quickly closed and the species spread at a rate of some 50 to 80 km per season. Where conditions were good, cowpats, which had been such a serious problem, began to disappear within a day of being dropped. The experiment was a dramatic success but nevertheless it did not entirely save the situation. The first imported species soon reached its ecological limits, leaving vast areas of Australia without the benefits of its presence. The search had to continue.

By 1969 eight different species had been released, four from Africa, three from Mexico and one each from Java and Sri Lanka. By 1979 the number of imported species had risen to 52, 10 of which showed every sign of becoming very well established. It was felt that by the mid-1980s a total of some 160 species would have been tried in Australia.

The logistics of this operation are impressive. It is not simply a case of the wholesale export of live dung beetles. The numbers required are too large and there are fearsome contamination risks. For example, it would be disastrous if, unwittingly, foot and mouth disease were imported into a country whose cattle and sheep industry represented an important part of the economy. Once the dung beetle's cycle was understood, therefore, a large part of the programme was devoted to 'mass-producing' dung beetles in sterile conditions. In this way growth rates could be optimised and mortality rates reduced to the lowest possible level.

The export of eggs, from various countries, still continues and the whole programme is far from complete. It has spawned far-reaching research efforts and our understanding of the dung beetle, and other insects too, has expanded enormously. It pleases me to think that the lowly and hitherto undervalued dung beetle, from the Kalahari perhaps, has finally earned the recognition its status deserves. I like the idea that an elderly dung beetle, approaching the end of his days, can put his feet up, knowing that somewhere, on the other side of the world, his progeny are carrying on the good work.

One of the less pleasant inhabitants of the Kalahari's sands is the scorpion, and these creatures exist there in great abundance, the soft sand providing an ideal habitat for many species.

Scorpions are a very ancient order and

first emerged about 45 million years ago. There are many fallacies concerning the scorpion. It will *not* sting itself to death if cornered, nor is its toxicity related to its size or colour. There are about 100 species in Southern Africa, but they do not all live in the sand; some are rock dwelling and some are arboreal. They are not all equally distributed either. Those which prefer a sandy environment, such as that which the Kalahari provides, are uniquely adapted for it. Their legs have long rows of close-set hairs which serve to increase the surface area and gives them a better grip when they walk over sand or burrow down beneath it, to depths of as much as a metre.

Most scorpions can survive without food and water for only limited periods, about a month at best, but the desert species are somewhat hardier and, if satiated to begin with, can survive for as long as a year. Their prey is varied but mostly comprises soft-fleshed insects. There are some surprising exceptions and there is a report of one Kalahari species devouring a small rodent.[20]

Prey is detected by sensory hairs on the pincers and on the body. Scorpions are capable of detecting minute air currents and ground vibrations which are transmitted to them through these extraordinarily sensitive hairs. Scorpions do not chew their food. They grip it and pour onto it extremely powerful digestive fluids so that prey is actually pre-digested outside the body. The fluids are sucked back in until nothing is left of the prey but its skeleton, which is discarded.

The mating dance of scorpions is a well-reported phenomenon.[21] It is neither romantic nor esoteric, but purely functional. In the pincer-grasping dance, the male steps backwards and forwards, pulling and pushing the female. In doing so, the space beneath them is cleared of larger soil particles. The grip is changed from claw-to-claw to mouth-to-mouth and the male deposits, in the cleared area, a small sack, or spermatophore, in which his sperm is contained. The female is manoeuvred over it and she evacuates the sperm from it.

Once insemination is complete the couple disengages and the male makes aggressive advances to the female, who is driven from

▲Flowers bring beauty to the desert sands

▼Ostrich chick explores its world

▼Fat-tailed gecko, Tsabong

▼Tampan ticks

▼Barn owl shams dead

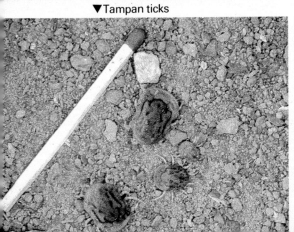

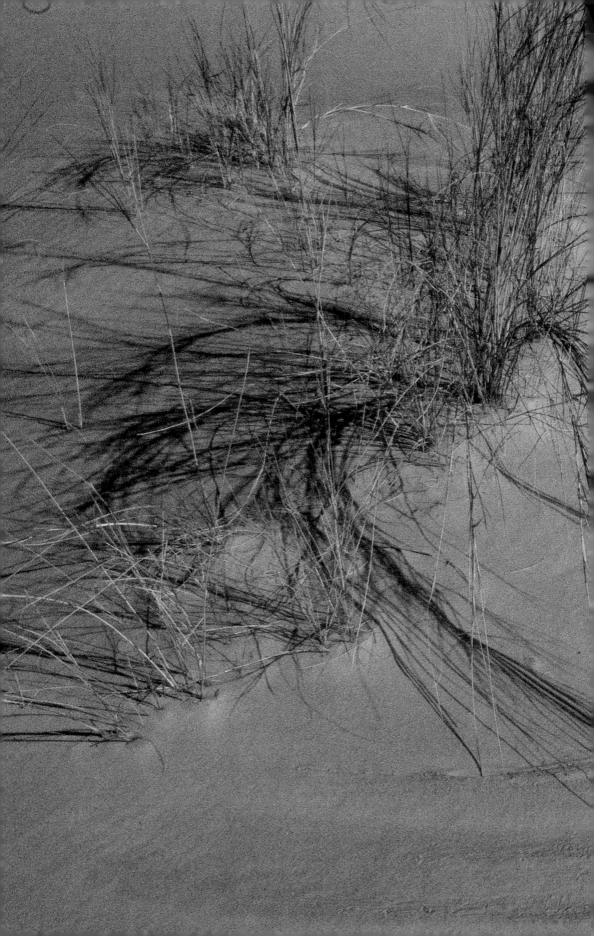

A tuft of grass traces circles in the sand

▲Red velvet mite, Ngamiland

▲Jumping spider, Ghanzi

▲Centipede, Ngamiland

▲Fat mouse, Savuti

▼Tracks in the sand betray the activities of nocturnal fauna

the 'dance' area. There is no evidence to support the tale that the female devours the male after mating. Scorpion young are contained in a small sac, which is slit open by the mother, whereupon they scramble out and crawl onto her back.

The reputation of the severity of the scorpion's sting is widespread and not altogether without foundation. There is much variety, however, and the sting is not necessarily painful or serious; a great deal depends on the amount of venom delivered and on the size of the victim. The most lethal of scorpions is not found in Southern Africa but comes from the north. The poison of *Androctonus australis* is said to be able to kill a man in four hours and a dog in seven minutes.[22] The venom is one of the most powerful biological toxins known to man.

There is a handy and fairly accurate way of judging the potency of a scorpion's sting. For this purpose scorpions can be divided into two groups – those which have thick, powerful-looking stings and relatively slender pincers, and those with powerful, heavy pincers and relatively slender stings. The former do not rely on strength to capture their prey. Instead, it is the venom that kills. They are the dangerous ones! When they strike, it is with great speed and much force. The heavy-pincered variety crush their prey and use their stings only for defence. Although they can still inflict a painful sting, it is not as serious.

It is often said (and sometimes disputed) that scorpions can spray their venom. According to Dr Gerry Newlands, one of South Africa's scorpion experts, scorpions which are capable of delivering large quantities of venom sometimes squirt it in the form of a fine jet when alarmed.[23] It is not aimed in any particular direction and it is more a muscular reflex, caused by the alarm, than a premeditated offensive action. The consequences can be very serious, though, and the effect is as serious as being struck in the eye with venom from a spitting cobra. It is a rare occurrence and only one incident has been recorded. Some species can squirt their venom for distances up to a metre. The treatment is the same as for spitting cobras. As quickly as possible, the eyes must be washed out, preferably with a diluted anti-venom solution or with water.

The question of what to do about treating a scorpion sting is a vexing one. The experts will give you certain advice, regarding with some scepticism any alternative method. On the other hand, Africa is rife with 'dependable' cures and there seems to be little agreement as to the most effective. Technical advice maintains that the best course of action is to administer scorpion anti-venom. Whilst this is available at most major centres, it is not the sort of thing you can buy in the local Kalahari store. I have never met anybody who carries it. Those who spend their time in the 'bush' tend to adopt a rather pragmatic attitude towards the risks of a scorpion sting and seem to prefer to suffer, not always in silence. There is, in addition, the danger of an adverse reaction to anti-venom and, for this reason, adrenaline or soluble corticosteroid should also be available. Perhaps it is these complications that make scorpion anti-venom less popular than it might otherwise be.

In the absence of anti-venom, it is recommended that the bite be bandaged with crêpe, immobilised and drenched with iced water. One piece of advice that is absolutely critical is never to use barbiturates, morphine derivatives or meperidine, since these drugs compound the venom's effect and increase the possibility of death.[24]

'Bush' cures for scorpion stings are legion and I am not going to enumerate them here. However, one particular cure strikes me as having some sort of logic behind it and it is certainly one I would not hesitate to try in an emergency. Besides, I heard it from the person who used it – and it worked!

Jimmy Kalafatis is a big, jovial man, who likes to hunt in the Kalahari.[25] In August 1981 he was hunting, not far from Lone Tree Pan. It was morning. He felt something moving on the inside of his right trouser leg. Unthinkingly, he brushed at it with his hand. After stinging him, a small scorpion fell to the ground. He killed it and threw it aside. Within seconds, the pain was exceedingly severe. Initially, it was centred at the bite but within two or three minutes he could physically feel it moving up his leg towards his groin. It was excruciating. In desperation he took a sharp knife and made a small, 5 mm long cut across the wound, just deep enough to break the skin. It bled a little. He poured on whisky – a measure of Jimmy's concern! It made no difference. He tried petrol – that did not help. The pain was now overpowering. Jimmy had with him a Bushman assistant, who had stood by throughout the whole incident doing nothing to help, grinning and laughing to himself. Eventually, he offered help.

He located the dead scorpion and removed its tail at the base. Using the sting itself, at the tip of the tail, like a sharp instrument, he made a series of criss-cross cuts over the sting site. He then took the scorpion's body, which had been decapitated and which was now also minus a tail, and squeezed the contents into the palm of his hand. He mixed them into a paste and applied the paste to the wound. The effect was dramatic.

The pain immediately diminished. Starting from the groin glands, relief was soon felt, travelling quickly down the leg to the bite. Jimmy claims he actually felt it moving! Within two minutes all pain was gone. He was left with a slight tingling sensation at the sting site for about a day and a half. I wrote to Gerry about the incident and saw him some months later. Above all, Gerry is a scientist, and a good one too. He smiled, said he'd received the letter and made no further comment.

Perhaps the best way of treating scorpion stings is to avoid getting them in the first place. Easier said than done, perhaps, but there are certain sensible precautions worth taking. Shake out clothing and footwear before putting them on. Be very careful if you are picking up or turning over stones, as many scorpions live beneath them and they resent intrusion. Picking up firewood is another way in which people frequently get stung. I always insist that people with me kick it and knock it about a little first. All sorts of creatures live in fallen wood, not only scorpions, and none of them particularly likes being disturbed.

Surprisingly, several species of scorpion can actually produce sound. They have no vocal cords with which to do so but manage a stridulating noise by scraping the sting over a series of small, sharp ridges on the top surface of the first two tail segments. Exactly why this is done is not known.

Another curious aspect is the scorpion's ability to glow in the dark – at least under ultra-violet light.[26] The phenomenon is not related to phosphorescence but to fluorescence: when the light source is removed the glow immediately stops. Apparently there is a wide range of attractive colours, although I have only seen shades of green, purple and yellow. Since the colour patterns appear to be species specific, it may have something to do with species recognition. Remarkably, the phenomenon persists after death and has been noted in one specimen that had been preserved in alcohol for seventy years – the alcohol also fluoresced a little – and in another that was collected and dried by Linnaeus in the eighteenth century! Scorpions are not the only creatures that fluoresce. So, apparently, do some spiders, dragonflies, millipedes, termites, geckos, crickets, and the cocoons of some caterpillars.

The arboreal scorpions are of interest if only because of some of the unusual places they appear and the ways in which they get there. An example is the species *Opisthacanthus*, which occur in the high rainfall areas of tropical Africa, and are expected, although none has been recorded there so far, to occur in the Okavango Delta. Although America has many of its own scorpions, this particular species is the only one of its family which occurs in the Americas and is the only American scorpion which is morphologically similar to African species. It is therefore almost certainly an 'import'. It is believed to have crossed the oceans from its African home on fallen tree-trunks.[27] Under-cutting rivers fell large trees which float to the sea and are delivered to far shores by ocean currents. These scorpions also occur in Madagascar and a few specimens have been reported from the East Indies.

Spiders are a fascinating source of interest, but regrettably the Kalahari's spiders are woefully under-researched. Thousands of species undoubtedly await identification. It is estimated that less than half the world's spiders are known to science – and 30 000 have been named so far! Unfortunately, there are simply not enough skilled researchers to finish the task quickly – and there are strong indications to suggest that it will prove to be an exciting and stimulating field. Take flying spiders, for example.

The phenomenon of flying spiders has been known, or guessed at, for a very long time. Pliny wrote that it 'rained wool' and Darwin, in 1839, described the 'air being full of patches of flocculent wool'.[28] Some spiders ensure their world-wide distribution by flying the jet-streams from one continent to another. Aerial migrations of spiders have been quite widely studied and have been reported, mostly, from North America and Australia. Such migrations are usually made up of young spiders and many hundreds of thousands may be involved. Spiders have been found great distances from the nearest continents: an American species was recovered in Antarctica. One researcher collected four species at 1 524 m, whilst another found twenty different species in the stomachs of swifts, obviously taken in the air. How does it come about?

The mechanism is simple, although the whys and wherefores are not so well understood. Would-be flying spiders simply lay out a long line of silk which catches the wind and eventually creates sufficient drag to pull them off their perch and hold them aloft. Scientists call this technique 'ballooning' and many spider species use it, among them the button spiders, of which the notorious black widow is one.

Universally feared, almost all of the button spiders are poisonous to man, but it is the black widow whose bite is the most severe. Easily confused with several less poisonous species, the bite of the black widow can induce painful cramps, profuse sweating and excessive salivation. The spider injects a neurotoxin which affects the spinal cord and nervous system. Mortality, in untreated cases, is low however – between 4 and 6 per cent.

Spiders are extraordinarily adaptive creatures and seem to have acquired a remarkable number of skills, allowing them to exploit a wide range of habitats. There are spiders with well-developed navigational skills which make use of the sun and stars. There are spiders that 'fish', spiders

that live in highly developed communities, some that use a net to catch their prey and others which prey on birds and lizards.

Many spiders living on or near riverbanks actually venture out onto the surface of the water in search of prey. It can be readily appreciated that such creatures, once removed from the familiar confines of the shore, could use with advantage, some system of navigation that would allow them to return to the point from which they came. In a slow-moving stream, for instance, where the body of the water is in motion, or in the event of a long chase, the spider might find itself far from its home. How does it know where 'home' is?

Dr Florian Papi,[29] in a series of experiments conducted in Italy, has shown how several species use the position of the sun and the direction of vibration of polarised light to orientate themselves on water.[30] In addition to the sun, spiders will also use landmarks on the shore but, curiously, they prefer using the sun, if it is shining, to terrestrial markers. It is not possible to use the sun efficiently as a navigational aid without also being equipped with an 'internal clock', by means of which allowances can be made for its daily movement. Bees, fish and birds all share this timing mechanism and, like spiders, they also use the sun as an aid in direction finding.

One species which exhibits this interesting behaviour is the wolf spider, commonly found on Kalahari sands, in the Okavango Delta and along the banks of the Kalahari rivers. No serious research has been conducted on this spider in Southern Africa and the occurrence of this behaviour in other African spiders is yet to be demonstrated.

The fishing spider is probably equipped with these skills because it, too, spends a great deal of time skating across the surface of the water. About 30 mm long, the fishing spider's prey consists of aquatic insects but also includes small fish, crayfish, tadpoles and frogs. Its method of fishing is most interesting.[31] Anchoring itself with its two rearmost pairs of legs to a rock or firm piece of vegetation, the fishing spider waits, watching beneath the water for suitable prey to approach. When prey draws near the spider 'shuffles' its legs on the surface, arousing the victim's curiosity and attracting it to within snatching distance. The method seems effective, as a success rate of 60 per cent has been recorded. Often, if frightened, or if pulled under by its prey, the spider will be submerged; experiments show that it can remain underwater for at least twenty-three minutes. Like scorpions, spiders do not chew their prey. Instead, a digestive secretion floods out over their meal and it is, literally, sucked off the bone.

Spiders, like all other creatures, must rely on special adaptations to permit their survival in the semi-arid areas of the Kalahari. For example, mobile hunters are much more common than web-makers. There is also a higher incidence of nocturnal and burrowing spiders – obviously a heat-avoidance strategy. The trapdoor spider, for example, can create a well-controlled micro-climate in its silk-lined, air-tight, waterproof burrow and many spiders seal their young in burrows, where they await the right environmental conditions before emerging. Some spiders, aware of the small predators which will try to enter their burrows, rig an elaborate tunnel-blocking mechanism in the shape of a silk bag of soil which collapses and blocks the tunnel's entrance if moved by any but the spider itself.

Other spiders rely on camouflage to escape detection and many are almost indistinguishable from the dry desert grasses. Not only their colour, but their shape, too, allows them to stretch their narrow length along a grass stem, making them all but disappear against the drab, grey background. Spiders also adapt physiologically to the rigours of an arid environment. Many have highly distendable abdomens so that they can gorge themselves in times of plenty. Some can vary their rate of reproduction in relation to the abundance of food. Most have a high resistance to starvation and can last without food for as long as six months.

Rare among spiders, one species, found mostly in the Kalahari, lives in a community. *Stegodyphus* can be found in groups of several hundred and in a ratio of females to males of about thirteen to one.[32] As natural increase leads to overcrowding,

the community splits and a new one is formed. Spider communities are unusual because many spider traits must be changed to allow it to happen. There must be cooperation between creatures and the normal aggressiveness of spiders cannot be permitted. Often, it is said, these spiders will overcome their prey by sheer weight of numbers. In such communities there is collective brood care and feeding takes place as foraging members of the community return to the nest and regurgitate food for the young.

One of the most interesting adaptations exhibited by spiders is seen in those which mimic ants. Not only do these creatures grow to look like ants, with the same colouring and body shape, but their movement is carefully designed to imitate that of ants. Some copy ants' characteristic jerking movement and others walk with their front legs raised so that they look like antennae![33] This phenomenon is frequently seen in desert environments, perhaps because ants are more common and, due to the lack of vegetation cover, more conspicuous.

Despite being in the minority, there are many web-using spiders in the Kalahari. One that occurs widely is sufficiently large and strong enough to capture small birds such as fire-finches, drongos and small kingfishers. Among the species that do this are some of the button spiders, whose powerful toxins make short work of struggling birds. Another curious spider, reported from Natal, but believed to occur in the Kalahari, possesses unusually long front legs. This creature makes a web which, at first sight, appears to be exceptionally small. However, as a moth or similar prey approaches, the spider, making use of its long legs, flips open hidden folds in its web which suddenly expands to more than four times its original size and, rather like a Roman gladiator of old, ensnares its prey.[34] There are others which are specialised cannibals, in the dark hours of the night creeping stealthily into a victim's web and, gently tugging the supporting strands, luring its meal out into the open. Surprise, speed and the accuracy with which it places its bite are all essential to its success.[35] Some experts believe that more spiders are killed yearly by their own kind than by any other order of invertebrates. The family is not common in Southern Africa but is found in collections and is believed to occur in the Kalahari.

In the last three chapters we have talked of the animals, large and small, that have chosen to live in the Kalahari. All of them exhibit marvellous adaptations which allow them to exist within this most inhospitable of environments. The diversity of these various species and the amazing range and ingenuity of their adaptations is to me a constant source of wonder, especially when one considers how little active research has taken place in this remote area and, therefore, how much more remains to be discovered.

## REFERENCES

1. **Coaton, W G H.** 'Survey of the Termites (*Isoptera*) of the Kalahari Thornveld and the Shrub Bushveld of the R.S.A.' In *Koedoe*, Vol 6, 1963, pp 38-50
2. **Collins, M.** 'The Importance of Being a Bugga-Bug'. In *New Scientist*, June 1982, pp 834-7
3. **Wilson, D S and Clark, A B** 'Defensive Strategies in Harvester Termites'. In *Journal of the Entomological Society of Southern Africa*, Vol 40, No 2, 1977, pp 271-82
4. **Velcich, G.** 'Diet of Flying Ants'. In *baNtu*, June 1963, pp 326-9
5. **Newell, I M and Tevis, L.** '*Angelothrombium pandorae* N. G., Sp. (*Acari, Trombidiidae*), and Notes on the Biology of the Giant Red Velvet Mites'. In *Annals of the Entomological Society of America*. Vol 53, No 3, May 1960, pp 203-95
6. **Holm E.** Personal communication, May 1984
7. **Theiler, G.** 'The Sand Tampan (*Ornithodoros Savignyi*): An Ecological Puzzle and an Economic Problem'. In *Annals of the Cape Province Museum*, II, 1962, pp 212-22
8. **Bothma, J du P.** 'Shepard's Tree, a Shady Haven for Strange Creatures'. In *Custos*, Vol 11, No 10, January 1983, pp 22-3
9. **Spickett, A M.** 'Kalahari's Sand Tampan, a Remarkable Creature'. In *Custos*, Vol 13, No 4, July 1984, pp 39-41
10. **Bothma, J du P.** Op cit
11. **Theiler, G.** Op cit
12. Ibid, p 217
13. **Penrith, M.** Personal communication, May 1984
14. **Scholtz, C H.** 'Aptery in Trox (*Coleoptera: Trogidae*): morphological changes and their relationship to habitat'. In *Journal of the Entomological Society of Southern Africa*, Vol 44, No 1, 1981, pp 83-7
15. **Penrith, M.** Op cit
16. **Brits, J A.** 'The Physiology of the Defensive Glands of *Parastizopus armaticeps* Peringuey (*Coleoptera: Tenebrionidae*). In *Journal of the Entomological Society of Southern Africa*, Vol 44, No 2, 1981, pp 297-313
17. **Waterhouse, D F.** 'The Biological Control of Dung'. In *Scientific American*, Vol 230, No 4, 1974, pp 101-08
18. **Bornemissza, G E.** 'The Australian Dung Beetle Project, 1965 - 1975'. Australian Meat Research Committee, Review. Sydney, Australia. No 30, August 1976, pp 1-32
19. **Scholtz, C H and De Villiers, W M.** *Dung Beetles.* Cape Town, 1983
20. **Newlands, G.** *Biogeography and Ecology of Southern Africa.* Edited by Werger, M J A. The Hague: Dr W Junk, 1978, pp 687-90
21. **Alexander, A J.** 'The Courtship and Mating of the Scorpion, *Opisthophthalmus Latimanus.* In *Proceedings of the Zoological Society of London,* Vol 128, Part 4, pp 529-44
22. **Newlands, G.** 'Transvaal Scorpions'. In *Fauna and Flora*, No 25, August 1974, pp 3-7
23. Ibid
24. **Newlands, G.** 'Review of Southern African Scorpions and Scorpionism'. In *South African Medical Journal*, Vol 54, No 7, October 1978, pp 613-15
25. **Kalafatis, J.** Personal communication, July 1984
26. **Stahnke, H L.** 'UV Light, A Useful Field Tool'. In *BioScience*, Vol 22, No 10, pp 604-07
27. **Newlands, G.** *Biogeography and Ecology of Southern Africa.*
28. **Musgrave, A.** 'Spider Astronauts and Gossamer Web'. In *The Australian Museum Magazine.* 15 December 1950, pp 118-23
29. **Papi, F and Tongiorgi, P.** 'Innate and Learned Components in the Astronomical Orientation of Wolf Spiders'. In *Sonderdruck Aus Ergebnisse der Biologie/Advances in Biology.* Edited by Autrum, A. Vol 26, 1962, pp 259-80
30. **Papi, F.** 'The Astronomical Orientation in Species of the Gen. *Arctosa (Araneae Lycosidae).* In *Zeitschrift für Vergleichende Physiologie*, Vol 41, 1959, pp 481-89
31. **Le Roy, A.** 'The Habits of *Thalassius Spenceri.'* In Spider Club of South Africa *Newsletter*, No 24, December 1981, pp 7-8
32. **Le Roy, A.** 'Community Spiders: *Stegodyphus'.* In Spider Club of South Africa *Newsletter*, No 8, March 1978, pp 5-7
33. **Cloudsley-Thompson, J L.** 'Desert Adaptations in Spiders'. In *Journal of Arid Environments*, Vol 6, 1983, pp 307-17

34. **Akerman, C.** 'On the Spider *Canneus camelus* Pocock, which Constructs a Moth-catching, Expanding Snare'. In *Annals of the Natal Museum*, Vol V, Part 3, 1926, pp 411-23

35. **Lawrence, R F.** 'The Cannibal Spiders'. In *The Naturalist*, Vol 25, No 2, July 1981, pp 4-9

# 12. On the Evening of the Third Day

AS we now know, the Kalahari is not a true desert. Deep in loose sand it may be and covered by large areas of rolling ancient sand dunes it certainly is, but, although rainfall in some regions is very low indeed, nowhere does it approach the extreme aridity of places such as the Namib or Sahara. The Kalahari is quite densely covered with vegetation and the few places where bare sand is exposed exist more because of misuse of the land by man than as a natural consequence of limited rain. Grasses, shrubs and trees occur in great variety, all in one way or another exhibiting special adaptations which uniquely equip them for survival in the difficult Kalahari environment.

Despite the abundance of plant life in the Kalahari, one would probably not expect to encounter truffles. And truffles are certainly found there, sometimes in huge quantities. There are 36 species of truffle found in the world, 11 of them occur on the African continent and 3 are thought to grow in the Kalahari.[1] The most common variety is known as *Terfezia pfelii* and was named after Graf Joachim Pfeil, a German geographer and colonial politician who made several journeys of exploration into Southern Africa.[2] African truffles lack the aromatic flavour of their European cousins but they are tasty and nutritious nevertheless. They contain no vitamin C at all but are very high in fat, protein, fibre and B vitamins and are much favoured by the Bushmen.[3]

A special skill is required to find truffles, for, like the potatoes they resemble, they grow beneath the ground. In the Kalahari neither dogs nor pigs are used in this search, as they are in other areas; it is the Bushman, with his extraordinarily keen eyesight, whose task it is. In March to May, when the fungi are ready for collecting, the Bushman keeps his eye on the surface of the sand. Moistened and compacted by the rain, its surface will crack in a zig-zag pattern to accommodate the swelling growth below. It is these tell-tale cracks the Bushman searches for and, using a special digging stick, he will expertly remove the fungi from where it grows just beneath the surface. The availability of truffles is directly linked to the right quantity of rain at the right time and several years may pass with no sign of them at all. Under ideal conditions, however, truffles can be collected by the bucketful.[4]

One of the most common of the Kalahari's trees, especially in the drier regions, is the shepherd's tree, or *Boscia albitrunca*. It is not particularly attractive but its ecological role in the Kalahari is important and the myths that are associated with it, as well as the unusual properties of its leaves and roots, make it worthy of attention. *B. albitrunca* is easily identified by its very round shape, with branches that often reach down to the ground, and a trunk which is typically stocky and conspicuously white or grey.[5] The shade given by the tree is important in a hot and often shadeless region. The cavern of cool shadow that it creates will frequently be occupied by lion or leopard, for the temperature within it can be as much as 21 °C lower than the open air.[6] Browsers among the Kalahari's ungulates, and cattle too, have been saved from starvation by the evergreen foliage in times of drought. The leaves and twigs are rich in vitamins and have a protein value of 14,5 per cent. Many farmers in the Kalahari liken it to lucerne in value, despite the fact that cows which eat it will produce tainted milk.

The shepherd's tree is a member of the caper family and the preserved flower buds are regarded as being of a standard equal to those of European capers. The white wood is hard and quite useful for making household furniture, although many African tribes are forbidden by tribal law to cut the tree, whilst others believe that to burn the wood will cause all the local cows to bear only bull-calves.

The uses of the tree are legion. Apart from the fact that their hollow stems often hold water for long periods of time after the rains have departed, they have medicinal uses as well. An infusion of the leaves is used to treat eye complaints in cattle and the treated fruits can assist in the control of epilepsy. I have no idea how it was discovered, but a decoction of the roots is apparently a helpful cure for piles! It is, however, the preservative properties of the powdered root which I find fascinating. Some indigenous people use the powdered root to preserve butter-fat and this aspect has been scientifically investigated, with remarkable results. When 0,5 per cent of the ground, freeze-dried root was added to milk at a temperature of 30 °C, the milk remained fresh for twenty-four hours, while a control sample soured after only twelve. Butter, made from cream treated in the same way, stayed fresh for nineteen days, when the untreated control went rancid after only three. Unfortunately, the characteristic taste of the tree's root was detectable in the butter. Other experiments have shown that the powdered root can prevent mould on oranges, tomatoes, bread and potatoes.[7]

An attractive, if somewhat unusual flower of the Kalahari is the stapelia. They look rather like aloes, with green, fleshy leaves, often spiked. I am told that biting off and chewing the tips of growing stems is a way of suppressing symptoms of thirst and hunger. However, this should be practised with caution for the method is so successful that renal damage can follow, due to dehydration.[8] Nevertheless, it is a useful piece of information to store away against some possible future emergency.

All stapelia share a common and unusual method of attracting insect pollinators. Whilst most plants appear to rely upon colour and what is to us a pleasant scent, stapelia have chosen a different mechanism. Their scent is particularly unappealing and their chosen pollinators are neither birds nor bees, but flies. It seems also that stapelia have a rather low opinion of the fly's intellect for, rather than chance that this small creature may pass them by, there are added inducements to attract its attention. Each flower has, set about the edges of its petals, a number of hair-like structures, called vibratile hairs.[9] They are not large, and the ones I have seen stood probably less than 2 to 4 mm high. Each slender filament carries upon its top a tiny, disk-like attachment. The whole thing looks rather like a hat-stand with a single hat upon it. The 'hat' is very loosely attached and it wobbles and moves easily. The slightest movement in the vicinity of the plant will set it in motion. Not even the smallest breeze is required; an animal passing by is sufficient to give movement to the hair. The buffeting gale from the beat of a fly's wing must make the head dance splendidly, an event which the fly apparently finds irresistible.

Without doubt, Africa's largest, best known and most easily recognised tree is the baobab. Grey, massive, almost overpowering, its huge, squat trunk and heavy-hung, bare branches are a familiar sight to visitors to Africa. Leafless for much of the year, it is easy to see how it earned its nickname of the 'upside down tree'. The Bushmen of Southern Africa tell a tale of how the baobab came to be planted this way. According to tradition, when the Great Spirit gave trees to the first men, he also gave one to every animal. The hyena was last in line and he received the baobab, the last tree left. He was so upset, say the Bushmen, that, in anger, he planted his the wrong way up – and so it has remained to this day.

An ancient tree, the baobab may have evolved in the area of what is now Madagascar for, of the nine species that exist in the world, seven of them are found there. Of the others, one grows in Australia and the other in Africa. Its distribution within Africa is limited mainly to the tropics and it prefers drier areas. The baobab has been a source of interest to African explorers since earliest times and they all took seeds with them when they left. Now occurring widely in India, it was probably introduced there in the thirteenth century. It has also been introduced as far afield as Mauritius, Malaya, Java, the West Indies and Guyana. It is said that French immigrants introduced the seed to Cuba from Haiti and that plants were taken from there to Florida in 1912, where they flourish still.[10] The trees have also been grown successfully in England and were first taken there in the early eighteenth century. Although most were killed in the severe frosts of 1740, others have been planted and, so far as I am aware, they grow there yet.[11]

The largest baobab in the world is said to be found on the south-east slopes of Mount Kilimanjaro in Tanzania. It is recorded as having a girth of over 28 m,[12] and there are many trees in the Kalahari which are almost as large. Such an enormous size suggests a long period of growth and it is being increasingly recognised that the lifespan of the baobab is remarkably long.

One of the ways in which trees can be dated is by counting their annual rings. Some trees do not easily show such rings, the baobab among them, and for a long time it was claimed that they did not possess them at all. However, the pioneering work of Dr Graham Guy seems set to change this situation. Convinced that baobabs do have annual rings, he experimented with dyes until he was able to show, quite clearly, that this is indeed the case.[13] By taking cores from tree specimens of known age, he was able to use his techniques to estimate age to within 2 per cent. The discovery is important because much information of archaeological and climatological interest can be gained from it too.

The study of trees, their annual growth rings and what they reveal about past climates, is called dendrochronology. A fascinating study has been made by the University of the Witwatersrand, in which the potential for this kind of information of all Southern African trees has been evaluated.[14] Unfortunately, of all the hundreds of different trees found in the sub-continent, only six score highly enough on a range of selection criteria to offer worthwhile research possibilities. The seventh tree is the baobab. It is generally agreed that the tree may live from 1 500 to 4 000 years and if a way could be found to unravel its secrets, much vital information could be discovered about, for example, earlier climates at archaeological sites.

The city of Great Zimbabwe is known to have been vacated, over a relatively short period of time, in about 1450, and there has been much speculation as to the cause. Local environmental collapse, caused by the demands of too large a number of people, concentrated in too small an area, is one of the possible reasons. Local baobabs, of which there are many and which were undoubtedly living at that time, might well hold the key to the mystery.

Perhaps because of their great age, baobabs grow exceedingly slowly. One tree in the Kalahari was found to have grown only 0,8 m in over 90 years and many have been found actually to have shrunk over time. Graham Guy located a tree measured by Livingstone in 1853, and found its girth to be less than it was in the explorer's day – by more than 1,6 m. Trial plots of baobabs have been in existence for nearly 40 years and it is from these it has been learnt that the average increase in circumference is a little under 5 mm a year! Often, in very dry years, the trees will temporarily shrink and this can sometimes be seen by the considerable gap that appears between the soil and the base of the trunk.

Pollination of the baobab remains a mystery. The flower is a beautiful cream-coloured, hanging bell. It is unusual in that it lasts only 24 hours. As the long shadows of Africa's brief twilight reach out across the land, its petals slowly unfurl, like some exotic nuptial bed to greet, seductively, the creatures of the night. In the morning, its pollen spent, the flower curls away from the harsh sunlight and quickly closes. By the end of the day, its task complete, it falls softly to the ground. Numerous pollinators have been suggested for this tree but the exact mechanism remains obscure. A popular suggestion is the bush-baby but, if this creature is responsible, it cannot be the only pollinator, for its distribution is far less widespread than that of baobabs. Bats are known to be attracted to the flowers, as are moths and several kinds of insects.

In the harsh environment of Africa, baobabs have long been useful to man in many ways. Not only do they provide food and medicine, but water, clothing and shelter as well. Frequently, these immense trees become hollow and hold large quantities of water. Sometimes the water collects only in the natural pool formed by the junction of the main branches, but at other times a reservoir actually develops inside the tree and rainwater is led into it along the branches. Occasionally the process is assisted by man who channels the water to the inner storage area. It is said that there is a chain of these trees across the Kalahari, spaced at about 100 km intervals, whose water has been invaluable to passing travellers.[15] I have not been able to verify this claim however. There are many baobabs in the Kalahari and many of them hold water, but there does not seem to be any traditional route that follows a particular line of trees.

In the Sudan some baobabs are regarded as personal property and are inherited and sold like any other piece of property. Details of ownership are kept in local government registers! The hollow trunk is not only used for storing water and there are countless tales from across the continent of ingenious uses. A baobab outside the District Commissioner's office in Katima Mulilo, in the Caprivi Strip, had been fitted out with a flushing toilet. Others have been used as tool-sheds, dairies and storerooms. There is one tree, reported from the area of Birchenough Bridge, in eastern Zimbabwe, which once served as a bus shelter and could hold thirty to forty persons. I think the hollow baobab outside the police station in Kasane, northern Botswana, has even been used, at least temporarily, as a prison.

When travelling the Kalahari with my children and a friend of theirs, Julian, we visited a group of baobabs made famous by the artist and explorer Thomas Baines. Known as the Seven Sisters, the group stands on the edge of a small salt pan, just to the south of Nxai Pan National Park in northern Botswana. We were interested to see what changes, if any, had taken place in the 123 years that had passed since

Baines had been there and painted them. Admittedly the detail of his painting did not allow for exact comparison, but there did not appear to be any changes at all. It was early January and the day was excruciatingly hot. Seduced by the dense and cooling shade of the trees in full leaf, we elected to remain in camp. Before long an exploration of the immediate area was in full swing and not very much later three young lads were high among the branches of the nearest baobab. In the central fork they discovered a large hole which disappeared down into the heart of the tree. Open at the top, it was in all about 3 m deep and 2 m across. Inside it was an odd assortment of animal bones, the fully feathered corpse of a barn owl, mummified by the heat, and a small electric torch. Thanking the tree for the torch, we turned our attention to its neighbour.

The next tree was also hollow. It was Jeremy who found an easy route to the entrance, which was open to the sky, although sheltered by the branches above. I looked inside. It was perfectly circular, about 2 m deep and the same in diameter. The floor was flat and soft, filled with the accumulated dust and detritus of ages. Huddled together at one side were two young barn owls. Completely feathered, they were just days away from flight. Clearly, never in their lives had their home been thus invaded. I, standing in the centre of the nest chamber, Jeremy halfway in, Julian and Andrew at the entrance, all of us peering down at the two unfortunate birds. They kept throwing sidelong glances at each other and one could imagine them thumbing through the range of their limited experience, wondering what to do next. Obviously neither had been prepared for such a situation and there was a lack of uniformity in their approach. One leapt forward in a hissing attack, a few small jumps accompanied by much fluttering of wings. The bird seemed nonplussed by its failure to elicit any response and promptly sat down quite comfortably at my feet, while it paused to consider its options. The second bird, having witnessed its companion's spectacular lack of success, decided on a most unusual ploy. It elected to 'play dead'. Rolling over onto its back, it folded its wings carefully by its sides, put its feet into the air with talons tightly closed and, after one last long look at me, flopped its head dramatically back onto the floor. It was a splendid performance, and most convincing. It would have remained so had the young owl not rather spoiled the effect by snatching its head back into the erect position every minute or so to check how its audience was reacting!

The baobab is a bountiful resource. The seeds, which are contained in brittle pods, are covered with a white, powdery deposit which has high concentrations of tartaric acid and are pleasant to suck. Mixed with water, they make a tasty and refreshing drink. The bark of the baobab has a high moisture content and is often consumed by wild animals, chief of which perhaps because it is best equipped for the job, is the elephant. Using their tusks, elephants lever away great patches of bark which they chew to extract the precious water. Man, too, makes great use of the bark of this tree. Twisted and rolled on the thigh, it makes a very strong cord, suitable for ropes, baskets, nets and cloth. I fear that we might have very few baobabs left to us, with all this removal of bark, were it not for another, unusual characteristic of the tree. It has the ability to regenerate bark, which not all trees can do, and, although the scars will remain, the tree can recover.

The wood of the baobab is of little practical use. It does make very good wrapping and writing paper but the cost of extracting the water is too high to make the proposition viable. The wood contains about 75 per cent water which makes it very spongy and difficult to cut with an axe. If left to dry after cutting, it disintegrates into long, powdery fibres and it is possibly this factor which gives rise to the oft-repeated tales of spontaneous combustion. There is probably some truth in them, for there are reports of trees becoming so dehydrated during times of drought that the massive branches, which owe their strength to the amount of water in them, suddenly snap off with a loud report and, occasionally, burst into flames.[16]

The sheer size of Africa's baobabs means that they often literally stand in the way of development and a number of interesting ways of getting rid of the bulky trees has been devised. I once attended a school in Tanzania which was housed in the abandoned buildings which had formed the headquarters of the infamous groundnut scheme. Huge areas, known as 'units', were cleared of all bush by a vast army of bulldozers and graders. Cleared, that is, of everything but its baobabs, for the monster trees proved to be tough customers. Even the biggest bulldozer could not push them over; blades were broken and tempers were lost in the attempt. Saws jammed and the trees refused to fall even when they were cut through, and they had to be pulled to the ground. When they did fall, they took up so much space it was eventually decided to leave them standing. Elsewhere in Africa, there have been similar problems. In Senegal the trees are injected with a cocktail of arsenic insecticide and caustic soda – a mixture which proves fatal in about 80 per cent of trees. In East Africa it has been found that a hawser, strung between two vehicles, can be pulled through a baobab, rather like a cheesewire, but again the tree then has to be pulled over afterwards.

There seems to be no immediate threat to the continued exstence of baobabs in Africa, although there is some evidence that their distribution is shrinking. Drought takes its toll for the tree cannot tolerate completely arid conditions. This is not to suggest, however, that the climate is changing: but the environment certainly is.

There is the inexorable increase of human populations, their spread into new rural areas of Africa and greater concentration in the old. Stock numbers increase, too, with a consequent reduction in vegetative cover. The resulting hard patches of exposed soil lead to increases in soil temperatures and rainwater run-off. The amount of water soaking into the ground decreases and the total effect is similar to a deterioration in climatic conditions. Ultimately the trees die.

One of the extraordinary phenomena of Africa, and one that is readily found in the Kalahari, is the so-called 'rain-tree'. Numerous reports from early explorers describe how they had been camping underneath a tree when, on a hot and sunny, cloudless day, rain would begin to fall from the branches of the tree above. In some cases the 'rain' would be sufficient to soak one's clothing and often trees would be encountered with a large, circular patch of wetness about their bases. There is one report, from the island of Hierro, where a tree was so prolific in its production of water that it met the entire needs of a small community. Another describes a tree in Pretoria that 'wept' for several weeks.

There are two explanations accounting for this strange rain. Some trees, if their roots are excessively moistened, do have special pores called hydathodes in their leaves, by which excess water can be discharged. This process takes place mainly at night and probably explains the Pretoria tree. The other explanation involves two similar species of insect that belong to the order Hemiptera and to the family Cercopidae. Other members of that family include what are commonly known as frog-hoppers, spittle-bugs or cuckoo spits. The rain insects, *Ptyelus grossus* and *P. flavescens* are less than a centimetre long and, although quite different from one another, share one particular characteristic. They both have long, sharp, almost needle-like mouthpieces. This they use like a probe to pierce the bark of young twigs in order to suck the cell-sap from within. The insects live on a number of different tree species but some are favoured more than others. It is for this reason that the 'rain-tree' of Africa *(Lonchocarpus capassa)* gets its name. The larvae and adult forms both exist on sap and both cause a liquid solution to pour over their bodies. The insects generally position themselves face-down and the fluid is either secreted anally or through special pores in the body. The excess falls to the ground as 'rain'. In some cases air is mixed with the fluid so that it bubbles up into a foam. It is very sticky and even rain will not wash it off.

The rate of fluid discharge has been measured in at least one case. A colony of 110 insects was located and its secretions measured. In a period of two hours, a minimum of 250 ml of moisture was produced. This is equivalent to about 1,1 ml of liquid per insect per hour.[17]. The colony was considered a small one and thus it is possible

to understand, with a large number of insects, reports which speak of such thorough wettings. The purpose of this sap-exuding behaviour is not fully understood. It may help prevent desiccation in the young, but a more likely explanation is that the insects are actually feeding from the sap juices. The nutritional value of this fluid is considered to be very low and one would therefore expect that a high volume would need to be processed so that the insects could fulfil their nutritional requirements. In these circumstances there would be a high waste rate, and it is of course this waste which appears to us as 'rain'.

Another creature that lives on trees is rather more directly useful to man; in fact, to some, it forms an essential part of their diet. This is a large, gaudy caterpillar which is found on the mopane tree. These creatures are collected, dried or cooked, and eaten with relish by certain rural communities. The mopane tree occurs in the north-eastern Kalahari. It prefers hot, low-lying areas, often forming pure stands, hence giving rise to the term 'mopane woodland'.

The leaves of this tree are the sole host for the caterpillar of the 'mopane moth' or Anomalous Emperor. The female lays her eggs on the underside of the leaves, within the first few weeks after rain. Overcast weather is important in the early stages, otherwise the newly hatched young die of sunburn! The young quickly grow into caterpillars which, at full size, measure between 5 and 8 cm in length. At the end of their growing period they drop to the ground and bury themselves in the soft earth beneath the tree. If the combination of late rains and temperature is right, a second hatching will take place in the same season; if not, the pupae will remain encapsulated until the following year.

Productivity of the hatchings is considerably reduced by the activities of a parasitic wasp. During the caterpillar stage this creature stings and lays an egg in the live caterpillar. The egg does not hatch and remains dormant within the crawler as it grows to its full size, drops off its leaf and enters the pupal stage. It is only when the caterpillar is safely in its chrysalis that the enemy from within strikes, literally, at the heart of its victim, whose body provides the young wasp with sufficient food to last it through to the next year, when it hatches and repeats the cycle. The predatory wasp is a fascinating example of the complex system of checks and balances that nature employs to keep the natural world in a state of equilibrium.

When the caterpillars or, as they are locally known, 'mopane worms' have reached full size, they are collected by the local people. Hundreds of women and children will descend on the trees, each carrying some sort of container. The crawlers are plucked from their leaves, the head is squeezed from the body and discarded, and the creature thrown into a bowl or dish. There it joins a writhing, squirming, decapitated mass in a sea of body fluids and blood. They are prepared for consumption by frying, roasting or stewing with vegetables. In years when conditions have been just right, there is an explosion in the caterpillar population. Hundreds of millions will swarm the trees, stripping them of every leaf, wreaking considerable damage. Faced with a dwindling food supply, the caterpillars sometimes migrate in search of new trees. So numerous are they that trains have been stopped at sidings, unable to move because of the solid mass of bodies making the lines too slippery for the wheels and sand has to be thrown onto the tracks to give the necessary traction.[18]

Not all the caterpillars are for home consumption. More often, the mopane worm is squeezed, dried and later sold. In Zimbabwe 50 kg of dried caterpillars will fetch $24,00 and roadside vendors selling them for just a few cents each are a common sight.[19] In the interests of research, I myself ate some of the dried caterpillars, and I have to admit that the thought is very much worse than the taste, which is not unlike bacon. The fresh-picked, cooked variety I have yet to sample – but I'll leave that for another occasion.

Squeamish though certain delicacies may make us feel, it is as well to recognise that many millions of people in Africa today take all, or at least a very large part, of their sustenance from the wild, where animals, plants and insects are all utilised as a food resource. I once attended a banquet celebrating the 10th Congress of the Association for the Taxonomic Study of the Flora of Tropical Africa. With some originality, the organisers chose to include on the menu only those items which came from the wild or from the sea. We dined most handsomely on guineafowl paté, truffles on sliced ostrich egg, fried porcupine served with herb stuffing, pickled mushrooms and sour-fig fruits. The main course was springbok pie with marula jelly and was accompanied by a salad with wild celery, watercress and wild garlic. For those with a thirst there was marula juice (and a supply of delicious Cape wine on the side!).

Another Kalahari tree, known for its prolific fruit, is the marula. It grows in open woodland and occurs throughout the Kalahari where there is firm soil, for it does not flourish in deep, wind-blown sand. Tall and beautifully shaped, it sometimes reaches as much as 15 m in height. Its fruit is a nut encased in soft white flesh and the tree is highly valued by the indigenous people of Africa. Both the flesh of the fruit and the nut within are utilised and uses vary from a sweet but potent alcoholic drink, to jellies, porridge, dried and fresh fruit. The real goodness comes from the kernel of the nut. The bark is used in treatment of malaria and is believed by some African tribes, if given to a pregnant woman, to determine the sex of her child.[20]

It is the fruit, however, that is both abundant and delicious. An average yield for some Kalahari trees is about 550 kg but trees producing over 1 000 kg of fruit have been recorded and somebody once counted more than 70 000 individual fruits from a single tree![21] There is a popular myth that claims that animals get drunk after eating the fruit, but recent research has shown that there is no truth in this at all. Chemical analysis shows that marula does contain alcohol and that the amount increases as the fruit ripens and rots. The highest level of alcohol is found in the rotting fruit but no animal, including the baboon, has been observed to eat fruit in such a state. Feeding trials on captive baboons also showed that they would not eat rotting fruit. If a baboon were to do so, it would need to consume approximately 400 marula berries or nearly 6 kg, before it had absorbed the amount of alcohol contained in a 340 ml can of beer. Baboons and other animals will eat the ripe fruit when it is freshly fallen. In this, of course, the alcohol level is lower and to obtain the same amount of alcohol the animal would need to eat 7,5 kg to achieve the same effect.[22]

There are two plant products of the wild which are of particular interest, one because it forms the staple diet of some Bushmen groups, and the other because it is an important raw material for a number of modern drugs. The mongongo tree grows in areas of higher rainfall only on Kalahari sand. It is a tree unique to the Kalahari. It has a straight bole and a broad crown and is often found in linear groves about 200 m wide, reaching across the flattened crests of the northern Kalahari's ancient dunes. The trees are widely separated so that a grove, often as large as 60 000 ha in extent, is a delightfully spacious and pleasant place to visit. This is perhaps as well, for the Bushmen spend a great deal of their time in the groves, gathering the mongongo nut.[23] The nut is very rich in protein and has a high level of natural fats. They are harvested from April right through to September and are used in a variety of ways. The fruit is cooked and the outer skin thrown away. A porridge or soup can be made from the flesh which has a pleasant, aromatic flavour and is often sweet, thanks to the high sugar content. The kernel of the nut is very tasty and can be eaten raw or roasted; it is not unlike a cashew nut. In dry years the Bushmen in whose area the trees occur depend heavily upon them as a mainstay in their vegetable diet.

The value of these nuts as a food resource has been recognised for some time. Several attempts have been made to exploit them commercially. From 1911 to 1914 the Germans exported about 2 000 tonnes a year from the Kalahari sands in northern Namibia. In 1916 similar amounts were exported to England for the manufacture of margarine. In the end, however, the project proved not to be viable and the trees have since been left alone.[24] They are of vital importance to some indigenous people and, in their enormous groves, are particularly beautiful. One is thankful that the densest

concentrations of these trees are located in some of the most remote regions of the Kalahari, where their isolation may help preserve their status and ensure that they continue to be available to those who need them most.

Another example of one of the Kalahari's rather unusual plants is the grapple plant or 'Devil's Claw' (Harpagophytum procumbens). The grapple is essentially a weed which shows a preference for disturbed areas and grows throughout the Kalahari sands. It consists of a number of tendrils, 1 to 2 m long, which radiate from a central underground tuber. They bear a fruit which illustrates a most unusual mechanism for seed dispersal. The seeds are contained in an oval, flattened pod, roughly 8 by 5 cm. Around the edges of the pod, when it is green, project a number of short, abruptly truncated stems about 7 cm in length. As the seed pod dries, the stems curl, twist and harden. The small fleshy protrusions become vicious hooks and barbs.

Toughened by the sun, the curled barbs stand proud above the pod, pointing slightly downwards towards its centre, waiting for some luckless animal to pass. When it does, and accidently steps upon the seed, its foot or hoof slips neatly between the curled stems – and cannot easily be withdrawn again. Usually, the pod is crushed and disintegrates, the seeds are widely – and very efficiently – dispersed and the animal continues on its way. Sometimes, however, the 'Devil's Claw' hangs on, painfully, to the hoof of the animal. The seed pod does not disintegrate and, once the wound festers, the animal dies. I know of springbok that have met their end this way. Occasionally, a grapple plant will catch one's shoe and the difficulty in removing it is enough to convince one of the effectiveness of this plant's method of seed dispersal.

The storage roots of the grapple plant, the tubers, can be harvested and they contain the raw material for a number of medicines and drugs used in the treatment of such human ailments as arthritis, and disorders of the stomach, gall-bladder and kidneys, as well as for the cure and relief of gall-stones, atherosclerosis, diabetes and menstruation problems.[25] The medicinal properties of the plant have been recognised for many years and it was harvested in Namibia long before its presence in Botswana's Kalahari was discovered. Inadequate control over harvesting, however, has resulted in the plant's scarcity in that country today and in some districts it has virtually been exterminated.

When organised exploitation began in the southern Kalahari in Botswana, it was hoped that careful farming methods would avoid this problem, a vain hope as it turned out. Grapple plant is a cash crop. Rural dwellers locating plants near their villages are encouraged to remove a portion of the tubers, which are dried and sold. Often the cash received is the harvester's only income. Under these circumstances, it is hardly surprising that the permit system, established to control off-take, breaks down. Too many tubers are taken from a single plant, which then dies. Control in the remote Kalahari is very difficult and in the past few years, the number of plants in certain areas has noticeably diminished. The Tsabong district was already quite denuded of the grapple before controls came into effect,[26] and it rather looks as if the story of Namibia is being repeated. Yet its contribution is important. In one district alone, over 600 people were employed in gathering grapple tubers and Botswana currently exports some 15 to 20 tonnes of the dried roots to Germany. This injects about P60 000 into the country's economy. Research into commercial exploitation of this plant is continuing and there will surely come a day when it is actively cultivated. The important short-term goal, however, is to prevent over-collection, not, one fears, an easy task.

The vegetation of the Kalahari is varied and interesting for its diversity and for the ways in which it has adapted to this extremely harsh environment. Only a few examples have been examined here but the list of other, equally fascinating plants is a long one. Increasingly, man is invading the Kalahari. His ways are often wasteful and destructive, unintentionally so, perhaps, but devastating nevertheless. It is, of course, the vegetation that suffers. The grass is consumed by his stock and trees used for hut-poles, fence-posts or fuel. One can but hope that, as a species, we will have learnt to respect our environment and to treat it with the care it deserves before it is too late.

## REFERENCES

1.  Pole Evans, I B. 'Notes on the Genus *Terfezia*; A Truffle from the Kalahari.' In *Transactions of the Royal Society of South Africa*. Vol 7, Part 2, 1918, pp 117-18
2.  Gunn, M and Codd, L E. *Botanical Exploration of Southern Africa*. Cape Town: A A Balkema, 1981, p 279
3.  Ackerman, L G J, Van Wyk, P J and Du Plessis, L M. 'Some Aspects of the Composition of the Kalahari Truffle or N'abba'. In *South African Food Review*, October 1975, p 145
4.  White, R. Personal communication, August 1984
5.  Coates Palgrave, K. *Trees of Southern Africa*. Cape Town: C Struik, 1981, pp 185-6
6.  Bothma, J du P. 'Shepard's Tree: a Shady Haven for Strange Creatures'. In *Custos*, Vol 11, No 10, January 1983, pp 22-3
7.  Bothma, J du P. 'There's no End to the Shepard's Tree'. In *Custos*, Vol 11, No 9, December 1982, pp 17-21
8.  Hardy, D. Personal communication, May 1984
9.  Smith, P. Personal communication, December 1984
10. Wickens, G E. 'The Baobab – Africa's Upside-down tree'. In *Kew Bulletin*, Vol 37 (2), 1982, pp 173-209
11. Palmer, E and Pitman, N. *Trees of Southern Africa, Vol 2*. Cape Town: A A Balkema, 1973, p 1466
12. Mogg, A O D. Trees in South Africa. January – March, 1950, p 14
13. Guy, G L. '*Adansonia digitata* and its Rate of Growth in Relation to Rainfall in South Central Africa'. In *Rhodesia Scientific Association*, Vol 54, Part 2, November 1970, p 70
14. Lilly, M A. *An Assessment of the Dendrochronological Potential of Indigenous Tree Species in South Africa*. Dept of Geography and Environmental Studies, Occasional Paper No 18, University of the Witwatersrand, 1977, pp 61-7
15. Mogg, A O D. Op cit
16. Wickens, G E. Op cit, p 184
17. Van Wyk, P. 'Raintrees – Fact or Fancy?' In *Custos*, Vol 2, No 5, April 1973, pp 34-7
18. Moss, H and Taylor, F W. *The Potential for Commercial Utilisation of Indigenous Plants and Insects in Botswana*. Vol 2. Ministry of Commerce and Industry, Government of Botswana, Gaborone, Botswana, pp 159-62

19. Van Voorthuizen, E G. 'The Mopane Tree'. In
    *Botswana Notes and Records,* Vol 8, 1976,
    pp 227-30
20. Coates Palgrave, K. Op cit, p 458
21. Moss, H and Taylor, F W. Op cit, p 33
22. De Klerk, W A and Watson, T G 'Baboons and
    Marulas'. In *Custos,* Vol 3, No 8, pp 33-7
23. Lee, R B. 'Mongongo: the Ethnography of a
    Major Wild Food Resource'. In *Ecology of Food
    and Nutrition,* Vol 2, 1973, pp 307-321

24. Vahrmeijer, J. *Ricinodendron rautanenii*
    Schinz, Manketti. Southern Africa plants
    No 4463,000-0010 (1976). Botanical Re-
    search Institute, Pretoria, South Africa
25. Tietema, T. *The Grapple Plant.* Unpublished
    project proposal. National Institute of Re-
    search, University of Botswana, Gaborone,
    Botswana. July 1982, pp 1-7
26. Campbell, A C. Personal communication,
    March 1986

# Part 5
# People of the Sands

# 13. Crackpots, Pans and the Southern Kalahari

WHAT excites more the imagination of red-blooded, adventure-loving men than tales of exotic lost cities in far-off, romantic and unknown places? Perhaps the idea appeals to some inner need to explore and discover for oneself. Or perhaps, in an age of microscopes and high technology, where adventure demands money and specialised skills, it is the old-fashioned 'blood, sweat and tears' which appeals. With satellites peering into every corner of the globe and professional cartographers filling in all those blank spaces on maps once illustrated with puffing cherubim, curiously imagined monsters and precious little else, the unknown is being taken away from us – and there are those who mourn its passing.

The lure of adventure seems to be missing in society today. Those exciting stories we remember from our youth, of lost continents, savage tribes, steaming jungles and barbaric empires, are all things of the past. I suppose we simply know too much now and tales of that nature somehow lack credibility. But the need for such stimulation must persist, as the story of the lost city of the Kalahari plainly shows. In a period of thirty-three years, twenty-six separate expeditions were launched in search of it, others have followed since and it remains a topic of conversation to this day.

In 1886 a gentleman by the name of G A Farini, otherwise known as William Leonard Hunt, published in England an account of his journey of exploration through the Kalahari. He had been accompanied by his photographer son, Lulu, and for five and a half months, in 1885, they had travelled from Cape Town to Lake Ngami and back. During the course of their travels they discovered what Farini claimed was a ruined city in the Kalahari. He described it as follows:

... beside a long line of stone which looked like the Chinese Wall after an earthquake, and which, on examination, proved to be the ruins of quite an extensive structure, in some places buried beneath the sand, but in others fully exposed to view. We traced the remains for nearly a mile, mostly a heap of huge stones, but all flat-sided, and here and there with the cement plainly visible between the layers. The top row of stones were worn away by the weather and the drifting sands, some of the uppermost ones curiously rubbed on the underside and standing out like a centre table on one short leg. The general outline of this wall was in the form of an arc, inside which lay at intervals of about forty feet apart a series of heaps of masonry in the shape of an oval or an obtuse ellipse, about a foot and a half deep ... some of these heaps were cut out of solid rock, others were formed of more than one piece of stone, fitted together very accurately ... (we) found that where the sand had protected the joints they were quite perfect ... On digging down nearly in the middle of the arc, we came upon a pavement about twenty feet wide, made of large stones. The outer stones were long ones, and lay at right angles to the inner ones. This pavement was intersected by another similar one at right angles, forming a Maltese cross, in the centre of which at one time must have stood an altar, column, or some

157

sort of monument, for the base was quite distinct, composed of loose pieces of fluted masonry. Having searched for hieroglyphics or inscriptions, and finding none, Lulu took several photographs and sketches . . .[1]

His report having aroused some interest in Europe, Farini was asked to address the Royal Geographic Society and, in his paper to them, he gave a slightly different version of his discovery.

> . . . we came across an irregular pile of stones that seemed in places to assume the shape of a wall, and on closer examination we traced what had evidently once been a huge walled enclosure, elliptical in form and about . . . a mile in length. The masonry was of a cyclopean character; here and there the gigantic square blocks still stood on each other . . . Near the base of the ruined walls were oval shaped rocks, hollowed out, some composed of one solid stone and others of several pieces joined together. These peculiar basin-shaped ovals were regularly distributed every few yards around the entire ellipse. In the middle was a kind of pavement of long narrow square blocks neatly fitted together, forming a cross, in the centre of which was what seemed to be a base for either a pedestal or a monument. We unearthed a broken column, a part of which was in a fair state of preservation, the four flat sides being fluted . . . The approximate latitude and longitude of this remarkable relic of antiquity were about 23,5 °S. lat. and 21,5 °E. long., near the tropic of Capricorn.[2]

After the publication of his book, his address to the Royal Geographic Society and an address to a similar society in Germany, Farini and the subject of his lost city seemed to slip into quiet quiescence. They might never have been remembered, had it not been for Professor E H L Schwarz of Rhodes University in South Africa, the same man whose wild imaginings gave Southern Africa the Schwarz Scheme in

the Okavango (see Chapter 7). Drawing attention, in 1923, to Farini's work and perhaps lending it some credibility by association with his own name, his interest inspired interest in others and the age of lost city expeditions began.

No one was ever able to prove that the lost city existed but some of the expeditions, and their results, give a fascinating insight into human nature. Courage, persistence, dogged stubbornness and wilful fabrication are all illustrated in the more than forty attempts, formal and informal, which were made to find the elusive city.

Albert Albath set off into the Kalahari in 1942, accompanied only by a donkey, its foal, his .22 rifle and twelve rounds of ammunition. It was said that he was seeking Farini's city but others, less charitable perhaps, thought he might have been avoiding internment, for he was a German, then living in South West Africa. Incredibly, he survived for two months, but not without great hardship. His rifle was hopelessly inadequate to supply him with food and he was eventually compelled to shoot the foal with his second-last round. The dried meat kept him going and when he could find no water (it was fairly plentiful for the recent rains had been good) he drank the donkey's milk. Finally he returned to the dry bed of the Nossob River and there, before being picked up by a rare passing car, he faced the last adventure of his extraordinary escapade. Finding a water-hole in the riverbed, he was denied access by a face to face encounter with an angry lion. He realised that his last round would have been quite ineffective against it and he could not bear the thought of offering his faithful donkey in sacrifice. In desperation he took the only remaining course of action – as loudly as he could, he screamed at the lion to go away. It turned tail and fled! [3]

In 1948 François Balsan, the well-known French explorer, walked 280 km through the most arid and inhospitable part of the Kalahari's southern region, searching for the lost city. He was alone but for two guides and some pack animals and completed what must have been a most arduous journey in just eight days. In 1951, this time leading the best equipped and most expensive expedition ever to search for the city, he combed the area again – but the 'Panhard-Capricorn expedition' found nothing of Farini's ruins.

Even governments were not above the lure of lost cities, and a South African Air Force Dakota officially completed an aerial search of 4 million ha in 1949. As failure followed failure it seemed not to deter successive attempts but rather, such is human nature, to encourage them. In the more imaginative minds, despite the paucity of Farini's description, the city began to assume its own identity. It became a desert terminus for Berber traders, built in Moorish style, providing a market-place for the exchange of exotic goods from firearms to ivory, glass beads to Bushman girls. By the 1960s expeditions were leaving from South Africa at a rate of three a year.[4]

Of course, there were also those whose reports, unwittingly perhaps, provided just the right amount of encouragement that others were waiting for – the air force pilot who actually saw the city when flying over the Kalahari; the geologist who also found it, but lost it again in a sandstorm; the police patrol, bedding down in a sandstorm, who saw the ruins before them, only to have them disappear again in the night, following another storm. Some reports strained the imagination. Mr G H Raubenheimer said he'd photographed the ruins, which were of Arabic origin. He described a temple with traces of ebony and gold and boasted of an Arabic parchment he possessed – the world never got to share his finds with him. Mr L S du Plessis was fortunate enough to find not only Farini's lost city, but two others as well! He never revealed the whereabouts of the two new finds, however, nor of Farini's city, which he described as being underground with curse-protected treasure vaults and ancient links with Atlantis.[5]

And so the lost city remains a mystery to all those who have tried to find it. Did it ever exist at all? To answer that question we need to meet Farini himself and consider an excellent analytical work produced by Dr A J Clement.

Farini was born William Leonard Hunt in 1839. Show business was his life. Acrobat and entertainer, he made his living in the early years by his wits. In 1864, at the age of twenty-five, he gained some fame by walking across the Niagara Falls on a tightrope. By 1884 he was established with a show in London for which he imported such exotic items as pygmies ('Dwarf Earthmen from the Interior of Africa') and whales. The show's star turns included 'Stalking the Lion' and 'Exciting Torture Dances over War Captives'. What inclination, if any, such a person might have had to invent a tale of a lost city can only be left to our imagination.

Dr A J Clement, in *The Kalahari and its Lost City*, meticulously analyses Farini's reports and his conclusions place a question mark over the existence of the ruins at all.[6] His evidence is convincing and exhaustive and is based on a long list of inaccuracies and inexplicable statements made by Farini. Farini said he spent 255 days in the Kalahari, yet Union Castle Line steamship bookings show that he was only in Southern Africa for 175 days. Working from Farini's own reports, the time taken up in preparation, getting to the Kalahari and back to Cape Town, as well as the rest periods he described, left our showman/ explorer with only 61 days in which to cover the route he claimed. To have done so by ox-wagon would have meant travelling an impossible 80 km a day. No unretouched photographs of the ruins are in existence today, yet Lulu proved himself elsewhere on the journey to be a very competent photographer.

It has also been suggested that, on his way through Kimberley in 1885, Farini secured the personal notes of a Mr D D Pritchard and that he copied these extensively in his own work, using them to support his claims to have visited places that he had in fact not been to at all. Pritchard was a mining engineer in the service of Cecil John Rhodes, who undertook a journey through the Kalahari and South West Africa in the 1870s. His notes include a list of supplies carried on his journey, in which mention was made of a theodolite. Farini's list is identical – except for the surveying instrument. Farini, who had no known geological background, observes in his book how a particular place, Tunobis, had risen in elevation by 3 m since 1851. Without an instrument to measure this fact, it is curious to know how it came into his possession – and even more curious when Pritchard makes that very observation in his own notes.[7]

The case against Farini looks grim and it seems almost certain that he misled all who listened to him, as his directions and descriptions are too vague to be comprehensible. Was there, then, nothing at all in this tale? Was it a figment of his imagination or did something inspire his showman's propensity to exaggerate and indulge in a flight of fancy? There are some that think this was so and many believe that the source of that inspiration was a place called Eierdop Koppies (Egg-shell Hills). These hills are to the south of the Nossob River, not to the north of it where Farini located his ruins, but they are well within the range of the travelling that he could possibly have done, even within the constraints that Clement has shown existed.

I have been to these hills myself and there is no doubt that at first sight they look remarkably like a ruined city on a vast scale. To reach them one passes across several large pans, set in hilly country. The track then winds up through the hills into increasingly rocky ground until, when the crest is reached, Farini's city stands, for one brief moment, in front of you. It is only a moment for, despite the illusion, one quickly realises that it is an entirely natural feature. The boulders are black, rectangular and, indeed, 'cyclopean'. They sit, several high in places, one atop another, some forming 'walls' which run for long distances. In other parts the boulders are ranged one behind the other, climbing the steep hillside in neatly ordered ranks, so that the impression of a ruined wall is heightened. Upon the flat top there are many curious wind-carved, rocky features, some of which closely resemble pedestals. The soil is not sand, but rock, and nowhere did I see anything that looked like an area of paving. However, the hills are very extensive and I cannot deny that such a thing exists or that Farini saw it – if indeed he ever went there at all.

Of mortar and cement I saw no sign, but a hard, white deposit on some of the rocks was quite common, although there was nothing about it to suggest it being placed there by human hand.

The rock is dolorite, which was forced up from within the molten interior of the earth during the period of Karoo vulcanism some 140 – 220 million years ago. Penetrating and infiltrating the overlying layers of sedimentary rock, the molten dolorite forced its way between the sedimentary bedding planes or up through existing cracks. During cooling, the rock typically shrinks and cracks along vertical and horizontal lines of weakness. In time the softer sedimentary rocks are worn away and it is into the exposed cracks that rainwaters flow. Erosion follows and weathering produces rock patterns that do look curiously like massive stone walls. Exposed boulders, especially on the crests of plateau heights, are subject to undercutting from sandblasting, which is always more pronounced nearer ground level, and in this way table-like structures are easily formed. The white deposit is a calcium carbonate and it is derived from weathering of the calcium in chemicals contained within the dolorite.[8]

This, then, is some of the evidence for and against Farini's lost city. Did he really find it and fail to log its position accurately? If he did, why did he never return to it? Was it just a figment of his imagination, inspired by the intriguing rock formations at Eierdop Koppies? We will never know. There is no doubt that the gravest suspicion has been cast upon Farini's claims and years of search in the sprawling Kalahari have produced not one iota of proof. Nevertheless the legend has lingered for nearly a hundred years. I suspect for some it lingers still and I doubt that we have heard the last of the lost city of the Kalahari.

Unless one is following an old and well-known route or employs the services of a guide, navigation in the flat, featureless Kalahari can present major difficulties, as it undoubtedly did to every one of the lost city's seekers. Maps proliferated but they were all based on dead reckoning and had to be used by the same method. The usual features, such as mountains, hills, rivers, streams and valleys, by means of which maps are read, are absent and there is little hope of comparing a physical location with some point on the map to confirm your precise position. Even with the advent of aerial photography, the problems of off-road navigation remain, as dead reckoning must still be relied upon. For this reason, explorers of the Kalahari have made much use of guides and traditional routes.

These routes have been established over several hundred years and, typically, follow the only features which are in any way distinctive, namely the salt pans of the Kalahari. They are ubiquitous throughout the sands but only in the southern Kalahari are they so numerous, so large and impressive. They become the focal point of life in this arid area, a place of departure and of arrival, a nucleus for cells of human existence and the anchor points by which a web of human occupation can spread across the endless wastes.

So far as I know, the pans of the Kalahari have never been counted. It would be a difficult task, for there are many thousands of them and the range in size and shape is great. A typical pan might be round or oval, a kilometre or more across, with a floor of smooth, hard clay, quite firm enough to take the weight of a vehicle, and upon which, mostly, nothing grows at all. When the rains fall the pans, which form a natural drainage basin for a sometimes considerable area, may fill with water and this is what makes them play such an important part in man's occupation of the Kalahari. The water can remain for several months, providing an oasis for animal life and affording it the opportunity to regain condition and prepare for the long, waterless months ahead. Man quickly found that by digging deep wells at the edges of a pan, he could often find supplies of fresh water sufficient to sustain him and his stock throughout the year. In this way a settlement would be established and, if the water supply was reliable and the location suitable, a village would grow and, in time, a small town emerge. I think, without exception, all the towns and villages of the Kalahari are located near major pans.

The depression area of the largest of the Kalahari's pans, at Ukwi, is more than 16 km$^2$ in extent, but most pans are between 2 and 8 km$^2$. Most commonly, they are excavated entirely on Kalahari sands, although in some, where the covering of sand is thin, rocks are exposed. Most, however, are not associated with rocks,

which may lie at depths of 25 to 30 m below the surface. The occurrence of such a large number of pans, concentrated as they are in a relatively small area, has naturally given rise to much speculation as to their origins.

A prominent feature of pan distribution in the Kalahari is their apparent concentration along a barely perceptible ridge which strikes north-westwards from the vicinity of Lobatse, across the Kalahari into Namibia, and which serves as a watershed, dividing this part of the Kalahari into two separate hydrological basins. Some have suggested that the pans are the remnants of ancient drainage lines, that they are sand choked, fossilised drainage systems. Others dispute this and have used sophisticated statistical techniques to show that, although the pans are locally clustered, they form no aligned groupings and that their distribution is random. There seems to be no relationship between the location of pans and the old drainage links with the Okwa or Molopo/ Nossob river systems of today.

Still the greatest puzzle is how these pans originated – and here there is little agreement. The most common theory presupposes the existence of a natural depression, created or maintained and enlarged by wind deflation, and into which seasonal waters flow and fine detritus accumulates. Under the hard, grey-white surface of the pan lie deep layers of a greasy, grey-green, calcerous, saline and sometimes sandy clay. Chemically, this clay is low in alumina and high in silica and alkalis. The constantly evaporating waters lead to a steady collection of salts and these, in turn, attract game which digs and paws at the surface of the pan, exposing concentrations of the salt, a necessary part of their diet. The constant passage of hooves pounds and reduces the surface clays to a powder, which are then carried away by the winds. Sandy soils have a low mineral content and often the pans are the only source of salt for wild animals. Salt licks are therefore common in pans, and game trails will lead directly to them. They are often near the centre, at the lowest point, where the salt is most concentrated. Sometimes there will be a heavily trampled area where up to a metre of soil has been scraped away and eaten.

Pans represent a highly dynamic system. Wind and falling rain sweeps dust, sand and organic waste onto the surface. The flow of water tends to sort these materials so that the coarser materials are left at the pan's edge, while the minerals and finer substances end up at the lowest point. Animals churn and pound the surface clay and the wind sweeps it on again. It is this action of the wind which forms the remarkable dunes that are typical of almost every significant pan.

On the south or south-western side of almost all of the Kalahari's larger pans is a conspicuous dune feature. Typically, close examination will reveal that this comprises two dunes and they are quite unlike any of the other dunes which are so abundant throughout the Kalahari. Both are crescent shaped. The outer one may be anything from 20 to 30 m high and between 1 and 1,5 km from the edge of the pan itself. The inner dune is smaller and closer to the pan, usually not more than 10 to 20 m high and 5 to 8 m from the pan. Sometimes the dunes merge, but mostly they are separated by a shallow depression. The regular occurrence of this feature, so faithfully repeated at pan after pan, with the dunes nearly always in the same compass direction, is not accidental and considerable research has been carried out to discover why this should be so.

Generally, it is now believed both dunes are formed by wind and their location reflects the direction from which it came at a time when winds were stronger, the Kalahari was more like a true desert and the sand was much more mobile than it is today. Nick Lancaster, who has spent a great deal of time studying these pans and their dune formations, believes that the outer, larger dune was formed during the original deflation of the pan surface.[9] As the size and height of the dune increases, it 'moves' downwind, creating the curved, crescent shape which is so typical of the dunes we see today. The inner dune was formed at a more recent time and is the product of a very slightly different wind direction.

The material of the two dunes is different. The outer one typically consists of the red to yellow, wind-blown aeolian sand, while the inner is more grey in colour, and its silty sands are derived from deposits on the pan's surface, after it has been formed. The inner sands are not as well sorted, with as much as 20 per cent silt and clay-sized particles.[10] From this information it is concluded that there have been at least two distinct periods of pan formation, the first more active and prolonged than the second. Between them was a very wet period, during which the pans were filled, possibly throughout the year, and when, over time, the clays were deposited.

There is more evidence to support this idea. Many if not most of the pans have about their edges considerable deposits of calcrete (see Chapter 6) and at some, notably Ukwi, Khakhea and Sekoma pans, there are deep notches, obviously cut by wave action, in these low cliffs, suggesting water levels 3 to 5 m above the present pan surface and quantities of water two to three times those of the present. The sequence of deposits within the pans suggests gradual desiccation. Research at the now dry Lake Alexander, near the south-eastern edge of the Kalahari and sufficiently close to it to be a good indicator of climate, has given some idea of how much wetter the wet periods might have been, when the pans were full. Once this lake was 44 km$^2$ in extent and to sustain a lake of that size about 16 000 years ago would have needed rainfall 125 per cent of the present level, assuming that the temperatures would have been about 6° lower than they are today. Given the same temperatures in the Kalahari, rainfall of twice today's level would have been necessary to turn the pans into permanent lakes.[11]

The game of the Kalahari depends heavily upon its pans. Not only do pans provide the only source of surface water, albeit for only a few months of the year, but they also yield essential salts and, because of the moisture that collects about them, offer green grazing for longer than anywhere else in the Kalahari. Vegetation around a pan is typically zoned and reflects the plants' different levels of toleration for salinity and inundation by water. As a general rule, the closer one is to the pan, the higher the salt content in the soil. Thus it is that usually only grasses are found at the edges. As one moves away from the pan, so low shrubs, bushes and finally trees appear.

Apart from the Stone Age inhabitants of the Kalahari, man has only begun to make use of the pans in comparatively recent times. Among the first to settle on the eastern and southern edges of the Kalahari was a sub-group of the Sotho-Tswana people who, because of their close proximity to the Kalahari, were called the Kgalagadi. These people, although of the same tribal group as the Tswana, were considered by the latter to be inferior, and when the Tswana began to expand eastwards towards the Kalahari, they forced the Kgalagadi into the arid lands to the west. By 1750 the Kgalagadi were well established in the Kalahari, using the pans to provide seasonal water for themselves and their cattle. The village of Lehututu was settled by then and within fifty years there were large villages at Hukuntsi, Tshane and many other places.[12] To begin with, the number of cattle held in these Kalahari villages was small, but over the years stock increased.

Research has shown that human occupation has brought a number of significant and far-reaching changes to inhabited pans. Typically, there is a reduction in perennial grass cover and an increase in the number of shrubs. Large villages result in the disappearance of wildlife in their vicinity, although in the smaller and temporary villages, wildlife and livestock do mix. Once almost the sole users of the Kalahari's pans, which, with their water, salt and grazing, were vital to their survival, most of the wildlife has, since man's arrival, been denied access and consequently its total range has been reduced. As we will see in later chapters, this has had a telling effect on overall numbers.

The unfavourable impact of man in the Kalahari is long-lasting. His abuse of the fragile environment through lack of awareness of proper range management techniques, leaves almost indelible scars. For example, the pan of Mabuasehube, in the southern Kalahari, was abandoned as a settlement in 1948 but even now, nearly forty years later, the expert eye can still see the effects in the highly modified appearance of the vegetation. Dr Graham Child, an FAO ecologist working with the Department of Wildlife and National Parks in Botswana, was able to illustrate the depressive effects on the vegetation of human occupation around two of the Kalahari's pans, after twenty-five and thirty-eight years respectively.[13]

The southern portion of the Kalahari, strictly speaking, begins on the north bank of the Orange River, which is one of the provincial boundaries of South Africa. The area of Kalahari sands to the north of it and between it and Botswana's Molopo River is known as the Gordonia District of the Northern Cape (see colour map of Southern Kalahari). Many people, when visualising the Kalahari, tend to think of it as occupying central Botswana, and yet Gordonia is every bit as much a part of the Kalahari. Indeed, in terms of its sand and sand dunes, low rainfall and sparse vegetation, it more nearly approaches a true desert than almost any region of the Kalahari further north. It would not be appropriate to talk of the southern regions of the Kalahari without describing this rather unusual and sometimes forgotten area, and its warm, generous farming community.

Prior to the turn of the century Gordonia seems to have been largely uninhabited by any settled community and was considered to be something of a 'no man's land'. Bushmen had certainly been living in the area before that time and this has been confirmed by the occasional discovery of a secret Bushman water cache. Bushmen are renowned for their foresight in building up emergency supplies of water at remote parts of their ranges. To do so, they carefully pierce and empty the contents of fresh ostrich eggs. The shell is then filled with water and the hole plugged with a specially shaped piece of wood or length of twisted grass. A number of these eggs will be cached together, buried in the sand against future use. The shifting nature of the sand sometimes lays bare these hoards and it was in this way that some in Gordonia were discovered, the water long since dried and gone, though, and only grains of sand in its place.

The first serious attempt at settlement followed the Anglo-Boer War when many of the Coloured people who had fought with the British were given farms in the area. It was at that time quite undeveloped. There were no proper roads, no electricity, no water, nor services of any kind. The only town of importance was far away on the Orange River at Upington. In such circumstances, and probably with little capital or expertise, the new farms got off to a shaky start. Within a few years most had changed hands as the Coloured people sold out and Afrikaans farming families took their places. In those days farms were sold for as little as one shilling a morgen (about 2 acres or ,85 of a hectare).

Despite the low rainfall, the succulent vegetation offers good grazing and the dry conditions reduce the problems of wetter climes, so that ticks and parasite infestations are less troublesome than elsewhere. The early settlers relied almost totally upon dorper and merino sheep and they also raised goats, donkeys and some cattle. Each homestead had to be entirely self-sufficient and self-reliance was the keynote for survival.

The donkey's role was particularly important. It replaced the horse, which so frequently succumbed to horse-sickness which was rife in the area, as well as the ox. Most of the oxen had been killed off by rinderpest and the local people were too poor to replace them. The donkey drove drilling rigs and water pumps, pulled ploughs, levelled roads and provided pack and passenger transport. The return journey by donkey cart to the only market-place, at Upington, took a full month. The donkey's part in the development of Gordonia has not gone unnoticed, and in the 1980s the municipality of Upington set plans in motion to raise a statue to the animal. Piet Venter, the man behind the project, believes it will be the only one of its kind in the world.[14]

Life in those early years was not easy. What wheat could be grown, and it was often planted on the moist pan surfaces after the rains, was threshed on stone floors by donkeys or horses walking over it. Winnowing was done by hand, in the wind. In the days before drilling machinery, wells were dug by hand too and some families used to specialise in this work. Dirk and

Johannes Human were well known for their skills and could dig down 30 m or more, lining their wells with stones as they went. Falling stone and sand were a hazard, however, and it was a risky business.[15]

Pedlars in motor lorries were a feature of the time. Long before the first roads were built they used to nose their way along the donkey tracks, visiting farm after farm, trading sugar, flour and household necessities for wool, skins and produce. Itinerant speculators would buy cattle and sheep and herd their stock back to the markets at Upington. In those days prices were low and a full fleece of merino wool would fetch sixpence, and a whole sheep a pound. Gertie Stadler, who has lived and taught in the area for almost all her life, remembers the school where she first started teaching in 1930.[15] There were no benches and the children sat on planks supported by empty four-gallon petrol tins. Some of the children had not been to school before and started at the age of fifteen. Gertie recalls a newly married couple who came to Upington from Kuruman – for £10 they purchased a saddle and all the groceries they needed for a month!

Farm produce had to be of the type that could be stored easily and represented a high value in a small volume, so that it could be moved without difficulty. It was for this reason that wool sheep were so popular but sand in the wool downgraded the product and the early farmers were not very successful. It took the coming of the karakul sheep to change the situation.

The same creature which in the Middle East produces astrakhan, the karakul had been introduced into South West Africa some years before and a highly protected but burgeoning industry had been established. The protectionist laws prohibited the sale or movement of karakul stock out of South West Africa but, as both buyer and seller were willing participants, the karakul began to spread. By way of the boot of a car, the first seven karakuls appeared in Gordonia in 1934. Here they flourished and it is not an exaggeration to say that the whole economy of Gordonia has been built upon these animals. Initially the pelts were sold in Germany, but after the war the chief market-place was London where it has

remained ever since. In recent years fluct-
uating prices and more attractive altern-
atives have drawn interest away from karakuls, while improved roads in Gordonia
and efficient transport have made beef and
mutton production more viable.

Today the farming community of Gordonia is well established, wealthy and
successful. Land prices have risen in eighty
years from a shilling a morgen to more
than R28. These achievements demonstrate
how productive the Kalahari can be if good
agricultural techniques are employed.
There is no doubt that abuse of the grazing
resource has also taken place here, as it
has elsewhere in the Kalahari, but strict
controls are now enforced. Carrying capacities are established for every individual
farm and are regularly reassessed. The
range-lands support far less stock than is
the case further north, with anything between 22 and 35 ha per single head of
livestock and between 4,5 and 6 ha per
sheep, depending on the type and quality
of land.[16] Undoubtedly, some of the success
is attributable to heavy government sub-
sidies, a typical example of which is a
massive irrigation scheme which is currently being installed. At a cost of some
R12 to 14 m, 480 000 ha on 52 farms are
being supplied with water from the Orange
River.[17] Nevertheless, it seems clear that
the Kalahari can be productive, given sufficient time, effort, skills and capital.

The Molopo River flows in a great curve
from the east to the south and separates
Botswana from the northern Cape. It is
contained in a huge valley, evidence of its
powerful flow in former times, but today it
remains dry and has never been known in
this century to flow its full length to the
point where it pours into the Orange River.
There have been exceptional years when
the Molopo and its major tributaries, the
Kuruman, Nossob and Auob, have all flooded. The year 1934 was one and 1976 was
another, but in neither was the volume of
water sufficient to breach the shifting sand
dunes which now block the river's lower
course and eventual exit to the Orange.

Textbooks have it that a large pan known
as Abiquasputs is where the Molopo flow
ends, but this is not so. In both those flood
years it went further. In 1934 it reached
the settlement of Noenieput, 27 km downstream. In 1976 it reached Springbok Vlei,
15 km from Abiquasputs. On those rare
occasions when the floods do come, life in
the Kalahari changes dramatically.

Christo Botha and his wife have a lovely
farmhouse right on the very edge of Abiquasputs and they well remember the seasons following the 1976 flood. Usually the
pan stretches dry and dusty all about them,
to the foot of the rocky hills that rise in the
west, in Mier Country. As the Molopo came
down that year, the pan filled and soon,
instead of grey columns of swirling whirlwinds, a great sea appeared. It had taken
from April to May to fill. At the centre it
was 3 to 4 m deep and they were even able
to water-ski. The flooded area was far greater, but they had nearly 5 km$^2$ in which they
could safely use a power-boat. The water
stood for more than two years before it
finally dried and soaked away. When it
did, millions of fish were left to suffocate
upon the surface.

The fish were an amazing phenomenon.
Nowhere along the Auob or the Nossob is
there standing water. Both the Kuruman
and the Molopo rivers start from springs,
the former from a most unusually powerful
one that delivers 20 million litres a day.
However, both, within a few kilometres of
their source, run dry and for the remainder
of their length are rivers of sand where
water only occasionally flows, and then for
only short distances. There are barbel and
carp at both sources, of the type that were
so abundant at Abiquasputs, but it seems
incredible that two such small populations
could have spawned the colossal numbers
needed to repopulate so many kilometres
of river. As the waters at Abiquasputs began to fall and the fish became more densely concentrated, food supply became critical and they would strike at almost anything, orange peel and even unbaited
hooks. In the end, of course, they could not
escape their fate and millions died in the
frothing mud as they gasped and flapped
their way to unhappy extinction.

'Mier Country' is the name given to a
district of rocky outcrops, pans and broken
stretches of Kalahari sand that lies to the
west of the Molopo as it turns south to meet
the Orange. It is in this area that Eierdop

Koppies is to be found, the possible inspiration for Farini's ruined city, and here is a most remarkable collection of names that reflect the mixed origins of the people who have lived here. Christo Botha's farm takes its name from the original Hottentot. It seems that Hottentot nomads had lived in this area before the coming of the first Coloured farmers. They called their present farm Obobogorob, a reference to the small holes dug in the pan surface by porcupines looking for water. The pronunciation of this word is beyond my understanding since it seems to bear no resemblence to the letters which make it up. Correctly said, it sounds like 'Key-bee-key-ghora'!

Clearly, at some time in the past, a surveyor of Scottish ancestry worked in the area. He gave to some of the larger pans such enchanting and evocative names as Loch Marie, Erin, Loch Mcgar, Linlithgow, Oxford and Loch Broom. But for all their stark and baking beauty they are a far cry from the gorse and bracken covered highlands of the Scottish north and I fancy that the surveyor may have been a homesick man.

Far away from the controls and regulations of the authorities, life in the southern Kalahari was not without a certain amount of lawlessness – most of it fairly harmless and regarded with understanding when brought to officialdom's attention. Klaas Brink was one of the great early characters of the area. He was a man who found the lion, across the Molopo in what was then British Bechuanaland, quite irresistible. His hunting activities were well known and policemen from the remote station at Witdraai, in Gordonia, would set out regularly on the weary task of finding Klaas to hand him yet another summons for poaching. In the end a satisfactory arrangement was concluded. Since his nefarious activities frequently took him past the police station, it was agreed that the police would hold the summonses there for him – if he would be obliging enough to pop in and collect them – which he did!

Across the Molopo, in Botswana, poaching has always been difficult to control. Game being more plentiful there than in Gordonia, it was not only Klaas Brink who made the surreptitious journey over the

dry river bed. It was an attempt to bring this to a halt and to win at least one battle in the never-ending campaign against poaching, that prompted Major Nigel Bowen to announce the 'Last Parade of the Bechuanaland Camel Corps'.

Nigel Bowen was evidently another of the memorable characters of the southern Kalahari. At the time, in the early 1960s, he was District Commissioner at Tsabong and was known for his rather individualistic and 'not altogether by the book' approach to problem solving. He knew that most of his problem came from across the border but he had neither the men nor the resources to put an effective stop to it – until he thought up his grand scheme. There was then operating from Mafikeng a radio service known as Radio Molopo, which had a wide listenership on both sides of the river. The story [17] goes that on a certain day Bowen broadcast an entirely fictitious report, announcing the 'last parade of the Bechuanaland Camel Corps'. Despite surprised enquiries from the British Administration at Mafikeng and from the press, Bowen maintained the fiction and invited them along. On the appointed day two aircraft arrived at Tsabong, loaded with the press and representatives from the Bechuanaland Protectorate Administration and Information Offices. They found no one to meet them and a hot and dusty investigation on foot revealed, much to the irritation of the visitors, that the police station, the camp and the entire village were deserted, almost to a man. They waited about but finally left empty-handed, while many ominous things were said about the future of Bowen's career.

In the meantime, Bowen had taken every single available man and had stationed them at every known border crossing point between Bokspits and Werda. He had guessed, correctly as it turned out, that the southern listeners, thinking that the police would be fully occupied, would choose that day for an illegal hunting expedition. He briefed his men to allow all incoming traffic to pass freely, but anyone trying to cross the river from the north was to be stopped, searched and, if meat was found in their possession, arrested. He made a magnificent haul and spent the next few days hold-ing impromptu courts all the way along the river bank. Meat, rifles and vehicles were confiscated and all were taken to Mafikeng. There, Major Bowen, himself ex-Hobson's Horse, Indian Army, lined the offending vehicles up in a formal parade before the Secretariat and, tongue in cheek no doubt, invited Sir Peter Fawcus to review it! Nearly £200 000 was raised from the sale, which went into the Protectorate Development Fund.

This was not the only occasion Major Bo-wen held impromptu courts under the trees in the wilds of Africa. In the mid 1960s, in cooperation with the staff of the Kalahari Gemsbok National Park to the west of Tsa-bong, he carried out another anti-poaching campaign. As a result, more than sixty local inhabitants were arrested. Albeit in some-what unusual circumstances, they were all subjected to the due process of law – be-neath the spreading acacia trees in the bed of the Nossob River![18] It is also said that Bowen, who could speak several dialects of Persian, submitted for publication his own translation of *The Rubáiyát*. Some claim it was a finer work than that of Fitz-gerald but it was never published.[19]

Charlie Webb preceded Nigel Bowen as DC at Tsabong by some years. He was stationed there during the Second World War and, because of the shortage of man-power, was not allowed to volunteer for call-up to the forces. He remained instead, throughout those years, at Tsabong, where he was responsible for the police function as well as administration. Finding himself bored and frustrated, to add some spice and interest to his otherwise empty days, he took to being DC in the morning and Police Commander in the afternoon. I have been told, but have not been able to verify, that there is in the National Archives in Gaborone a considerable quantity of official correspondence between these two posi-tions. It seems that Charlie, as the Police Commander, would amuse himself by writ-ing a strongly-worded letter of complaint to the DC and send it across to the latter's office by messenger. The following morn-ing, as DC, Charlie would be furious at the lack of cooperation, understanding and goodwill exhibited by the Police and would

pen an equally strong reply![20] The corres-pondence apparently continued for several years.

Poaching in the southern Kalahari has always been a problem and has become more so recently as the game outside the protected area of the Kalahari Gemsbok National Park slowly disappears. This huge park, far larger than the better-known Kruger National Park, is equally shared between South Africa and Botswana. It is administered by South Africa and the Bo-tswana section remains purposely undevel-oped so as to provide a reservoir into which the game can retreat. It still needs to be patrolled, however, and while in the old days camels used to be used for the job, today, when poachers are equipped with fast and powerful vehicles, aircraft and four-wheel-drive trucks are employed.

Rian Labuschagne, who worked for some years in the park, told me an interesting story about some of the less professional poachers they sometimes encountered.[21] He was on a routine patrol of the Botswana side of the park with the warden, Elias Le Riche. An aircraft patrol had spotted deep wheel tracks leading into the park from Botswana and Rian's ground vehicle was directed to the scene by radio, where an extraordinary sight met their eyes. Along-side a seven-tonne truck with rock-hard tyres were fourteen exhausted Batswana, four dogs, one with a bandaged muzzle, and a dead gemsbok. There were three rifles between the fourteen men, all of which were exceedingly ancient and only one actually worked. Enquiry about the truck's tyres revealed that they had no tools, no jack and no spare wheel. The tyres had been inflated in order to reduce the risk of puncture but, in consequence, the wheels had dug deep into the soft sand. The gen-eral consensus was that they had pushed the vehicle most, if not all, of the 100 km so far travelled, accounting for their state of exhaustion.

Their somewhat inadequate fire-power restricted their choice of victim. Eventually they came across an aged gemsbok stand-ing in the shade of a tree, peacefully pass-ing away its last days. Its age and condition allowed the hunters to sneak up close to it and, from practically point-blank range (for the only working rifle was not capable of anything better), a single shot was fired, which felled the beast. Unfortunately, one of the dogs was on the other side of the animal when it was shot, and it too was struck. The bullet had gone right through the gemsbok and hit the dog in the jaw. After such an unhappy chain of events, Elias decided to dispense a very fair rough justice. The rifles and meat were confiscated, the poachers were sent packing and a letter was sent to the Botswana police at Tsabong, merely advising them of the incident.

Four generations of Le Riches have run the Kalahari Gemsbok Park since it started in 1931. Johannes Le Riche, Elias's uncle, was warden until 1934 when he, and many of the early park's staff, died of malaria which followed the great floods of that year. Johannes's brother then took over the job, 'temporarily', for the next thirty-six years, before handing over to his eldest son, Stoffel. When his brother died in 1980 Elias became warden. Poaching has always been a major problem. Elias tells a delightful story of his father whose practice it was to visit the local church every Sunday morning. His objective, however, was not devotion, but to scan the pews to see which seats were vacant and to guess who he might meet on his next anti-poaching patrol!

Before responsibility for anti-poaching patrols within the park became that of its administration, the job was done by the police at Tsabong. For this and their own patrol work, camels were extensively used. Mike Leech, who served at one time in the Bechuanaland Police and retired as a superintendent some years ago, believes that he was the last white officer to serve at Tsabong and to complete a camel patrol. It was August 1964 and he was on patrol for eighteen days, during which time his party of seven camels and five men covered over 800 km. Maps and radios were not available then and the patrol was completed successfully by a combination of common sense, guides and the reliability of the camel itself. The camel, according to Mike, is a much maligned creature. He never found them bad tempered and maintains that they were very gregarious. They were ideal for patrolling in the Kalahari's sands, comfortable, tough and much more suited than horses to the sandy terrain, the vegetation and the scarcity of water.[22]

The Botswana police still use camels today, although not as much as formerly. There are fifty-three on strength altogether and the majority are still at Tsabong.[23] They wander freely round the village but from time to time take it into their heads to go off and explore the world. In 1983 a party of tourists in the Kalahari Gemsbok Park, whilst enjoying a picnic lunch, were somewhat taken aback to see four camels walking by. Eventually the camels were tracked down by the park's staff and, in due course, were herded back to Tsabong, where it was learnt that seven camels had been missing for six months. Occasional reports of sightings suggested that they had wandered over 600 km in that time – a testament to their successful adaptation to the Kalahari.[24]

The southern Kalahari is, for me, a place of fascination. It is a region that has seen much development but, somehow, all the best of the past seems not to have been forgotten. Perhaps this is because its people have changed little and the memories live on in them today, linking the present more firmly with the past and providing a greater continuity.

## REFERENCES

1.  **Farini, G A.** *Through the Kalahari Desert.* London: Sampson Low, Marston, Searle & Rivington, 1886, **pp 357-9**
2.  **Farini, G A.** 'A Recent Journey in the Kalahari'. In *Proceedings of the Royal Geographical Society.* 2nd series, Vol 8, 1886, **p 447**
3.  **Barrow, B.** *Song of a Dry River.* Cape Town: Purnell and Sons, 1975, **pp 110-12**
4.  Ibid, **p 114**
5.  Ibid, **pp 116-17**
6.  **Clement, A J.** *The Kalahari and its Lost City.* Cape Town: Longmans, 1967, **p 145**
7.  *Comparison of the D.D. Pritchard Notes and 'Through the Kalahari Desert', 1886, by G.A. Farini.* Author unknown. Copy supplied by E. Le Riche, Kalahari Gemsbok National Park, South Africa, September 1984
8.  **Clement, A J.** Op cit, **p 150**
9.  **Lancaster, I N.** 'The Pans of the Southern Kalahari, Botswana'. In *Geographical Journal,* Vols 144-145, 1978-1979, **pp 81-98**

10. **Lancaster, I N.** 'Pans of the Southern Kalahari'. In *Botswana Notes and Records*, Vol 6, 1974, **pp 157-69**

11. **Lancaster, I N.** 'The Pans of the Southern Kalahari, Botswana'. In *Geographical Journal*, Vols 144-145, 1978-1979, **p 96**

12. **Campbell, A C.** 'Kalahari Pans, Source of Life in the Desert'. In *Botswana*, No 4 (no date). Department of Information Services, Botswana Government, Gaborone, **pp 5-11**

13. **Parris, R and Child, G.** 'The Importance of Pans to Wildlife in the Kalahari and the Effect of Human Settlement on these Areas'. In *Journal of Southern African Wildlife Management Association*, 3 (1), **pp 1-8**

14. **Venter, P.** Personal communication, September 1984

15. **Stadler, G.** Personal communication, September 1984

16. **Botha, C.** Personal communication, September 1984

17. **White, R H.** Personal communication, August 1984

18. **Le Riche, E.** Personal communication, August 1984

19. **Campbell, A C.** Personal communication, March 1986

20. **Condy, J.** Personal communication, April 1984

21. **Labuschagne, R.** Personal communication, August 1984

22. **Leech, M.** Personal communication, July 1984

23. **Selerio, M.** Personal communication, August 1984

24. **Labuschagne, R.** Op cit

# 14. Stone Age in the Sands

MANY of us are accustomed to thinking of the Stone Age, the Bronze Age and the Iron Age simply as periods of time. In a sense, they are, but it is less confusing to think of them as a way or mode of life. After all, the people who lived during those times did not use these terms to describe themselves; it is only we, many thousands of years later, who have invented labels as a handy way of referring to the past. The terms were chosen because they highlighted a particularly dominant aspect of the culture. The time element only becomes important with regard to a particular part of the world. For example, it may be that the Stone Age in Mongolia began very much later than it did in Africa but long before its beginnings in Tierra del Fuego, if it ever appeared there at all.

By accepting the 'ages' as a way of life rather than periods of time, it is easier to understand that two of these 'ages' can exist concurrently – that people of a Stone Age culture can live with and among people of a more modern Iron Age culture. This is exactly what has happened in Southern Africa, and particularly in the Kalahari.

In central and southern Africa, there was no Bronze Age – just a transition, slow in some places, quick in others, from the Stone Age to the Age of Iron, although iron was not exclusively used during the latter. Copper and other metals were also worked.

Compared with the information we have of more recent times, we know very little about the Stone Age. There are two reasons for this. First of all, archaeologists rely, almost exclusively, on material remains to help them unravel the past. The arrangement of living space is also important, but there have to be material clues to explain how it was used. So far as we can tell, Stone Age man had few durable posses-

sions and none but the most durable items has survived. Almost all that we have of the Stone Age are the stone tools that were used.

In various ways it has been possible to establish a date at which the tools were discarded. From this information, archaeologists have been able to separate the Stone Age, simply for the sake of convenience, into three distinct sections – the Early, the Middle and the Late. The distinction, of course, is arbitrary. It did not occur suddenly, nor did it occur simultaneously in all places. Once again, the references are to the people of the time and their lifestyles, as indicated by the type of tools they used.

Tools from the Early Stone Age (ESA) are easy to recognise. They are big, clumsy, heavy and of fairly limited variety. They were not hafted, but hand-held and used for hitting, digging and cutting. In Southern Africa we speak of the ESA ending about 200 000 years ago. It began, perhaps, about a million or so years before that.

The Middle Stone Age (MSA) tools display much more variety and they are smaller and better made. Occurring, mostly, between 150 000 and 50 000 years ago, they include such relatively sophisticated tools as scrapers and points for spears. This is not to say that the separate divisions of the Stone Ages represent clearly differentiated technologies. This is not the case at all. The process was an evolutionary one in which new techniques emerged, coexisted with the old and, in time, replaced them. The flowering of Stone Age technology really only came quite recently, in the Late Stone Age (LSA), which began approximately 30 000 years ago and ended, in the Kalahari regions, where it seems to have persisted for longest, only within the last 200

Ancient pottery from the edge of
Botswana's Kalahari, dated *c.* AD 400

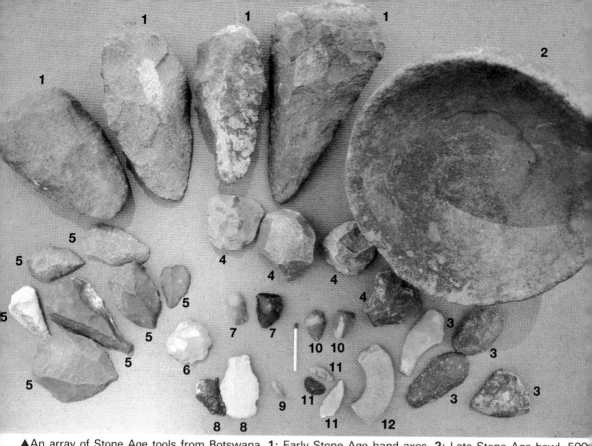

▲An array of Stone Age tools from Botswana. **1:** Early Stone Age hand axes. **2:** Late Stone Age bowl, 500 BC–AD 300. **3:** Late Stone Age scrapers, 9000 BC–AD 1700. **4:** Middle Stone Age cores. **5:** Middle Stone Age points, possibly spear heads, 150 000–50 000 BC. **6-11:** Late Stone Age tools including cores, side and end scrapers and blades. **12:** Fragment of Late Stone Age bored stone ▼Hand-made baskets awaiting sale at Etsha

mily Cooper, descendant
f Simon Cooper, Lokgwabe

▲Witsands, Northern Cape ▼Golden grass at Nxai Pan

years, or even later. This era saw the most delicately beautiful, tiny tools. Exquisitely made, minutely chipped to perfection, they included many specialised scrapers, extremely sharp blades and arrowheads.[1] It is currently accepted that LSA peoples did not make clay pots, except perhaps in the last 2 000 years when they acquired the skills from others, and they certainly did not work iron.

Who were these Stone Age people? There is no certain answer, but most experts in this part of the world agree that they were the ancestors of the modern Bushman. In other words, the Bushman, or Khoisan, as he is more properly called, is a direct descendant of Stone Age people and he and his recent forebears are the product of more than a million years of human evolution in this part of Africa. This to me is an exciting image, and it is tantalising to think that our interest has been aroused just a few hundred years too late to see man as the pure hunter and gatherer, quite untouched by modern civilisation, which he has been for most of his existence on earth.

It is also generally agreed that the Khoisan, prior to about 3 000 years ago, enjoyed possibly exclusive occupancy of the whole of southern, central and parts of eastern Africa. They lived by hunting game and gathering wild foods from the bush. In the absence of human competition, all their energies could be devoted to the single purpose of survival, at which they were most adept and, if the evidence from the Kalahari is correct, left them with time to develop an elaborate social and artistic life. There is no evidence to suggest that the Stone Age people of the Kalahari, who are known to have lived in parts of it for at least 40 000 years, were refugees or that they lived there for any other reason than that they chose to. They became an extremely adaptable people. Only as a result of increasing competition in very recent times is it likely that the Khoisan have moved into the less hospitable reaches of the Kalahari, where many are found today.

Why did the situation change? Who were the Bantu and where did they come from? There is little dispute now, among archaeologists, as to the point of origin of the proto-Bantu people. It is generally accepted that they spread through to central and southern Africa from a point in west Africa, somewhere near the Cameroons. Between 6 000 and 12 000 years ago, the Sahara Desert was a verdant, lake-studded savannah and, undoubtedly, naturally expanding populations moved into it and occupied it. Then the climate changed, and by 4 000 years ago the Sahara had turned back into the desert we know today,[2] compelling the people who had lived in it to leave. It may have been this factor that initiated the migration of proto-Bantu populations, about 3 000 BC.

Until quite recently a fairly simplistic model has been used to explain the advent of the Iron Age in Southern Africa. Basically, it says that the proto-Bantu spread eastwards from western Africa, moving around or through the Congo Basin, and made contact with the Nilotic peoples of eastern Africa. These people possessed cattle and possibly the knowledge of ironworking, which may have been transferred to the proto-Bantu. The new knowledge increased the human productivity of the proto-Bantu who continued to expand the area they occupied, but now in a southerly direction, crossing the Zambezi River, with their clay pots, iron and cattle, some time about AD 250. From that time they rapidly expanded to fill the sub-continent.

This explanation of Bantu origins in Southern Africa is no longer uncritically accepted. It is the very nature of archaeology, a dynamic and rapidly changing field, that hypotheses are constructed to explain known facts, only to be destroyed and replaced with new interpretations as new information comes to light. Criticism of this hypothesis centres on its inability to account for several important facts.

We know there were sheep in the Cape around 100 BC, and in Namibia by AD 300. For this to have happened, livestock raising must have already crossed the Zambezi by 200 or 300 BC.[3] We also know that the first Bantu pastoralists only appeared south of the Zambezi after AD 250, so how could the sheep have reached the Cape? Who took them there? The puzzle is made more complex by the occurrence of pottery in the Cape region dating from about AD 120.[4] Since pottery is one of the trade marks of Iron Age people, the model is at a loss to explain this occurrence, since, at that time, the Iron Age, pot-making people had not yet appeared in Southern Africa.

Another weakness of the model lies in the most curious fact that the 'cattle-words' used by Bantu in Southern Africa south of the Limpopo have their linguistic origins not in Nilotic or even proto-Bantu words, but in the Khoisan group of languages![5] If there are no words in your language for a particular activity which you learn from another group, experience shows that you will choose similar words to those used by the people from whom the new knowledge was gained. Why are the southern Bantu using cattle-words from Stone Age people? The conclusion seems inescapable – rather than Bantu introducing domestic stock to the Stone Age people, it may very well have been the other way round. In addition, it seems that the knowledge of pottery was not the exclusive preserve of the Bantu people, who brought it to Southern Africa. It may well be that the technology had preceded them and that the agent responsible was a hitherto over-looked, so-called Stone Age man. The evidence is slowly accumulating to suggest that the diffusion of some components of Iron Age technology had actually taken place sooner than was first thought and that the Khoisan played a major role in this.

How, then, should the model be changed to account for these new facts? Whilst the eastward spread of the proto-Bantu is not disputed, there is much disagreement over the route that they took. Was it north of the Congo rain forests, or through them, or both? The issue is undecided. The weight of evidence suggests that the route lay through the rain forests – and if this is so it carries important implications. The proto-Bantu used pottery and, although there is a great deal of debate on the subject, it seems that they also understood the use of iron.[6] Certainly, they had been pastoralists, and had kept cattle. Passing through the tsetse-fly belts of central Africa, they gradually lost their stock and, in time, the words that were associated with them. When those who passed through the forest regions emerged again into the savannah, the only

proto-Bantu cattle-word that survived was re-applied, in the absence of cattle, to the buffalo.[7]

It would be a mistake to think of the Bantu migration as an exodus or an organised mass movement. It is almost certain that there was no formality to it all. It was simply a continuous process of suffusion and expansion into areas of least population. It followed, by canoe, the shores, rivers and streams, and on foot the ancient paths and tracks of Africa.

Whilst this eastern movement of proto-Bantu was gaining momentum, Nilotic and Cushite people had moved down from the north and settled into eastern Africa, although never further south than the northern parts of Tanzania. The southern Cushites were the first food-producing immigrants in this region and were established by about 3 000 BC.[8] They were pastoralists who were later to acquire the technology for making iron. When the protoBantu, moving slowly eastwards, entered the eastern side of Africa in the first century BC,[9] it was with these people that contact was made. Reintroduced to cattle, they acquired new words of east African origin for them, words like *Mombe* and *Ngombe*.

Not all the proto-Bantu had travelled due east. It is now supposed that the wanderings of many groups in the forest areas had, in fact, led them in a south to southeasterly direction, where they emerged on the central African plateau, far south of the areas occupied by the eastern Nilotic people. The interesting fact is, however, that they acquired cattle from whatever people they met there and, more interesting still, they acquired the words those people used.

As already mentioned, in Southern Africa it is generally true to say that all the cattle-words used by present-day Bantu people who live south of a line roughly parallel to the Limpopo River, have their origins in the Khoisan language group. For example, the words for cattle are *Kgomo* and *Inkomo* and for sheep, *Nku* and *Imvu*. Between the Limpopo and the Zambezi there is a mixture of words with Khoisan and east African origins. North of the Zambezi, the Nilotic base predominates, and *Mombe* and *Ngombe* are the everyday terms. This discovery leads to some interesting conclusions.

It seems evident that at least some of the Bantu who now inhabit Southern Africa, having lost, in their passage through the equatorial regions, their cattle and their cattle-words, now re-acquired both from what could only have been a Khoisan people, with whom they made contact after emerging from the forests. This in turn implies that the early Khoisan acquired cattle and stock, probably from the area of East Africa, long before the modern Bantu appeared. This theory, although fairly new, is not unreasonable in view of the distribution of the Khoisan. They must surely have been in contact with the Nilotic, cattle-owning peoples of East Africa, and there is reason to suppose that they would have acquired goats and perhaps cattle, and that the knowledge would have suffused through their own regional groupings. That all the Khoisan did not then become a permanent pastoralist people is not surprising. Given their high level of adaptation to their environment and their preference for a nomadic life, it may be that ownership of stock was not considered to be necessarily advantageous in all places at all times.

Suffice it to say that the old model, which suggested Stone Age man in Southern Africa being exposed to the 'high tech' invasions of a Bantu people, equipped with the knowledge of cattle-rearing, pottery-making and iron-smelting, to which he was introduced for the first time, must now be questioned. Already, in some Kalahari sites, bones of domestic stock and fragments of pottery are being found, very much further back in time than was expected, and restructuring of some old ideas may well be necessary.

The trans-continental movement of proto-Bantu did not stop either in East or in Central Africa. Equipped with their technology and skills, cattle and cattle-words, the movement continued, swinging round into a southerly direction. The current view on the occupation of Southern Africa suggests that there were three 'streams', or gradual movements, of people.[10] One, down the east coast, may well have been sea-borne, as they moved fairly quickly. They had no cattle but they were agriculturists and they brought with them the use of iron. Another, more central group, with iron-working skills and possessing cattle, came through Malawi, which they reached by about AD 200, and through Zimbabwe, in which the earliest sites are dated to about AD 300. The third, western stream, came south through the area of Zambia and Angola, also bringing cattle and iron. The Iron Age had arrived in Southern Africa.

This southerly movement of Bantu was not a mass migration, leaving nothing behind it. The movement was slow and might have been powered only by a natural increase in population. One could think of it in terms of younger generations moving on, seeking new pastures, whilst the old remained where they were, creating the nucleus for the many different tribes of Africa today.

The Khoisan, upon whose wide and empty world this human activity was superimposed, seemed simply to fade away. There are remnant populations of Khoisan-like people in East Africa but there is now no continuous link to associate them with the Khoisan of Southern Africa. We are unable to account for their demise. They are a gentle, peace-loving people but, on the evidence of more recent history, are not above considering cattle in the same category as game – and helping themselves accordingly. This may have brought them into conflict with the Bantu, as it did with the white settlers in the very south of the continent. If provoked, history has shown them to be formidable adversaries. It is also possible, even probable, that the original Khoisan adapted to new ways of living, among the Bantu, becoming absorbed genetically and culturally.

It is difficult to keep abreast of the Iron Age in Southern Africa. It is the field in which the most intensive research is taking place, where the greatest controversy occurs and where the steady flow of new information upsets old ideas with some regularity. Nowhere is this more true than in the Kalahari. Traditionally, there has been a low regard for the Kalahari as potential for Iron Age sites, but this has recently been changed by the work of Dr Jim Denbow.

Jim is a towering American from the Mid-West who has a penchant for animated camp-fire arguments, an astounding capacity for alcoholic beverages and an unfortunate propensity for doing painful things to his thumb, when he is not polluting the air with his dreadful pipe! He is also a first-rate archaeologist and can claim much of the credit for putting the Kalahari onto the Iron Age map, where it clearly has an important place.

Jim's first outstanding success was to use aerial photographs to locate non-walled Iron Age sites. By that time he was aware that most of these sites had had cattle kept in or near them. It is a phenomenon of this part of the world that a particular grass, Cenchrus ciliaris, grows rankly on old cattle middens. It has a bold, white flowering head and, if it occurs in sufficient quantity, appears clearly on good aerial photographs. In this way Jim found enough sites to keep him occupied for a number of years. Many of the sites that he located by this interesting method were more than a thousand years old, and most of them were close to the eastern edge of the Kalahari.

More recently he has focused his attention on sites within the area of Kalahari sands and has found at least ten, yielding dates from the first millenium AD.[11] This has been a dramatic discovery and has placed agricultural-pastoral settlements over a thousand years earlier in time than was previously estimated. In all of them there is evidence of early Iron Age pottery and metal tools, mixed, at some sites, with LSA artefacts. This is remarkable evidence of contact and exchange between LSA and Iron Age communities and, as Jim suggests, implies the existence of compound economies, linking together the Stone Age Khoisan and the pastoralist into a complex of social and economic relationships.

Cowrie shells and glass beads also indicate that there was at least indirect trading contact with the east coast. Clearly, this is only the beginning of new discoveries. Jim works more or less on his own, as the resources for archaeological exploration and discovery are woefully slim; despite this, new finds are constantly being made. In one of his most recent discoveries, yet to be properly examined and evaluated, is pot-tery that looks as if it may date from somewhere between 200 BC and AD 200. If this turns out to be the case, it will create more problems than it solves – since pottery and the associated Iron Age is not thought to have started in this area until very much later. Again, it will add weight to the theory that pottery and domestic stock preceded the Bantu in Southern Africa. It also emphasises the hitherto unexpected richness of the Kalahari's Iron Age sites. A further discovery, along the Boteti River and near the Makgadikgadi Pans, suggests that for at least 2 000 years Stone Age hunter-gatherers have adapted to an aquatic environment, which included fish and hippo, as well as the usual game.

The previously wide distribution of the Khoisan and their contact with pastoralists in eastern Africa, together with the fact that the Khoisan undoubtedly transferred a knowledge of cattle to at least some of the proto-Bantu, suggests their introduction of limited pastoralism into Southern Africa. It also makes possible that this took place well in advance of the accepted start of the Iron Age and the arrival of the first Bantu people. If it was not the Khoisan who were responsible for this, who else could it possibly have been? As yet, we do not have the answer but, increasingly, the evidence points to an under-estimation of the role played by the Khoisan in the peopling of the southern sub-continent.

There are other small clues which support the theory of acquaintance with pottery and cattle among the late Stone Age Khoisan people. An interesting example comes from medical studies of the Khoisan in the Kalahari.[12] Among a sample tested, a very high rate of lactose intolerance was detected. This is not unexpected. After weaning, the presence of an intestinal lactase which can digest the lactose contained in milk, is, strangely enough, restricted almost solely to Caucasoids of north-western Europe, America and a few pastoral peoples, of whom the Khoisan are not one. The trait is dominantly inherited although, more rarely, it can be acquired by continuing milk consumption over a long period of time. The interesting point about the survey was not so much the number of Khoisan who exhibited lactose intolerance but the 3, out of a sample of 110, who showed tolerance. Where did they acquire it? Drs Nurse and Jenkins suggest it points to one possibility, namely that these Khoisan have reverted to a hunter-gatherer way of life after a previous period of pastoralism or settlement.

With a better understanding of their past and the role that they may have played in the spreading of new cultures through the continent, we will now take a closer look at these fascinating people, the Khoisan. Descendants of man's distant past, these warm, friendly people are with us still. It is an unfortunate fact of life that, though they will continue among us, their traditional way of life will not.

## REFERENCES

1. **Denbow, J.** Personal communication, January 1985
2. **Ambrose, S H.** 'Archaeology and Linguistic Reconstructions of History in East Africa'. In *The Archaeological and Linguistic Reconstruction of African History.* Edited by Ehret, C and Posnansky, M. Berkeley: University of California Press, 1982, **pp 137-8**
3. **Ehret, C.** 'The First Spread of Food Production to Southern Africa'. In Ibid, **pp 158-71**
4. **Denbow, J R and Campbell, A.** *The Early Stages of Food Production in Southern Africa.* Unpublished paper. Gaborone, 1985
5. **Denbow, J R and Campbell, A.** Op cit
6. **David, N.** 'Prehistory and Historical Linguistics in Central Africa: Points of Contact'. *The Archaeological and Linguistic Reconstruction of African History.* Edited by Ehret, C and Posnansky, M. Berkeley; University of California Press, 1982, **pp 78-95**
7. **Ehret, C.** 'Linguistic Inferences about Early Bantu History'. In Ibid, **pp 57-65**
8. **Ambrose, S H.** Op cit
9. **David, N.** Op cit, **p 94**
10. **Huffman, T.** Personal communication, April 1984
11. **Denbow, J R and Wilmsen, E N.** 'Iron Age Pastoral Settlements in Botswana'. In *South African Journal of Science,* Vol 79, No 10, **pp 405-08**
12. **Nurse, G T and Jenkins, T.** 'Health and the Hunter-Gatherer'. In *Monographs in Human Genetics,* Vol 8, Edited by Beckman, L and Hauge, M. S Karger, Switzerland, 1977, **pp 25-7**

# 15. The Gentle People

SO much has been written about the Bushmen, or San, that one would think we must have learnt all there is to know about these people, and yet experience shows that this is not so. The Bushmen are undergoing a fundamental change at this very moment (detailed in Chapter 18) and in helping them through this transitional period, thorough understanding of the San people is very important. If success to date is anything to judge by, so far we do not seem to have mastered this.

We have already seen, in the previous chapter, how widely dispersed the San once were and how they have lived on this continent and in the Kalahari for a very long time. Consistently, in the last two millenia, others have competed with them for their territory and consistently, looking at the numbers that are left and the area they occupy, they have been ousted. We do not know how this occurred, whether by warfare and annihilation or by absorption. In eastern and central Africa there seems little evidence to support either view; in Southern Africa there is evidence for both. The San languages are the only ones in which the distinctive 'click' sounds are a natural, original component. That echoes of these clicks now occur in such languages as Zulu, Xhosa and Tswana, is taken as evidence of intermarriage and absorption over long periods of time. There is also direct evidence of persecution. Everywhere, it seems, the San have clashed with pastoralists due, no doubt, to the very different views held by the San on their right to kill and consume the cattle of others.

Nowhere is this more amply illustrated than in the records of early Cape settlement. Here, the growing white settler community depended in some large measure on their herds of cattle, and raiding San were a serious cause of stock loss. San were declared vermin and were hunted to the death. Records show that in the last ten years of the Dutch East India Company's rule, from 1786 to 1795, 2 480 San were killed and 654 taken prisoner.[1] Other records suggest that as many as 200 000 San may have been killed in Southern Africa in the two hundred years following 1652 and the arrival of the first settlers.[2] Nor, it is said, was the killing one-sided. The San were ferocious adversaries, and cruel too. In addition to stealing livestock, they plundered homesteads and killed many settlers. In some areas it was a case of open warfare.

Although the San were eliminated in vast areas of their range, they did survive in the more inaccessible places. Estimates of their numbers today are not entirely reliable but frequently quoted figures suggest that in excess of 55 000 San remain, of which 60 per cent are found in Botswana, 36 per cent in Namibia and the rest scattered through Angola, Zambia and South Africa.[3] These figures are probably too low because almost everywhere today the San population is increasing. There seems little danger of these people disappearing as a race and they are not threatened with extinction, as many seem to think. However, San living as traditional hunter-gatherers are, indeed, becoming a thing of the past. There are probably no San alive today who remain untouched, in some way, by modern civilisation. Of their total number I would expect there to be less than 2 000 San who live solely as hunter-gatherers the year round. It is not the people who face extinction, but the way of life.

Very little is known of the origins of the so-called Bushmen. Without going into too much detail, it is perhaps enough to say that within the general term Khoisan are included two major divisions of people, the San and the Khoi. Of the Bushman or Khoisan types who live in Southern Africa, there are three separate groups: the northern, central and southern groups.[4] The northern San group consists mainly of the !Kung people and related sub-groups who occupy the area west of the Okavango and north of Ghanzi. Representatives of this group are found as far afield as Angola. The southern San include the !Ko people and their related groups and live in the area between Kang and Bokspits in Botswana. The central group is of the Khoi branch and lives in central Botswana; elsewhere they are known as Hottentots. To the north they extend around the eastern Okavango to Kasane and, to the west, into Namibia. There, the Nama people, who look the same and speak the same language, but are known by a different name, spread westwards to the coast and southwards across the Orange River, reaching almost as far as the Cape.

One of the fascinating features of these three separate groups is that their languages are at once similar and yet very different. All share the clicks that are unique to the Bushman tongues, yet each language is quite different from the others, so much so that there is little or no mutual understanding among the groups.

! is a click sign that signifies the sound made when the tongue is pulled away from the roof of the mouth, creating a slight vacuum.

X is an alveolar or lateral click. It is made when the tongue is sucked away from behind the teeth on the upper, right side of the mouth.

C stands for a dental click. The tongue is placed behind the two top teeth, creating a vacuum when it is pulled back.

There are many dialects of the three languages and, whilst those of the north and south have some similarities, those of the central group are very far removed from either of the other two. This indicates a common origin but a long period of isolation.

The central group is the remnant of a population which lived long ago in the area of what is today north-eastern Botswana. Somehow they had acquired sheep and cattle, although from whom and when is not known. It was possibly as early as the first millenium, or even earlier. The practice of keeping and herding stock spread through the then widely dispersed population across the central Kalahari, south-west into Namibia and down to the coast. Over time, it seems, some of these Khoi Bushmen appear to have lost their cattle and sheep because local climatic conditions were no longer favourable. Others, however, retained them – and still do to this day. It is probable that the people who lost their herds owing to a changing environment are those known now as the central group. Possibly the central Khoi were the victims of a general drying-up of the Kalahari which has recently been reported and is believed to have taken place about AD 500.[5]

Since about that date, all the San have been, in one degree or another, in contact with cattle-keeping people and traded with them for commodities such as iron, copper and salt. In return, the San were providers of skins, ivory, horn, feathers and other game products. Many anthropologists, by studying the San peoples today, hope to learn how the earliest hunter-gatherers lived. However, other authorities point out that this is not a valid proposition, for the San have now been in contact with food-producing peoples for over 1 500 years and it is known that they have intermarried with Bantu peoples, traded with them and, when periods of high rainfall allowed it, have been owners and herders of their own cattle, sheep and goats. Also, unrestricted movement of the San has been inhibited throughout the Kalahari for much of that time owing to the presence within the area, or on its boundaries, of Bantu and non-San people. For these reasons, it may not be valid to generalise about the San today and the earliest humans; they are barely comparable.

'Hunter-gatherer' is an excellent term with which to describe the San, because it accurately describes the way they live. The San are good hunters and proficient weapon-makers. It is the men who hunt, while the women's task is to gather wild foods from the bush, although, to a much lesser extent, the men are also gatherers. Generally speaking, a child of twelve will be able to recognise and name about 200 plant species and an adult more than 300.[6] A hunter-gatherer existence implies a certain degree of mobility and the San are highly mobile. Having no pack animals, everything that is owned must be carried, so the number of personal possessions is small. The shelters in which the San live are necessarily easily and quickly constructed, for the duration of their use is likely to be short. The growing of any kind of crop is not feasible, for this would impose constraints on the need for mobility.

A hunting and gathering way of life imposes certain societal imperatives on a community. The number of people who can occupy any area must be a function of the ability of that area to provide them with sufficient food. The abundance of game and plant life is seasonal, and both do not necessarily occur in the same place. It follows, therefore, that if the food resource varies in size, so too must the population it supports. When game and plants are plentiful, San of a particular group will congregate into a relatively large community. Environmental constraints still operate, of course, even in times of plenty, and the group will seldom exceed 120 people. As the food resource diminishes, so the large group fragments into smaller units and, in very lean times, may consist of no more than a man, his wife and immediate family. Such a mode of life emphasises self-reliance and independence at the expense of interdependence among members of a large community.

There is among the San no centrally organised political system, no leader, chief or headman. Decisions are made by group consensus and there is little compulsion to conform. Among a people where social continuity is disrupted by a constant process of disintegration and amalgamation, one would expect to find mechanisms designed to cope with the unique stresses upon human relationships which would inevitably arise. This is indeed the case and behaviour patterns have evolved which allow for the release of tension and aggression and the establishment of a widespread network of obligations between individuals, both of which enhance the group's cohesion in an otherwise fluid situation.

Much is made of the San's phenomenal powers of endurance, eyesight and physical abilities, but to a large extent these are exaggerated and, despite the plethora of tales to the contrary, there are few measurable and significant physiological differences between San and other races in Southern Africa.

Colour blindness is rare among San hunter-gatherers and their eyesight, on average, is generally excellent, attributed to the relative absence of those abnormalities to which Negro and Caucasoid populations are prone. Because of this, tests have shown that visual acuity among San is higher than it is among whites and Bantu when the latter groups are without correcting lenses. With them, however, there are no significant differences. What this means is that if your eyesight is good, with or without glasses, you will be able to see as well as any Bushman. You may not be able to estimate size, at a distance, as well as the San, but this ability is not a function of eyesight alone. An often repeated myth about the San is that they do not have names for colours because they cannot see colours. This is not quite correct. Whilst it is true to say that in no San language is there an abundance of colour names, they have no difficulty whatsoever in distinguishing colour. The reason for the paucity of names results simply from a conceptual approach that is different to ours. To the San, colours do not exist on their own; they are an attribute of an object or a plant, for which there is already a detailed description.[7]

Scientists measure endurance by a test of maximum oxygen intake. In one test, twenty-four San males showed endurance capacity that was lower than that of Caucasoid or Negro athletes and lower than that of labourers and army recruits.[8] I have heard of informal races being organised in which Bushmen have been pitted against good marathon runners and the former have been hopelessly outclassed. In enduring pain, however, the San are remarkable. One man accidently cut his foot on a poisoned arrow. The cut was slight and the amount of poison small. Despite this the wound festered and, in the absence of any medical assistance, he amputated his own foot. He recovered from this self-surgery and may still be living today, limping about on his home-made crutch. Another man survived an unarmed fight with a leopard. Today his face is paralysed and his arm and fingers suffered permanent damage, but he did kill the animal with his bare hands![9]

It would be a mistake to give the impression that San are not in any way more suited to their environment than you or I. They most certainly are, but the adaptations are mostly not physiological: they are the result of experience and constant practice. Their hearing is better than ours because it is more important to them than it is to us, and they are accustomed to listening for sounds with which we are no longer familiar. They are better at gauging size over a long distance because they do it all the time. They live under open skies where vast distances are an everyday part of their lives. Their tracking ability is not a function of eyesight but of practice. They know what to look for and how to interpret what they see. Almost any one of us, given the same circumstances, could acquire the same skills.

Tony Trail, a linguist who has spent much time among the San, told me once how he took a small group of San into a large city. They were as disorientated and afraid there as a city-dweller who had never left its confines would be if he were suddenly taken into the wastes of the Kalahari. The survival skills of the San are not magical, although to us they may appear so. Close examination shows that they are logical and learned, but nonetheless marvellous illustrations of the adaptability of the human race.

Although it can be misleading to generalise, because the regional variation within the Kalahari is so great, and because there are great differences between different tribes and groups of San, it is generally true that more than 90 per cent of the water they consume actually comes from plants. They live in a region where there is likely to be no standing water for at least 300 days in the year. Can you imagine what

that would be like for the city-dweller, used to running water, showers and baths? How would he cope, standing beside the drying mud of the last water-hole, knowing that nearly a year will pass before rain comes again? And yet the San cope very well.

Water is often stored in empty ostrich eggs and throughout their range the Bushmen know of hollow trees where water lingers well into the dry season. The tsamma melon is a member of the cucumber family. Tasteless and insipid, it grows in widely scattered patches and ripens in mid-winter. The roasted seeds are a delicacy and when ground they provide a coarse white flour. The flesh of the plant is more than 90 per cent liquid and it is said that a man can live on tsamma alone for more than six weeks. Much of the gathering effort in the dry season is aimed at finding succulent, moisture-filled roots and tubers and it is these that provide the San's major source of liquid. In some areas conditions favour the construction of what have come to be called Bushman 'sip-wells'. Opportunities for these 'wells' are not frequent, nor do they supply great quantities of water – but they are enough to save a life.

Certain plants indicate a damp place, where, for some reason, the sand below the surface may be more moist than usual. It will usually be an old woman who will make and use the well. She will dig a hole, large enough for her hand, scraping into the sand as far as she can reach. A hollow reed or grass-stem is placed in the hole and the lower end of it tightly packed with a nest of fine grass or roots. The sand is replaced and very firmly tramped down. The well is left for an hour or more, after which the woman will return and begin sucking at the end of the protruding reed. This she will do for an hour or more, before the reduction in atmospheric pressure draws the water away from the sand grains up the hollow tube. When the water rises a second, shorter reed is placed in the mouth and this is used to transfer the water to some suitable container, usually an empty ostrich egg. There is one report that tells how two men and four donkeys were kept alive in this way for two weeks by an old San woman. During that time they were able to dig a well and were down 10 m before they found water. This was how the present-day settlement of Khakhea came to be established.[10]

It is often said that Bushmen are the most prodigious eaters when there is a surplus of meat available. I have not been able to verify this from my own experience but know of at least one reliable report to support the claim, in which a 45 kg Bushman is alleged to have eaten 26 kg of meat in a single day.[11] Perhaps happily for their digestive systems, such vast amounts of meat are not always available; indeed, hunting requires a great deal of time and effort and is far from always successful. Usually a hunt is organised by a small band of between two and five men, who will set out into the bush in search of game for the whole group. It is only when game is sighted that the hunt really begins.

If there are two men, as soon as their potential prey is located, they will sit and study it carefully, watching its behaviour, deciding how best to approach it and anticipating in which direction it will flee. This process may take many hours and often a kill is only attempted towards the the end of the day. One of the men will try and take up a position where he can see both the animal and his companion so that he can signal any unexpected activity beyond the sight of the second man, who begins to make his approach. The Bushmen are masters at the art of stalking and every imaginable scrap of cover will be used during the approach. When he is within range, between 15 and 20 m, the hunter will loose his arrow, aiming for a soft or fleshy part of the animal. The arrow is designed in such a way that it can separate when the animal takes flight. The head and its short stem will remain embedded in the flesh whilst the shaft will fall away. The arrow-head is poisoned and, properly struck, the beast's fate is sealed.

There are number of natural sources of poisons used by the tribes of Africa: vegetables, insects and the venom of snakes and scorpions. Almost all of the Kalahari's Bushmen, however, use the larvae of a leaf-cutting beetle, *Diamphidia simplex*. When the larvae pupate, they fall from the ends of the leaves on which they have grown and bury themselves in a small

cocoon some 20 to 30 cm below the ground. It is these that are retrieved by the San, who carry them around with them until they are needed. When an arrow is to be prepared, the cocoon is opened and the small grub inside carefully removed. It is rolled between the thumb and forefinger until the innards are liquefied, the head is nipped off and the contents spread upon the arrow-head. Eight to ten grubs are needed for one arrow.[12] There is no known antidote for a full dose of this poison although there is some controversy as to how long it retains its efficacy. Some claim that it is only for a few months and that often the San will run out of supplies during the course of a year. Others say that it will last for at least two years and one authoritative source claims that a sample, tested after 100 years was still active and had not changed either toxically or chemically in all that time.[13] The poison does affect different animals differently but all large creatures, including man, will die from its effect within ten to twenty hours.

When the prey is struck, all need for caution falls away. The hunters will follow the animal for a short distance to ensure that the arrow is safely home, to recover the fallen shaft, to establish the line of flight and to familiarise themselves with the creature's spoor. They do not follow far, for to do so frightens the animal and serves only to lengthen the distance it will run. Sure of their quarry, the hunters turn for their camp if it is close by, or prepare themselves for the night where they are.

The following day the spoor is followed and the dead or dying animal found. If necessary, it is despatched with spears and it is then that the job of transporting and utilising the carcass begins. Bushmen seldom, if ever, kill more than their immediate needs demand and very little that they do kill is wasted. The arrow-head is carefully removed and the meat from about it cut away and discarded. The liver of the animal may be eaten by the hunters straight away, as well as the more perishable parts which will not last the journey home. The rest of the meat and the blood, which is carried in stomach sacks is, however, subject to very firm rules. It belongs not to the person who killed it, but to the owner of the arrow used.

This curious custom has very important social implications and is part of a network of behaviour patterns that works to ensure the cohesion of the group as a whole. By using his own arrow, by borrowing the arrow of a friend or by accepting the offer of another person's arrow, the hunter is making an important statement about his place and role within the group. Over time a complex of obligations and 'debts' is built up so that every person within the group at one time or another is under obligation to others. This is in some measure illustrated by the way in which the meat is eventually distributed at the camp.

In the first distribution the meat is divided among the hunters themselves and the owner of the arrow. Each then distributes the meat to their closest kin and relatives. After this, there is another round of sharing where everyone who has received meat gives some to other people. In this way more debts are incurred, but nobody goes hungry. In one hunt, four hunters took eight days to find a large eland. It was wounded and followed for another three days and eventually died two days' walk from camp. Thirteen days, in all, had been involved. When the meat was finally brought back to camp a total of sixty-three gifts of raw meat were made. The giving is functional, it avoids jealousy and the generation of ill-will and it helps towards the maintenance of friendly relations within the group.[14]

The circumstances of the hunting expedition vary greatly. It may take the form of a large group or a man may be hunting just for himself and his family. Often the larger animals are not in evidence and it is then, in the leaner times, that there is heavy reliance on hunting skills which are both unusual and highly developed. Trapping and snaring are common methods employed to kill smaller game, and there are specialised techniques for hunting particular animals. A favourite delicacy is the porcupine and this is caught in a special way.

Porcupines live in burrows in the ground, to which there are often several entrances. When a San hunter finds a porcupine 'at home' he will quickly block all but one of the entrances and will then enter this last remaining tunnel himself. There is sufficient room for a man to slide forward along the tunnel, but very little room to manoeuvre. Pushing ahead of him a bundle of grass and twigs, he will eventually reach the central chamber of the burrow where the porcupine is waiting. It is at this point that the hunter must be particularly careful. Using his fingers and whatever sticks or stones he can find about him, he starts to loosen the sand, pushing it in front of him beneath his shield of branches. In this way he gradually fills the chamber, leaving the unfortunate porcupine with less and less room. The idea is to so cramp the animal and restrict its mobility that the hunter, reaching from under his shield, can take hold of one of its legs. He then reaches for the neck and throttles it.[15]

Hunting techniques seem to improve and change as new resources become available, as the following story illustrates. The San living in Ngamiland now own or have access to donkeys and they use these increasingly in their hunting. In late March or April, in a good year, the grass-heads are full and ripe and zebra find them irresistible. They gorge themselves and often stand about afterwards with woefully distended stomachs. It is this situation that the San watch for.

With perhaps ten or twelve donkeys, they surround the herd from some distance away and trot the donkeys in an ever tightening circle. The bloated zebra reluctantly begin to trot in the same circle. The San rest the donkeys, two or three at a time, but for the zebra there is no rest and, with their distended stomachs, they quickly tire. Eventually, when the animals can do no more than walk with painful slowness, some of the San will dismount and, each approaching a zebra, will thrust a spear through the anus, deep into the entrails. Incapacitated and certain to die, the creature is still able to walk. Terrified and in great pain, but quite docile, it is led back to the camp and slaughtered.[16]

An intriguing aspect of the Bushman's life is his total confidence in finding his way from one place to another in the Kalahari, where there is such a complete absence of the visual clues to which we are accustomed. Little research has been conducted in this particular field, yet there is no doubt that this uncanny skill exists among these people. It is frequently commented upon by those who have lived and worked with the San. Dr Tony Trail confirms this. Despite the fact that his San friends were totally confused and even terrified by their experiences in a big city, their faculty of direction finding did not desert them. A number of long-distance journeys in a motor vehicle were undertaken with these people, to various widely separated cities. At no time did they so much as hesitate in pointing out the direction of places they had come from or where they had been. It may be that this remarkable skill can be acquired by practice and that it is enhanced by numerous visual cues from a familiar local environment, but I suspect not. It seems to occur even when the environment is changed and it may be possible that some form of magnetic sense may be involved.

Until recently, the idea of a 'magnetic sense' might have been laughed at, but for the fascinating work of Dr Robin Baker at the University of Manchester. In a series of increasingly sophisticated and refined experiments, Dr Baker has established a convincing case that man has a sort of sixth sense that, in the absence of any other cues, such as the sun, noise or the wind, can help him set a direction for a particular, known destination. That this sense is dependent upon the earth's magnetic field is shown by the fact that it can be totally negated by placing bar magnets close to the head.

Despite its fairly recent discovery, this phenomenon is not all that surprising since many life-forms enjoy this faculty, among them some birds, bees, bacteria, salamanders and turtles. It seems that mammals are the only major group for which a magnetic sense had not been demonstrated, even though they are known to be affected by magnetic fields. In so far as the sense has been demonstrated among humans, it seems that it is more pronounced in men than women. However, it clearly has a survival value and one would not be surprised to find evidence of it among a people who still live so close to the natural world. Dr Baker has experimented among the Abo-

riginal people of Australia but, so far as I am aware, no work has been done among the San.[17]

Like mankind the world over, the San, gazing into the night skies of the Kalahari, have been no more able than others to resist weaving tales about them. Hundreds of kilometres away from the nearest pollution, the night sky in the Kalahari is breathtakingly beautiful. It has a matchless clarity and the stars seem more numerous, bigger, brighter and closer than anywhere else. On a moonless summer night, the air is warm and balmy, sometimes a perfect stillness falls, when the wind has dropped, the trees and grass stand silent and even the geckos have stopped their incessant calling. It is then, say the Bushmen, when the silence is so profound and the stars so bright and close, that you can actually hear them calling. And you can. I've heard it too – although I cannot be sure it was the stars.

The myths and tales of the San are many and they vary from region to region, and from clan to clan. One cannot say that one story holds true for all of them. Some groups will not acknowledge a particular story at all – others will know a variation of it. One should not generalise, but some of the tales are delightful and reflect the humour and humanity of these gentle people. One such story is of the birth of the stars.

The stars came into existence in a very simple way: there was once a girl of an ancient race, long before the San existed, and she wished for a little light so that the people might see to return home in the darkness. She reached down and threw some wood ashes high into the air – and of course, they stayed there and became the Milky Way.[18]

The San have names for many of the stars and, as with our own constellation names, these underline important aspects of their life and the way they see the world. The Southern Cross, so well known to us, is equally familiar to the San – except that the two 'pointers' represent two male lions whilst the stars of the cross itself are the females of the pride. There is a lovely story of Orion's Belt, told among the !Kung San of north-western Botswana. They say that the stars of the belt are three zebra. One day the Great God who lives in the eastern sky was out hunting. He saw the three animals, loosed an arrow from his bow, but missed and his arrow fell short. You can still see it there today, the !Kung say, and they point to what we call the dagger of Orion. The zebra, spared from the hunter, followed the wheel of stars around the sky and, one after another, daintily stepped down upon the earth.[19]

To the G/wi San of central Botswana the moon is a foolish and lazy man, whose activities are a constant source of mirth to them. These people have it that the moon hunts but once a month (naturally enough on those nights when he does not appear in the sky) and returns with the carcass of a wild animal. He feeds his family on the meat and makes a cloak out of the skin, which he uses to hide himself. It is then that an age-old theme, with which we are all familiar, asserts itself. His wife, who has no cloak, gets cold and night by night, gradually pulls the cloak away from her husband until, by the end of the month (and the full moon, of course) he has none of it. Slowly, he takes it back again until he has it all. By this time his children are hungry and they go to their father and eat the cloak, compelling him, once again, to hunt.[20]

This same group of San attribute the great rain storms of the Kalahari to a mythical giant leopard. When it is angry the lightning is the light of rage flashing in its eyes and at the same time its thunderous roar rolls round the land.

The G/wi believe in two supernatural beings who appear to be approximate equivalents of our 'good' and 'evil'. N!odima, who created the world, is invulnerable, invisible, all-powerful and appears to be living in a state of semi-retirement, since he takes very little active interest in the affairs of the world, apart from occasionally intervening and helping an individual. G//awama, although he has much less power, can appear in any guise at any time and place, and is responsible for most of the things that go wrong, including all disease, misfortune and the wrongdoings of man. His constant objective is to undo the perfection that N!odima vested in the

world when he made it. Unlike N!odima, G//awama is very much involved in the day to day affairs of men.

There is a tale told, in connection with G//awama, which illustrates not only the close, daily relationship which the G/wi have with the 'business end' of their religious hierarchy, but also their excellent powers of observation. The Okwa, a massive fossil river today, once carried large volumes of water into the great super-lake of northern Botswana. As the Okwa approached the shores of the lake, its course became far less pronounced and was all but lost amid a random spread of sandy ridges, hollows and dunes. Even from the air, it is very difficult today to discern the original pattern and the sequence of events. The Bushmen, however, seem to have known all about it for a very long time and, for them, G//awama himself was responsible. It happened like this.

Out hunting one day, G//awama was bitten by a python when he was in the far west of the Kalahari. He was in great pain and became feverish and thirsty. He needed water. The only place he knew of was what is today the village of Rakops, on the Boteti River. He limped off in that direction, dragging his affected leg. This dragging action, so say the G/wi, created the valley of the Okwa. They say that if you look carefully, you can see how, as G//awama came closer to the water in the river, he found new strength and hurried on, dragging his leg less heavily. As the smell of the water grew stronger, so G//awama was able to walk more upright until, eventually, his injured leg left no mark at all – which is why the Okwa does not quite reach the Boteti River today.[21]

It is because the San are in daily contact with the forces of good and evil that it is necessary for them frequently to indulge in what are widely called the 'trance' dances. This is a spontaneous event which involves a number of dancers, and usually, therefore, only takes place during the seasons of plenty, when the fragmented units of a band come together. It is, simply, a dance, but during the course of it one or more of the dancers may enter a supernatural state, during which they acquire 'power' and may attempt some healing. It is generally only the men who dance; the women sit upon the sand around the fire, marking the tempo and rhythm by singing and clapping.

A special fire may be lit, away from the usual hearth, and around it the dancers will gather. There is no direction, no organisation, it is all quite spontaneous. Someone will start a song, low and soft. The volume swells as more voices join and a rhythm of clapping punctuates the night. A single male voice will hurl a pure, clear note, high and sustained, out into the frozen air as a full moon inches out of the distant sand to begin its nightly circle of the sky.

A man rises to dance, others join him, stamping the beat into the yielding sand around the warmth of the fire. At first the rhythm is restrained, but one can sense the enormous tension, as if a flood of energy is being held back, tightly controlled. The women ululate, a clear, penetrating sound, shaped, sometimes, by a hand moving quickly back and forth across the open mouth. The beat quickens and the dance settles into its routine. The dancers sometimes wear chains of dried seed-pods round their legs or ankles so that the thud of a falling step is echoed by the rattle of hard wood. The rhythmic clapping, the melancholy song of the men, the stamp of feet and ululations from the women contorts the mind with a weird, strange and primitive appeal. One feels the power of millenia past, reaching out to tug gently at the soul and strange responses start from within. Someone throws more wood upon the fire and a shower of sparks streaks towards the heavens. The orange flames leap higher as the fuel is hungrily devoured and grotesquely moving shadows flicker with renewed energy across the faces of the women.

Each of the dancers seems to begin to close out the world and slowly slips into his own inner existence. The energetic movement produces a film of sweat which glistens blood-red in the flame-light. Only one or two of the men will achieve a true state of trance, however, in which the spirits of the world will become visible to them. Beyond the circle of firelight, at the very boundary of visibility, the spirits will sit, silent, impassive, watching. The dancer, in his altered state of consciousness, exhorts

and appeals to them with passion and sometimes violence. If the aim of a dance is to heal some affliction of a member of the group, the healer will draw into himself the patient's hurt, while he is in a trance. Having done so, he will rid himself of it with a terrifying shriek that explodes from his body as it hurls the 'evil' out into the cold air of the night.

Every San believes in n/um, a powerful healing force that lies dormant within most people. It can be activated in a number of ways but the most common is the dance. Some people possess it more than others and some can make it work more readily. It is especially the older people who have this skill, some of whom can enter a trance state almost at will.

The trance condition can be dangerous. Acquired during the course of a dance around the fire, the person who reaches it will usually collapse and, not infrequently, has to be rescued from the burning embers. There is a medical explanation as to how the trance state is reached: it is induced by a deliberate technique of breathing. Hours of energetic dancing attune every muscle to the rhythm, and there is an exact and monotonous balance between demand and supply of oxygen. In order to induce a state of trance, the dancer shortens his breathing, without reducing the level of his physical exertions. An oxygen deficiency is created which leads to drowsiness and profuse sweating. The heart pumps more strongly in order to circulate the blood through the lungs more rapidly and, at the same time, blood pressure in the brain is increased. Eventually, the man loses control of his conscious will and he collapses from a cramp in the heart brought about by the lack of oxygen.[22] What the medical world cannot tell us, though, is what the experience feels like. The San would not be interested in an explanation, for they believe in what they are doing and they 'know' that it is the spirits they meet. To them, the trance world is real, and survival in the living world is dependent upon successful communication with the non-living world.

The survival of San in the Kalahari is an excellent illustration of human adaptability but, as has been pointed out, this is not solely attributable to physiological factors or even experience. It is as much so because of their culture and the social systems they have evolved and which are so uniquely suited to the harsh environment. Every facet of human interaction within a San group seems geared towards the maintenance of friendly relations within the community. Personal possessions, already limited because of the necessity for mobility, are regarded among the San in quite a different way from how we look at them. Nothing is so personal that it cannot be borrowed by another. Permission must be sought but it cannot be lightly denied. When granted, it incurs an obligation which further binds lender and borrower to one another as they are bound in a matrix of debt to the group as a whole.

There is a strong need among the San to enjoy a sense of belonging and companionship, to feel part of the group, free from hostility and rejection. If this need is denied, a high level of insecurity results, which causes considerable distress. Life with a Bushman band sounds idyllic, but it is not necessarily so. There is often a marked absence of day to day friendliness as we understand it. For example one might see a person struggling with a particular task while others sit by and watch him, sometimes even laughing at his predicament. Much of the daily tension is channelled through a special kind of talking. Different from ordinary conversation, it revolves around some important, unresolved issue that affects the band as a whole. It will occur spontaneously and anyone who has anything to say joins in. There appear to be no rules and there are no reservations about what may be said or who may say it. Everybody speaks his mind and the occasion becomes an outlet for emotions, so that normal speech turns to shouting. But it is all a way of relieving tension and is highly functional in that a potentially serious outbreak of violence is ultimately avoided.[23]

Children of the San seem, by our standards, to lead a very comfortable life. They do not appear to be burdened with the responsibilities we load upon our own children and their time is largely free for them to spend as they wish. Children are not expected to take part in the gathering work and they spend days in camp, in the company of other children. They make very little social contribution and most of their time is taken up in play. Naturally enough, this takes place outdoors where the whole village and its immediate surrounds lie open to them. Surprisingly, perhaps, there seems to be little emphasis upon competition in the games that are played and some researchers have found this to be a feature that pervades San society. The emphasis falls not so much on being better than another, but on trying, rather, to become more accomplished for accomplishment's sake.[24]

It is generally agreed that San populations are increasing, which means, of course, that the birth rate has risen. This increase seems to be associated with a more settled way of life, induced by the provision of permanent water, schools, clinics and stores. In the more remote bands, untouched by these 'blessings' of civilisation, the birth rate is lower and the population grows slowly, if at all. Among the !Kung, for example, children are spaced roughly every four years, although it is not entirely clear how this is achieved. The San do know of plants that allegedly can bring about a miscarriage although there is no evidence that they make regular use of them, or that they work. There is a taboo against sex for six months after a child is born but this seems to be largely ignored.

The probable explanation for such successful natural spacing has several origins. San generally nurse their children for a long period of time – two or three years are not unusual. Stimulation of the nipple is known to produce a hormone, prolactin, which inhibits ovulation. While it does not prevent conception taking place, it certainly reduces the chances. It is also possible that the high level of energy expended in this nomadic way of life, combined with subsistence-level nutrition, does not leave sufficient surplus energy which is necessary to re-establish regular ovulation. It is interesting that this spacing of children, despite the fact that it is not apparently deliberate, is actually of vital importance to the survival of the group.[25]

Meat consumed by the San is almost totally supplied by the men, but meat does not account for a large proportion of the diet. Estimates vary by region and group, but generally speaking, it makes up only 20 to 40 per cent of the diet. While hunting may be the more strenuous activity, gathering is more continuous. The women are the major providers of vegetable foods. They will set off on foraging trips two or three times a week and each may cover as much as 15 to 20 km. Returning after a successful trip, they may be carrying up to 15 kg of vegetables, and probably a nursing child as well. This is a considerable load for a woman who, on average, will not weigh much more than 40 kg herself. Were children to be any more frequently spaced, a large part of the clan's labour force would have to be diverted to fulltime childcare. As it is, the mothers can only just cope. A four-year-old can accompany its mother on short trips or be left behind at the camp, but younger children would have to be carried. It would simply not be possible to carry two children and the normal load of vegetables.[26]

Unpleasant myths abound about the San's treatment of their aged, and there is little or no evidence to support them. It is often said that ageing people who can no longer fend for themselves are simply abandoned with nothing but a small container of water. I have found no reports confirming this, however. The nearest I know of is a case where a husband, anxious for the safety of his children, abandoned his wife, but the circumstances were exceptional and abandonment is definitely not the norm.[27]

The aged create the same problems in San society as they do in our own, but old people are regarded with greater respect. Each family looks after its own and, if there is no family, this responsibility devolves upon the group as a whole. Eventually, the aged do become totally dependent upon the group but they are not rejected on this account. Age, in fact, is important, and being born first by a matter of just a few hours can be a valuable advantage. Ownership of permanent water-holes is vested in the oldest of the clan and they are also the custodians of tradition, as well as the spiritual leaders of the group. We have already seen how *n/um* is most powerful in

the elderly and this undoubtedly plays a part in the way they are perceived and the respect accorded them.

Death and dying seem to be regarded much more pragmatically than in our society. If a child is born with a defect, it may be killed. Twins, likewise, are often not allowed to live – there are simply not the resources, human and nutritional, available. If a mother dies in childbirth, her baby may be buried with her if there is no one to look after it.[28] These are unpleasant realities of life in a hard and difficult world. The dead are buried in a deep hole. In some cases the body is orientated along a north-south line; in others, it rests in a squatting position. A few of the deceased's possessions are broken and placed upon the otherwise unmarked grave, to warn others of its presence – but the site is never visited again.[29]

The survival of the San as a race is no longer seriously doubted but, increasingly, their way of the life is changing. To their great credit, the Government of Botswana set aside a vast area of the Kalahari, the Central Kalahari Game Reserve, as a reserve not only for animals, but also for the exclusive use of Botswana's remaining San who still choose to live as traditional hunter-gatherers. So much is changing it is doubtful if the reserve is now being used as it was originally intended. One estimate suggests that, in good times, as many as 3 000 San may live within it in the old way, but when times are difficult this number may drop to as little as 800.[30] Already, the existence of the reserve is being challenged and discussion is taking place on how it should be used.

The phenomenon of change is easy to understand and the San cannot be blamed for being attracted to the material attributes of the different society that they see all about them. There is a steady trickle of people out of the deserted reaches of the Kalahari into the farms and tribal lands, as the San, forsaking their old ways, sell themselves into virtual slavery for the dubious rewards of cast-off clothing, hard labour, alcohol, tobacco and disease. One accepts that it is unavoidable but it is a pity that so supremely adapted a creature should see the worst of our civilisation as

▲Herero woman, Ghanzi
▼Bushman from the Central Kalahari

▲Rebecca Cooper, descendant of Simon Cooper, Lol
▼Bushman woman, Tsodilo Hills

more attractive than the free and open life that he lived in the past. That is, of course, a romantic outlook. The life itself has changed and, if it was once easy and comfortable, as we might like to believe, it is no longer so.

Man the pastoralist has invaded the Kalahari. His presence and demands have made it impossible for the large herds of game to exist as they once did. Cattle consume the plants. Thus the two mainstays of the San's existence are simultaneously diminishing. Apart from being attracted by a different civilisation, he is being impelled towards it too because the alternative is becoming increasingly less viable. The San, however, will not find the transition easy, as they move from the open, friendly egalitarianism of the small hunter-gatherer band to the individual isolation and competition that characterises the Western world.[31]

## REFERENCES

1. Hermans, J. 'Official Policy towards the Bushmen of Botswana: A Review, Part 1'. In *Botswana Notes and Records*, Vol 9, 1977, p 56

2. Shostak, M. *"Nisa". The Life and Words of a !Kung Woman*. London: Allen Lane, 1982, p 345

3. Tobias, P V. 'Bushman Hunter-Gatherers: A Study in Human Ecology. In *Ecological Studies in Southern Africa*. Edited by Davis, D H S. The Hague: Dr W Junk, 1964, p 69

4. Campbell, A C. Personal communication, March 1986

5. Cooke, H J. Personal communication, March 1986

6. Campbell, A C. *All Desert, but All trees*. Botswana, No 4, no date. Department of Information Services, Government of Botswana, Gaborone, p 39

7. Reuning, H and Wortley, W. 'Psychological Studies of the Bushmen'. In *Psychologia Africana*, Monograph Supplement No 7, 1973, pp 1-113

8. Nurse, G T and Jenkins, T. *Health and the Hunter-Gatherer. Monographs in Human Genetics*, Vol 8. Edited by Beckman, L. and Hauge, M. London: M S Karger, 1977, p 74

9. Lee, R B and De Vore, I. *Kalahari Hunter-Gatherers*. Massachusetts: Harvard University Press, 1976, p 170

10. Debenham, F. 'The Kalahari Today'. In *The Geographical Journal*, Vol 118, 1952, pp 18-19

11. Nurse, G T and Jenkins, T. Op cit

12. Silberbauer, G B. *Report to the Bechuanaland Government on the Bushman Survey*. Government of Botswana, Gaborone, Botswana, 1965, pp 56-8

13. Schapera, I. 'Bushman Arrow Poisons'. In *Bantu Studies*, Vol 2, 1923-1926, pp 208-209

14. Marshall, L. 'Sharing, Talking and Giving: Relief of Social Tensions among !Kung Bushmen'. In *Africa*, Vol 31, 1961 pp 236-8

15. Taylor, F. Personal communication, July 1984

16. Ibid

17. Baker, R R. *Human Navigation and the Sixth Sense*. London: Hodder & Stoughton, 1982

18. Bleek, W H I and Lloyd, L C. *A Brief Account of Bushman Folklore and other texts*. Cape Town: J C Juta, 1875, p 10

19. Marshall, L. 'Two Ju/wa Constellations'. In *Botswana Notes and Records*, Vol 7, 1975, pp 153-4

20. Silberbauer, G B. Op cit, p 101

21. Ibid, p 96

22. Bjerre, J. *Kalahari*. London: Michael Joseph, 1960, pp 171-2

23. Marshall, L. Op cit, pp 233-4

24. Shostak, M. Op cit, pp 108-9

25. Ibid, pp 65-9

26. Ibid

27. Nurse, G T and Jenkins, T. Op cit, p 77

28. Tobias, P V. Op cit, p 81

29. Silberbauer, G B. Op cit, p 102

30. Campbell, A C. 'Central Kalahari Game Reserve: II'. In *African Wild Life*, Vol 22, No 4, December 1968, pp 321-7

31. Biesele, M. 'Hunting in Semi-Arid Areas – The Kalahari Bushmen Today." In *Botswana Notes and Records*. Special Edition No 1. Proceedings of the Conference on Sustained Production from Semi-arid Areas. October 1971, Gaborone, Botswana, p 66

# 16. Cultures and Traditions

I suppose that it is almost axiomatic that man, in his spread across the continents, will choose first to settle in the most inviting and hospitable of regions, leaving the less attractive parts for later generations. We know that the Bushmen, or San, have been living in the Kalahari for many thousands of years but the present Bantu-speaking peoples may only have moved there in relatively recent times, within the last 250 years. The archaeological record of the Kalahari is only now being explored and early findings suggest more widespread Bantu occupation, and at an earlier date, than was first thought.

Some Bantu peoples have been living, perhaps intermittently, in the Kalahari during the last fifteen hundred years or more, possibly since the Bantu first arrived in Southern Africa. This very recent view, based on the latest archaeological evidence, recognises that for many in the distant past the Kalahari was not a place of last refuge, but was particularly fine cattle country and therefore much sought after.[1] How much continuity there has been between this occupation and the present time is difficult to say but, for the most part, the oral history of those who live in the Kalahari today implies that they are relative newcomers.

I cannot name all the different tribes, subtribes, clans and varying ethnic groupings which are now to be found upon the broad reaches of the Kalahari's sands. The remoteness of the Kalahari has provided a refuge for many groups of people in recent historical times, the admixture of which makes for a diverse and fascinating, polyglot population. The background of the Kalahari's people is described in greater detail in many authoritative works. We shall deal only briefly with a handful of them here – those whose origins are tragic and unusual, or who brought with them interesting skills and crafts that have remained in use to the present day.

The first recorded white man to visit the Kalahari was Jacobus Coetse Jansz who, in 1760, while on a journey of exploration from the Cape to Namaqualand, crossed the Orange River.[2] Among other achievements, he named some of the vegetation encountered. From his observations of giraffe eating the leaves of a thorny acacia tree, we have the name *Acacia giraffae* or, as he called it in early Dutch, *kameeldoornboom*. A second early visitor came in the following year. He was Johann Andreas Auge, at the time superintendent of the Dutch East India Company's garden at the Cape. He accompanied an expedition led by Captain Hendrik Hop and, as the first recognised botanist to visit the area, collected and named many new plants. Since then the lure of the unknown has drawn many men to the Kalahari's open spaces and a succession of explorers have travelled across its sands. Lichtenstein, William Burchell, Chapman, Baines, William Cotton Oswell and, the man he launched on a career of exploration, David Livingstone, are but a few of the famous characters who were unable to resist the mystery of the Kalahari.

Among the more interesting of the Kalahari's inhabitants are the river people of the Okavango Delta, the Hambukushu and the Bayei. These tribes, who have central African origins, were, in the eighteenth century, living on the Zambezi and Chobe rivers. At about that time, in what is now western Zambia, Chief Ngombela of the Balozi was expanding and unifying his empire. In doing so, he sought tribute from subordinate tribes, who were faced with the prospect of either meeting his demands or moving away. The Hambukushu, nearest to the seat of power at Katima Mulilo, on the Zambezi, were the first to move. Being a river people, they kept to the rivers and moved to the vicinity of the Chobe and Linyanti areas where they, in turn, dislodged the Bayei, who were already settled there.

The Bayei, by this time, had probably explored, and were familiar with, much of the Okavango and its connecting link to the Chobe, which is called today the Selinda Spillway. Under pressure from the Hambukushu, they moved to the area of the Okavango and Lake Ngami, which they called Ncama, from which the present name derives. From 1750 onwards, the slow expansion of Bayei occupation continued and, by about 1800, they were firmly established throughout the region.[3]

The Bayei may thus have been the earliest arrivals among present Bantu-speaking peoples in the Okavango and are now the largest single group. They were not, of course, the earliest Bantu-speakers in the area; such people may have been in the Kalahari as early as AD 500, as discussed in an earlier chapter. The Bayei were expert fishermen and preferred the shallower water; hence they tended to concentrate more in the southerly section of the Delta. They owned some cattle but these animals did not assume an important social status in their lives, as they did in those of the Tswana people who were to follow. The Bayei used their stock neither for ploughing nor for bride-wealth but as pack animals.

The Okavango was not unoccupied when the Bayei began to settle there. For many centuries before their arrival, there had lived in the Okavango a group of people about whom we know very little. The River Bushmen, or Banoka, as they have come to be called, were Khoi people who had successfully adapted to an aquatic environment. Groups of them lived throughout the Okavango and along the Boteti River. Those of the Banoka who lived outside the tsetse fly zone, kept cattle, much to the surprise of archaeologists studying the Iron Age, who

believed until recently that the herding of cattle was the exclusive preserve of the Bantu people.[4] They were also expert hunters of aquatic game and were accomplished fishermen. The Banoka did not have fishing nets but used instead woven baskets and stone weirs, some of which are still in existence. It was from the Bayei, and later the Hambukushu, that they learnt netting skills, and the exchange of knowledge was reciprocal, each tribe learning from the other.

The Banoka taught the newcomers how to build game-pits as a means of killing game. In the centre of a suitable game trail a deep pit would be dug, with sheer sides and the bottom set with sharp-pointed stakes. Covered over with thin dry poles, grass, soil and a layer of leaves, the pits would be indistinguishable to all but the most cautious animal. Skilled though the Banoka were, it was the Bayei who were masters of better technology. They introduced two new methods for killing hippo, a highly prized catch, as well as improved fishing techniques and the well-known dug-out canoe, the *mokoro*.

There were two ways in which the Bayei set about obtaining fresh hippo meat. Both methods demanded a great deal of luck and the first a great deal of courage. Being skilled iron-workers, the Bayei fashioned a barbed harpoon, with a detachable iron head, to which was attached a long rope. Out upon the placid waters of the Okavango, precariously balanced in their narrow canoes, the hunters would search out hippo herds and attempt to get close to them. This in itself is a dangerous activity since hippo are notoriously bad-tempered if they are interfered with in the water, and will not hesitate to attack. Like Captain Ahab, the moment was judged and the harpoon thrust deep into the animal. Instantly, pandemonium would break out, and the hippo would take flight, the barbed head embedded deep in its flesh. The *mokoro* and its hunters were towed behind it, their aim being to kill the hippo with their spears before it broke loose, or killed them! In the more popular hunting areas the hippo would become very shy of *mekoro* and it became necessary for the hunters to take account of this. They would

hide their canoes on rafts of floating papyrus reeds in order to get close to their prey.[5]

A less risky method of killing hippo –
although one inclined to produce a very
nervous breed of pedestrian – involved sus-
pending a heavily weighted spear in a vertical, point-down position above a trail
known to be used by grazing hippo. A
triggering mechanism on the ground was
sprung by the animal's tread, releasing the
spear which fell, under its own weight, deep
into the unfortunate creature's body.[6]

The dug-out canoe or *mokoro* was another innovation brought to the Delta by
the Bayei. It is ubiquitous in the Delta today
but it was not introduced until after 1750.
There is some suggestion that the Banoka
used primitive, roughly constructed vessels
but it was not until the arrival of the Bayei
that canoe construction was raised almost
to the level of an art. Certain families specialise in making these canoes, which are
hacked, trimmed and carved out of a single
tree. The heaviest end, usually that nearest
the roots, becomes the bow and construction proceeds without any prepared plan.
The finished product is largely the result of
care, good luck and experience. The boats
are narrow and, to the inexperienced, extremely unstable, since they have a
rounded bottom and no keel. They draw
very little water and a large *mokoro* can
seat four or five people, although two to
three passengers is the norm.

Today, the cost of one of these canoes is
fairly high, in the region of P200. They
used to be less expensive and the price
was determined in a rather unusual, if
highly practical, way. The prospective new
owner would arrive at the builder's home
on the appointed day, bringing with him a
number of people of 'average' size. Price
was determined by the simple expedient of
allowing £1 sterling for each person who
could fit into the canoe before it sank. As
far as I can see, the method had only two
minor drawbacks. It is possible to imagine
the arguments that might develop over the
definition of 'average', since it is clearly to
the advantage of the buyer to find the
largest, heaviest 'average' people he can,
whilst the seller would want to select the
smallest and lightest. The other disadvantage would seem to be that, as it is the

capacity of the boat that is being tested,
one assumes the last passenger must
necessarily be responsible for getting
everyone thoroughly drenched![7]

Among other innovations, the Bayei also
introduced improved fishing techniques.
Foremost of these was the fishing net and
the idea of trawling from canoes. Two
*mekoro* would drag an extended net out
into deep water, gradually pulling it into a
semi-circle between them and, in this way,
trapping fish. Today these techniques are
still used, although nylon has replaced the
original net-making fibre which came from
the leaves of succulent plants. Other
methods of fishing included the construction of reed-weirs across narrow streams
and inlets.

Having displaced the Bayei, the Hambukushu, who had initially settled on the
Chobe River, found that they had not escaped the attentions of the Balozi empire,
and moved again, this time to the Okavango River, just inside the border of present-day Angola. From there they spread
slowly down-river and by the early nineteenth century had populated most of the
northern or 'Panhandle' section of the Delta.
They too were iron-using, cattle-owning,
river people. Unlike the Bayei, however,
they preferred deeper waters and were thus
more at home on the upper reaches of the
Delta. The huts in which they live are unusual in Southern Africa, dwelling and
storage huts being mostly rectangular as
opposed to the more usual round shape
which, it is said, they adopted from the Bayei.[8]

The Hambukushu knew, of course, how
to build *mekoro* but it is interesting that
their preferred method of propulsion differs
from that of the Bayei. The latter, confined
by choice to shallower waters, use a pole,
whilst the Hambukushu prefer a paddle.
Both tribes are primarily agriculturists, as
well as hunters and fishermen, and both,
because of the unique nature of the Okavango, cultivated fields, some depending
on rainfall for success and others which
were planted on the moist flood-plains, after
the waters had receded.

The Hambukushu were the renowned
rainmakers of the area in which they lived
and showed some enterprise in selling their
skills at this art to native tribes far beyond

their own boundaries. The rain-invoking rituals necessitated the sacrifice of children and this, plus their involvement in the slave and ivory trade, encouraged many of their followers to flee to the Okavango and Ngamiland.

Tribal unity was eventually shattered by the feuding of rival claimants to the chiefdomship and its control of the profitable rain-making ceremonies.[9]

Unlikely as it may seem at so comparatively recent a date, there are references to the Hambukushu's participation in slavery. Apparently they were involved in assisting the traders not only in finding slaves from among neighbouring tribes, but also from among their own people. Colonel Rey, who was Resident Commissioner in British Bechuanaland in the 1930s, reported that the numbers of Hambukushu had declined considerably over the years owing to the depredations of the Arab slave traders who frequently went to the local headmen and, in exchange for guns, powder, lead and beads, often received entire villages.[10] 'Matabele' Wilson, an adventurer and explorer at the turn of the century, said that when he was in 'Ansaras' (Andara), in the Caprivi Strip, 'four Arabs arrived, no doubt for the purpose of buying slaves.' Although Wilson gives no dates it would appear to have been about the 1890s.[11] Another report holds that the Portuguese, with their Mambari slave traders, regularly travelled all the way from the Atlantic coast to Andara, there to barter for slaves and ivory. It also claims that slavers from the east coast penetrated as far as the Okavango.[12] The reference to 'Arabs' at such recent dates is a misnomer and is likely to have referred to a few Portuguese half-castes who still made a living from the trade.

Like the Bayei, the Hambukushu are iron-workers, and their supply of ore came originally from the Lozi in Zambia. As they were closer to the source, they were able to obtain the ore more easily and soon surpassed the Bayei as the finest iron-smiths in the area. It is still possible, at Shakawe, in the very north-east of Botswana, to find old men who use the traditional methods of forging metal, although this is, of course, a dying craft.

The Hambukushu brought with them their own specialised fishing techniques, some of which are still practised today. The traditional basket fishing of the northern Delta is a rare experience to watch. It is only performed by women, who wade into the shallow parts of the river, carrying their tall, funnel-shaped, reed baskets which they line up, side by side, across the river's current. After the line of baskets is laid, the women approach them from upstream, flushing the fish and driving them into the traps. The method is simple but it is not without considerable risk, for the crocodiles of the upper Delta are renowned for their size and ferocity. The danger is reduced by strategically placing *mekoro* around the fishing area so that it is effectively cordoned off. The craft are manned by small boys who beat the water or the side of their boats to make the crocodiles aware of their presence. However ineffective this precaution may seem to be, it apparently does work and the only fatality recently recorded during a communal fishing event was about twenty years ago. On that occasion, a badly laid *mekoro* screen was blamed for allowing a formidable 3 m crocodile to take and kill one of the women.

A variation of this technique, and one borrowed from the Bayei, is found a little further to the south, at Sepopa. Here, smaller baskets are used. They are sturdier and also funnel-shaped, except that the smallest end has an opening in it. Refined for use in the shallow lagoons, which are numerous in the area, the method is as effective as that used further upstream. Practised by both men and women, the first stage is to drive a herd of cattle through the chosen lagoon. This is done to churn up the mud on the bottom, presumably to confuse the fish, and possibly to suffocate them, as fish are often seen floating on the surface after the mud has been stirred. The cattle are followed by a line of people, each carrying a basket. These are held by the neck and plunged down onto the muddy bottom. The fisherman then puts his or her hand through the narrow opening at the top and feels around the entire basket for anything that might have been trapped within it. Once again, this method has its risks and quite often young crocodiles are caught in the baskets. The fishermen somehow seem to know when this is the case and there are few reports of missing hands or fingers to suggest unlucky encounters.[13]

John Seaman, who is 'Mr Crocodile' of the Okavango today and is a most engaging and generous host, has hunted crocodiles in the past and now breeds them. He has many a crocodile story to tell. The point of the crocodile's tail and the tips of the six un-nailed 'fingers' (four at the front and two at the rear), he says, are exceptionally sensitive. When the Bayei or the Hambukushu are out in the waters fishing, and are bitten by a small crocodile, they apparently quickly grasp the creature as its clings onto them, and clamp its toes or tail between their teeth. It immediately lets go![14]

The famed wood-carvers from Namibia's Caprivi Strip include Ovambo and Hambukushu. As there is a more plentiful supply of suitable wood in that area, this is where most of the wood-carving is done. Although they continue to produce the most magnificent work, the output of the Hambukushu on the Okavango today is very small. An interesting instrument that is hand-made still, is what is commonly called the friction or 'hippo' drum. Made out of a hollow piece of wood, it is small enough to hold in one hand. One of the open ends is covered with tightly stretched cowhide into which has been depressed, from the inside, a short length of wood, secured on the outside by a thong at the point where it is about to pierce the hide. The length of wood hangs, suspended, down the interior of the drum and can be easily grasped by inserting a hand in the open end. The instrument is played by sliding the hand up and down the wood inside – but there is a secret to it. The palm of the hand must be slightly moistened with spittle. The noise produced can be startlingly like that of a hippo. Jessie Neil, who runs a safari camp in the Okavango Delta, summons her guests to the evening meal in this unusual and delightful way.[15]

In 1969 there occurred a second wave of Hambukushu immigration into the Okavango, due to much the same causes of the first, nineteenth century event. Many thousands of these people, fearful for their lives because of the civil war raging in Angola, fled that country and requested refugee status in Botswana. Botswana, generous as always to such people, accepted them. At first, while a suitable location was being sought, the 5 000 Hambukushu lived at Shakawe, just inside the border. In time, a new settlement, called Etsha, was created, on the south-east side of the Delta. Interestingly, whilst awaiting their fate at Shakawe, the refugees spontaneously organised themselves into thirteen natural groups, probably based on family, clan or totem. When the time came to move to Etsha, these divisions were preserved and today you will find thirteen small villages, each just over a kilometre from its neighbour, lining the road which serves them all.

These people brought with them a traditional Hambukushu skill, which had not hitherto been commercially exploited in Ngamiland. The skill was basket weaving. Baskets had always been woven by Okavango residents but the fresh input from the new arrivals reasserted the strong traditional and cultural components of this craft. Today the work of the Okavango's basket weavers is internationally known for its high standards of design and finish.[16]

All the designs are drawn from incidents in traditional life and reflect the close association of these people with the world in which they live. One woman, after witnessing the killing of an animal for meat, produced a new motif which she called 'the tears of the giraffe'. Another design resulting from the same event is known as 'the ribs of the giraffe'. Other patterns include 'the forehead of the zebra', 'the knees of the tortoise' and, after the pattern of zig-zagging lines that it leaves, 'the bull's urine trail'!

The variety of baskets is astonishing, owing to their traditional origins, when they were designed to meet a wide range of specific needs. There are enormous baskets which are used to store grain, and others specifically for herbs, seeds and household articles. One particular basket has a special, tight weave and it is used for holding the local beer. It is not entirely waterproof, but the material of which it is made swells up on contact with the liquid, so that only the smallest quantity escapes. The 'sweating' effect thus produced helps keep the beer fresh and cool.[17]

Baskets are manufactured now as part of a flourishing cottage industry that brings much needed income to a people who, only fifteen years ago, started with nothing. More than 15 000 baskets are sold annually, providing employment and income for more than 3 000 people. A family can earn more than P800 a year from its weaving work. Care is taken, through a selective buying policy, to maintain the highest standards. At the same time, by encouraging quality and not quantity, it is hoped to reduce the catastrophic impact the industry has had on local vegetation.

All the raw materials of Hambukushu basket-work are natural in origin and are found locally. With the growth in sales, the calls upon the environment have been excessive. The vegetable ivory palm, the unopened leaves of which are used, is now in short supply. In some places women have to walk for three days to find a supply of leaves.[18] Replanting has been urgently advised by various authorities but it is taking time to organise and to convince the local people of its necessity. As a result, unfortunately, the future of the industry is being threatened and alternative materials are being sought.[19] Some of the dyes that are used come from the bark of acacia trees and from the roots of other trees, and many of them are now dying from over-exploitation. This is a recurring environmental problem in the face of development. As with the grapple plant in the southern Kalahari (Chapter 12), when a price is placed on a naturally occurring commodity, wide-scale decimation almost immediately follows.[20]

The arrival of cattle, on a large scale, did not occur in Ngamiland until the coming of the Batawana people. They settled first near lake Ngami in 1795, having split away from the Bangwato, as a result of a dispute, shortly before that date. The latter were the main tribal grouping of the Tswana people and lived in the east, on the edges of the Kalahari. The Batawana were followed to their Ngamiland retreat by a Bangwato army, led by Chief Kgari, but they defended themselves successfully and were able to set themselves up as an independent nation. Peace was not to last and they soon found themselves subordinated to another,

more powerful tribe. By the mid-nineteenth century they were established in peace and independence again, this time at Toteng, to the south of the Okavango.

They remained here until 1883, when they were attacked by marauding Matabele warriors from the capital of Chief Lobengula at Bulawayo, in what is now Zimbabwe. The attack was devastatingly successful. The Batawana lost large numbers of cattle and many of their Bushman slaves. Encouraged by their success, the Matabele attempted a second, more ambitious raid in 1885. The Batawana, however, had been forewarned. They used their special knowledge of the Delta and withdrew into its flooded wilderness, hiding their cattle on its thousand islands. Unwisely, the Matabele followed. During several battles at river crossings in the vicinity of present-day Thubu, in the Delta, south-east of Gomare, the Batawana ambushed and turned back the raiders, who suffered heavy losses from rifle-fire and drowning.

The survivors fled back to Bulawayo but on the journey further disaster awaited them. With excessive confidence, born of their first raid, they had brought food and supplies only for the outward journey. Forced to retreat without the food or cattle they had expected to plunder, many died of thirst, starvation and exhaustion.

In 1915 the Batawana moved their capital again and established it on the banks of the Thamalakane River, at the very foot of the Okavango Delta, in a town we know today as Maun.[21]

The Khoi, better known as Hottentots (from the Dutch 'to stutter'), are another of the Kalahari's fascinating peoples. Their origins are obscure. Neither plainly Bantu nor Bushman, it is thought that they may have moved into Southern Africa from somewhere to the north, about two thousand years ago. They more closely resemble Bushmen in both language and physique but their culture is very different indeed. Unlike the Bushmen, they have a centrally organised political system and they are herders of cattle and sheep. Although they did not know how to manufacture iron, they could produce copper and made pottery, but essentially they were pastoralists rather than agriculturists and seemed to practise no form of agriculture at all. By about AD 1600 the Hottentots occupied much of southern Namibia, western Cape and western Botswana. They were exposed to pressures from various competing groups and, by 1850, their nation had disintegrated as an organised structure. Fragmented, many of the smaller groups resorted to brigandage and, during the numerous tribal wars of the nineteenth century, were constantly involved in conflict.[22]

In 1884 the Germans occupied what became known as German South West Africa. They attempted to bring the inter-tribal fighting to a halt and, to that end, signed peace treaties with the Hottentots and the Herero. It is said that the Germans' treatment of the indigenous people, particularly the Herero, was extremely harsh. The Herero, a proud and independent people, eventually rose in rebellion and a bloody and vicious war ensued in which the Hottentots, too, became involved. In 1905, after a massacre of Hottentots under Hendrik Witbooi at Hornkranz, a certain Simon Cooper (variously spelt Koper, Coper and Kooper), who had hitherto held his group aloof from the conflict, committed his forces to the fray, disregarding the treaty he had signed with the Germans.

Leading what was known as the Franzmann tribe of Hottentots, Cooper organised a guerrilla-type of action and for some time operated effectively against the Germans. It is probable that he based himself inside British territory by crossing the western border of British Bechuanaland (later to become Botswana) and operating from there. 'For several years he was the terror of the German settlers and patrols on the eastern frontier . . .'.[23]

There is some divergence of opinion as to exactly what eventually happened, various sources giving the account matching most closely the political stance they wished to assume at the time. A supposedly independent source suggests that, tired of the activities of this highly successful rebel, the Germans actually entered British territory and surprised Cooper and his men in a place where he had thought himself safe from their attentions, some 70 km inside the Bechuanaland border.[24] They managed

to escape but Cooper must have realised that the game was up and that he was no longer safe from German retaliation. He decided to appeal to Britain for protection.

In what has been described as a singularly shabby deal, the group was allowed to settle at Lokgwabe, not far from Lehututu, one of the most remote spots in the Kalahari. The deal was described in such terms because, far from coming to blows with Germany over what was, after all, a violation of her territorial integrity, Britain co-operated with her. In an agreement between the two governments, German money was paid over to the British Foreign Office which, in turn, made a yearly payment of £60 to Simon Cooper on the understanding that he 'had pledged to cease hostilities against South West Africa and not to leave his present place of residence without permission'.[25] It was a piece of 'Realpolitik', on a small scale, of which Bismarck would have been justly proud! At a small cost to themselves, the Germans had removed a very troublesome thorn from their side and, with a modicum of adjustment to principles, an international incident had been avoided.

Simon Cooper died in 1913 and the descendants of his rebel group are now spread throughout many of the towns and villages of western and southern Botswana. The Cooper family still live in Lokgwabe and I went to see them there. Dignified and gentle people, they received me kindly and cordially but, alas, their star has not risen; they remain poor and not altogether accepted by the local populace. The Hottentot is not regarded with much status or respect by the Tswana, who call them, privately, 'Double-tots', an allusion to their apparent propensity for drink for which, it is sadly said, they will sell their last cow. I did not get this impression from my short visit.

Simon Cooper and his Hottentots were not the only refugees who fled German South West Africa in the early years of the twentieth century. Tired of being deprived of their land, which was given to German settlers, the Herero rose in rebellion in 1904. They struck first at the German farmers and before long 150 of the colonists had been murdered. The German response was typical of the time and they waged a war of extermination against the Herero. A decisive battle was fought at Waterberg in 1904 and those Herero who managed to escape fled to all parts of Southern Africa. Many sought refuge, like the Hottentots, in the Kalahari.

The Herero are pastoralists who have scant regard for agriculture. Their origins are obscure but it is thought that they may have arrived in Southern Africa about AD 1500 from somewhere in central Africa. They are not strangers to either the Kalahari or to Botswana. By 1600 they were settled in the western Kalahari in Namibia, but their wide-ranging pastoral activities took them frequently across a border that did not then exist. By 1820 they were in conflict with local residents over grazing rights near Lake Ngami and are known to have used the grazing in the Ghanzi District in 1830.[26]

Strictly speaking, the Herero people can be divided into three or four groups, only one of which is properly called Herero. The others are Mbanderu, Tjimba and Himba. The reasons for this differentiation are not clear, even among the Herero themselves. It may be that the splintering took place shortly after the arrival of these people in the sub-continent.[27] In any event, among the three main Herero groups who still retain them, cattle are of great importance, not only for subsistence but for religious reasons.

Ownership of cattle is the central point of existence; their lives and deaths are closely involved with these animals. During his life, a man will single out his favourite oxen and others that are to be killed on his death. When he dies the favourite is killed immediately and he is buried in its skin. The other animals, for fear of the ancestors' anger if it is not done, are killed and eaten, and their skulls placed on the man's grave. Sometimes this slaughter will involve as many as 200 cattle.[28] In earlier times, so strong were these religious and cultural prohibitions that Herero were forbidden to sell their cattle.

It is estimated that some 2 000 to 3 000 of the Mbanderu Herero escaped from Namibia to the Kalahari and today they are widely distributed throughout Botswana. When they arrived they were without cattle, and for many years those in Ngamiland, for example, worked in servitude for the Batawana. They were paid in milk and the use of bulls for stud. Sometimes they would be given a calf or two as a bonus at year end. From the milk they received, they made butter and a cheese-like substance which they sold to the Batawana. Every available cent was used to buy more cattle. It took time but within twenty or thirty years the Herero were able to build up their herds and gain economic independence from the Batawana.

The experience had radically changed them as a people, however, and they did not go back to the old ways. Now, for the first time, they began to sell livestock, traditionally a forbidden practice. The traditions died slowly among the older people but not so the younger gereration. More and more, the Mbanderu raised cattle for commercial rather than religious purposes. Among the Botswana Herero, the sacred role of cattle is a thing of the past. They are now only their means of economic independence.[29]

Above all, the Herero are a proud people, yet resilient and capable of adapting to change. They have a deep respect for their nationality and their traditions. Despite the changes, they are still staunch traditionalists in some respects. They keep very much to themselves as a community and marriage outside it is uncommon. The females are also distinctive as to the manner of their dress. Subjected to missionary influence in the nineteenth century, the women adopted the full, ankle-length dress that was common in those days. Combined with unique headwear, made from material folded in a special way, this mode of dress still persists to this day. The drab, dusty streets of many a Kalahari town are brightened by the attractive, colourful sight of Herero women as they go about their daily business.

The importance of cattle in the lives of some Southern African pastoral peoples has an unexpected consequence in the rate of the occurrence of albinism in the sub-continent.[30] In some ethnic groups, notably the Tswana, its incidence is unusually high and this is attributed by some researchers to the relationship between marriage partners and cattle ownership. Albinism is a heriditary defect in the metabolism of melanin and it results in a decrease or absence of this pigment in the skin. Bantu people who are affected by it often have a chalky-white or pink-tinged skin and white or sandy-coloured hair. Contrary to common belief, albinism does not carry with it any impairment of intellectual faculties.

The occurrence of albinism is expressed as a rate of one in so many thousand, and it occurs universally. In Holland, for example, the rate is 1 in 20 000, in Northern Ireland 1 in 10 000 and in Nigeria as 1 in 5 000. Studies among Bantu ethnic groups in Southern Africa have revealed some interesting statistics. The rate among the Southern Sotho people, of whom the Tswana are part, is 1 in 2 254, among the Xhosa it is 1 in 4 700, the Pedi, 1 in 9 700 and the Shangaan, 1 in 28 614. Why do these rates vary so much and why is the incidence of albinism so high among the Tswana?

Among livestock-owning tribes, cattle are not only a source of food but, even more important, of wealth and status. When marriages are arranged cattle are given as gifts to the bride's family. Some of the tribal groups in Southern Africa arrange marriages, where possible, among close relatives, thereby ensuring that the cattle remain within the family, or among those relatives through whom the family can increase its political influence. This practice is particularly marked among the Sotho people; there are two Tswana proverbs which explain the reasons for marriages to blood relations: 'Child of my paternal uncle, marry me, so that the cattle should return to our kraal', and 'Side by side with his cousin, a man is always happy'.

Investigation of the tribal rules regarding such marriages shows that they vary considerably. Among the Zulu, for example, marriage between relatives is virtually taboo and prospective partners must be at least four generations removed, on the mother's or father's side. Marriages among the Zulu to blood relations is 4 per cent, whilst the among the Tswana it is 41 per cent, the latter society encouraging marriage between cousins. The advantage for the Tswana lies in retaining cattle-wealth within the larger family group; the disadvantage, however, is of increasing the spread of genetic disorders, hence the high rate of albinism, for example.

The Kalahari is home to numerous small groups of people, torn by strife and conflict from far distant homelands, who have settled there as a place of last refuge. With its endless spaces the Kalahari finds room for them all and offers a chance to start again with a promise of peace, stability and freedom from interference.

## REFERENCES

1. **Campbell, A C**. Personal communication, March 1986
2. **Leistner, O A**. *The Plant Ecology of the Southern Kalahari*. Government of South Africa, Department of Agricultural Services, Botanical Memoir No 38, Govt Printer, Pretoria, 1967, pp 31-2
3. **Campbell, A C**. *The Guide to Botswana*. Gaborone: Winchester Press, 3rd edition, 1980, pp 74-7
4. **Campbell, A C**. Personal communication, March 1986
5. Ibid
6. **Tlou, T**. The Taming of the Okavango Swamps — the Utilization of a Riverine Environment ±1 750 - ±1 800'. In *Botswana Notes and Records*, Vol 6, 1972, pp 147-59
7. **Campbell, A C**. *The Swamp Boats. Botswana, No 4*. Government of Botswana, Department of Information Services, Gaborone (no date), pp 64-9
8. **Campbell, A C**. Personal communication, March 1986
9. **Larson, T J**. 'The Hambukushu of Ngamiland'. In *Botswana Notes and Records*, Vol 3, 1969, pp 29-44
10. **Rey, C F**. Ngamiland and the Kalahari. Address to the Royal Geographic Society (?), 6 June 1932 (no other references), p 305
11. **Wilson, W**. *The Northern Kalahari Desert*. Rhodesia Scientific Association, Vol 5, Part 2, p 31
12. **Larson, T J**. Op cit, p 30
13. **Mamashela, L D**. *The Weird Art of Basket Fishing. Botswana, No 4*. Government of Botswana, Department of Information Services, Gaborone, (no date), pp 30-37
14. **Seaman, J**. Personal communication, December 1984
15. **Neil, J**. Personal communication, October 1983

16. **Thomas, M.** Personal communication, December 1984

17. **Yoffe, M.** *Baskets that Tell a Story. Botswana, No. 5.* Government of Botswana, Department of Information Services, Gaborone, Botswana (no date), **pp 16-21**

18. **Tshweneagae, M.** Personal communication, December 1984

19. **Ibid**

20. **Moss, H.** Personal communication, July 1984

21. **Potten, D H.** 'Aspects of the Recent History of Ngamiland'. In *Botswana Notes and Records,* Vol 8, 1974, **pp 63-86**

22. **Campbell, A C.** *The Guide to Botswana.* Gaborone: Winchester Press, 3rd edition, 1980, **pp 91-5**

23. **British Govt.** *Union of South Africa: Report on the Natives of South West Africa and their Treatment by Germany.* Administration office, Windhoek, South West Africa, Her Majesty's Stationery Office, London, Jan. 1918, **p 83**

24. **Trail, A.** Personal communication, May 1984

25. **Jerve, A M.** *Cattle and Inequality. A study in rural economic differentiation from southern Kgalakgadi in Botswana.* The CHR, Michelsen Institute, Dept of Social Science and Development, Norway. DERAP publication number 143, September 1982, **p 132**

26. **Campbell, A C.** *The Guide to Botswana.* Gaborone: Winchester Press, 3rd edition, 1980, **pp 77-85**

27. **Vivelo, F R.** 'The Entry of the Herero into Botswana'. In *Botswana Notes and Records,* Vol 8, 1976, **pp 39-46**

28. **Campbell, A C.** *The Guide to Botswana.* Gaborone: Winchester Press, 3rd ed., 1980., **p 81**

29. **Vivelo, F R.** Op cit. **p 43**

30. **Kromberg, G R C.** 'Prevalence of Albinism in the South African Negro'. In *South African Medical Journal.* 13 March 1982, **p 383-6**

# 17. No Man's Land

TOWARDS the west of the Kalahari there is a town in Botswana called Ghanzi. It is, essentially, a cattle town and a centre for the administration of the vast Ghanzi District. The town sits atop a great ridge of limestone that curves south from Lake Ngami and then west, fetching across an enormous stretch of Kalahari sands until it merges with the foothills of the mountains where you will find the city of Windhoek, capital of Namibia. To call it a 'great' ridge is, in one sense, misleading. Few features, amid the unrelenting flatness of the Kalahari, qualify for such an appellation, at least in terms of height. You can hardly discern the ridge from the air, and not at all from the ground, but it is appropriately named nevertheless because it runs continuously for over 500 km and, say the experts, includes some of the finest cattle country in the world. There is another reason for its great attraction. In the limestone, below its shallow surface sands, there appear to exist unlimited quantities of good, sweet water. It is these two features, the grazing and plentiful water, which have attracted man to this area.

Even today, Ghanzi is remote. It is served by major roads from the east, west and north. It has an airfield, but there is no regular service and a journey upon any of the roads is not lightly attempted; they are execrable and the distances are vast. Although it might have been a little more comfortable, travel in earlier times was probably even more difficult, as there were no roads at all and Ghanzi was not on the way to anywhere.

As far as can be established, the first white person there was an Englishman by the name of Moyle, in 1840.[1] He had got into difficulties on a hunting trip and the perennial springs that existed on the ridge

at the time saved his life. Over the next forty years many of the era's famous explorers passed along the ridge: Andersson, Galton, Baines, Chapman and the German, Schinz. Somewhere about 1868 a man named Hendrik Matthys van Zyl made his first appearance in the area.

Few more ruthless, rugged and independent men have walked the sands of the Kalahari. Van Zyl is a legendary figure, but surprisingly little is known, and even less has been written, about him. Such facts as have survived, emphasise these qualities, and show that he was indeed an exceptional person.

Van Zyl is thought to have been born in about 1830, in the Cape Province, and may well have moved to what was to become the Transvaal with the Great Trek.[2] At one time he was a Member of Parliament in the cabinet of the South African Republic, but after his involvement in a scandal following his divorce, he left the country.[3] He was clearly a man of some intelligence and, possibly, some wealth. Whatever the cause of his departure from the Boer Republics, he appears to have devoted himself to life on the western sands. It is said that he planned to establish a community, with himself as president, near Rietfontein, about 70 km west of Ghanzi, but the idea seems not to have materialised. There is a suggestion that he might have visited Gootsa Pan, north of the giant Ntwetwe Pan in central Botswana, as the initials 'H.v.Z.' are said to be carved on a tree there, with the date 1858.

In 1868 Van Zyl travelled to Hereroland, in Namibia, by way of Lake Ngami, from which journey he returned to the Transvaal with many ostrich skins and, some claim, with child slaves. He had gained the friendship and respect of the local chiefs and this may have laid the foundations for his future in the Kalahari. From 1868 to 1872 he hunted extensively in the Ghanzi District and at the end of that time, he decided to leave the Transvaal permanently and return to Ghanzi.

One cannot help but wonder what sort of person would forsake every vestige of civilisation and take his wife and children to a completely remote place, where there was no one else at all, except perhaps for a handful of nomadic Bushmen. His confidence must have been awesome. It was necessary to take with him everything that he could possibly need and he had to be prepared to deal with every emergency with only the help of his family. There was nobody else to call upon.

Records show that Van Zyl spent six months on the banks of the Limpopo River in 1873,[4] and whilst there made purchases from a passing trader of guns, ammunition and sundry goods to the value of £1 200, for which he paid in gold. Obviously, he was not without financial resources. He moved across the Kalahari in the wet season and settled first near Lake Ngami in early 1874. (There is some confusion as to whether he settled here or moved on, immediately, to Ghanzi.[5]) His entourage was not unsubstantial; we know that he had five wagons, breeding cattle and 'salted' horses. Near the lake he set up a temporary home for one year, and here he and his sons hunted successfully. At some stage during his travels, Van Zyl had inadvertently stabbed himself in the eye while skinning a hippo. His eye never recovered, but he had special sights fitted to his rifle and he remained, for the rest of his life, an excellent shot. During his stay at Ngami, he appears to have usurped King Moremi's minority, and virtually ruled the Tawana people, extracting taxes from them for the privilege of so doing.

At the end of the year, he set off for Cape Town by way of Walvis Bay, on Namibia's coast. His wanderings, by ox-wagon, had taken him more than halfway across the continent. The proceeds of his sales in the Cape brought him a large sum of money and it was with this capital that he returned once more to Ghanzi, there to establish his renowned home. We know that he was set-

tled by 1877, although it might have been as early as the end of 1875. In any event, it was at about this time that his infamous hunting exploits were recorded.

His sons were hunters too and it is believed that from time to time he also used the services of passing visitors to the area. In his first year at Ghanzi he and his party killed 400 elephant, acquiring in the process a conservatively estimated 4 tonnes of ivory. The following year, 1878, they slaughtered 103 elephant in a single afternoon. Apparently the herd was in the vicinity of a pan, now known as Olifants Pan. Shots were fired and the herd stampeded straight into the pan. At the time it must have been moist, for the herd ran blindly into it and were soon caught fast in a mire of mud and clay. The hunters sat around the edge, picking off the animals at their leisure.

There were six hunters present that day, three of whom were Van Zyls. There is some doubt as to whether the father was one of them, or whether they were all his sons. In either event, all were in his employ and the ivory went to him.

When the slaughter was over the victorious hunters carved their names on a baobab tree near the pan. Ever after, the tree was known as the 'Hunters' Tree' and those who thought their deeds worthy of commemoration, added their names to the list. I have not seen this tree, which is said still to exist, and I am not entirely convinced that this story is true – or that the tree exists. Elephant are wily creatures and I cannot imagine them making so fatal a mistake. However, there seems to be no way, now, to verify the tale.

The house that Van Zyl built in Ghanzi has become a legend in itself. It is said to have been a double-storey and furnished at great expense with French furniture. Even today, you will be told that the windows were of stained glass. It is difficult to verify any of this and the truth may simply be that Van Zyl built a very large house which, to those who visited it, deprived as they were after months in the bush of any kind of luxury, was lavish in the extreme. The ruins of the house can be seen today on the farm Ghanzi Number 1, presently owned by Dick Eaton. Nothing but the foundations remain, and I found it difficult to trace them.

Tom Kayes recalled building a house on Ghanzi Number 1 in 1914, within 100 m of Van Zyl's old house, and he says it was in ruins then.[6] The highest standing wall was no more than 0,5 m high and there was a huge mound of rubble in the centre. Tom found some pieces of coloured glass at the site which he described as the stippled variety 'that you used to get in those fancy doors'. The insides of the remaining walls were plastered and coloured blue and pink. He saw no sign of a roof, nor of thatching nor any trace of poles. It is his opinion that the house was a single-storey because, he said, there was not enough rubble and the ground plan was so large there was no need to go up.

Tales of Van Zyl's success as a hunter spread, and after his death a swarm of human vultures descended. His house was probably ransacked, since it is believed that his family abandoned it, and the ruins have been deeply quarried by generations since, by those looking for hidden wealth. This, in Dick Eaton's opinion, explains the mound of rubble.[7] Another explanation may be that many of the buildings and water reservoirs erected in that vicinity since the turn of the century used stone taken from the walls of Van Zyl's house. Today, the ruins are under state protection and perhaps, at some future date, resources will be made available to investigate them properly, and to learn more of how this extraordinary man lived.

That he lived like a sultan and considered himself 'Laird of Ghanzi' is widely told. He organised great hunting expeditions from his castle in the veld. He is supposed to have employed more than a hundred Bushmen in his lands and fields. After some time four other hunters and a trader with his family joined him at Ghanzi, but who these people were we have no idea. Van Zyl was certainly a very successful hunter and, so the tales go, great loads of ivory, feathers, skins and trophies were sent down to Walvis Bay and the Cape. There were rumours that he buried much of his treasure at Drotsky's Cave but, if true, we may wait a long time before it is recovered as a thorough search would take a lifetime.

The first of the Dorsland Trekkers, of whom we will learn more later on, were not impressed with Van Zyl. They had had an extraordinarily difficult journey, but he was unwilling to give them water, lest their animals damage the sides of his wells! He eventually relented, but not before these hardy trekkers had decided that they were not going to place themselves under the jurisdiction of an imperious and ambitious man like Van Zyl. They moved on to Rietfontein.

Van Zyl was not without some loyalty to his fellow Boers, however, and when he heard that one of their party, a youth named William Frederick Prinsloo, had been murdered by Bushmen, he took it upon himself to seek revenge. His method was simple, if barbaric. Through his servants, he put out the word that he was giving a party for the Bushmen, with free tobacco and brandy for all. Within a few days, groups of Bushmen began to arrive and they were accommodated in a specially built stockade. When Van Zyl judged that sufficient men had collected he ordered them to be caught and bound. They were taken to the edge of the pan where the Prinsloo boy had been murdered. There, in cold blood, Van Zyl shot thirty-three of them. That night, perhaps to make peace with his Creator, Van Zyl held a service in which he quoted the passage 'An eye for an eye and a tooth for a tooth.'

There are at least five different accounts of Van Zyl's death. It is not even certain when it occurred, although 1879 or 1880 seem the most likely years. Some say he was murdered by Bushmen in retaliation for his slaughter of their companions. Others say a dissatisfied Bushman servant, whom he had reared from childhood, killed him. There is a tale that he once sheltered Chief Moremi in his house, hiding him behind the folds of the cloth on the dining-room table, while his pursuers searched the room. It is said that this interference in native affairs earned him the anger of the Tawana's enemies, the Damara. He seems also, to have earned the disapprobation of the Hottentots and, in a different version, of the Tawana. The most authoritative source claims that he appeared before the magistrate, Palgrave, at Gobabis in 1880, on

charges of general banditry. He was cleared and went on to Ovamboland, where he
was murdered by Hottentots.

Whatever his fate and however unpleasant it might have been, it seems to have
been appropriate. Van Zyl was a man who
lived by the sword and it was fitting that he
should die that way. It seems remarkable
that so little should be known about so
notorious a person. The tales of his death,
where they mention it at all, all say his wife
escaped and returned to the Transvaal. But
he had at least three sons – Andrew, the
eldest, Jan and Pieter, and also a daughter.
Nothing is said about what happened to
them.

In the last quarter of the nineteenth century there occurred a most extraordinary
movement of Afrikaner people, whose jour-
neyings took them for many thousands of
kilometres through the sands of the Kalahari. In an exodus from the Transvaal, hundreds of people, taking with them their cattle, horses and all their worldly possessions,
set out across the sandy wastes in ox-
wagons, with no definite objective in mind
and, did they but know it, nothing but a
bleak and tragic future ahead of them. The
Dorsland or Thirstland Trek, at it came to
be known, touched lightly upon the affairs
of Ghanzi, but the trekkers did pass through
the area and some lingered there for years.

The Boer farmer had, historically, proved
to be a tough and extremely independent
individual. Any knowledge of South African history will show that the 'trekboer'
has always been a part of it. From earliest
times there have been individuals whose
whole lives have been devoted to living
alone, with their families and animals, far
out in the veld, away from every semblance
of rule and regulation that organised society demands. The Dutch East India Company, in the old days of the Cape, tried,
unsuccessfully, to control their wanderings.
Later administrations also attempted the
task, with an equal lack of success. Increasingly, as the Afrikaner nation took on
an identity of its own, dissatisfaction with
the Government and the way it governed,
grew. The people resorted to a traditional
solution – they trekked. To most, it was a
means of wiping the slate clean, of starting
again and of doing things 'their' way. To

some, trekking was an incurable disease.

While Africa remained empty and under-
populated, trekking was an approach that
had its merits, but by 1870 this was no
longer the case; it was no longer possible
to head for the horizon and to find a new
place to start again. The continent was becoming crowded and the best areas were
already occupied. Old habits and traditions
die hard, however, as the Dorsland Trekkers found out, at appalling cost.

To many, the Great Trek of 1836 had
been successful. The tyranny of British
Government had been left behind, the slate
had indeed been wiped clean, and they
were content with the way in which the
South African Republic was being run.
There were others who were not as satisfied.[8] They did not care for President Bur-
gers' new laws, nor did they care for his
religious learnings; there was fear, too, of
British designs on the new republic. This
group once more looked to the old solution
and began to think of another trek. Reports
emanating from people such as Van Zyl
spoke of the lush pastures in the Kalahari
and wistful minds turned to thoughts of a
new, better and freer country.

There were, in fact, three Dorsland Treks
– the first was led by Gert Alberts, the second by Louwrens du Plessis and the third
by J F Botha. They left the Transvaal at different times but joined forces in the region
of the Okavango. No group appeared to
have a clear aim of what they were going
to do, or where they were going. Crossing
the Kalahari seemed the immediate objective. Although it was claimed that their intention was the establishment of an independent republic, in truth it was more likely to have been a manifestation of an un-
controllable urge, simply to trek, as they
and their kind had always done.

Alberts' party crossed the Kalahari with
little difficulty. They assembled on the Limpopo in mid-1875 and, by the end of September, had secured the permission of
Khama, the Bechuana Chief at Shoshong,
to pass through his territory. They left Shoshong in the third week of November, at
the start of the rainy season, to cross the
sands to the Boteti River, with ten or twelve
families, forty to fifty wagons and about
1 400 cattle. As they had been advised to

do, they travelled in small groups. There was good reason for this advice. Pans were few and small; scarce water resources could better handle a large number of small groups, spaced apart, than a single large group at one time.

The party reached Lake Ngami after losing only a few cattle to tsetse fly. Some of their stray cattle had been killed and eaten by Tawana warriors but, on learning of this, chief Moremi replaced the animals and allowed the travellers to pass, otherwise unmolested, through his territory. Early in 1876 the first of their party reached Ghanzi, where they met Van Zyl. They then moved further west, to Rietfontein, which became their base for the next two years. There they hunted, tended their cattle and explored north and north-east, towards the Okavango River and Delta, while they waited for the other trekkers to join them.

The second group were altogether less successful. The reasons for this are not clear but there are two possible explanations. Firstly, the trek seemed constantly beset by leadership disputes. The lack of sound leadership led to the making of poor decisions and this, in turn, resulted in tragic loss of life. The second reason may be the fact that this party was very much larger.

The second trek began to collect on the banks of the Limpopo, in the Marico District, in April 1876. They remained there for over eighteen months, during which time approaches to two rulers were made. The first was to Lobengula, in Bulawayo, to assure him that he had nothing to fear from the trek which had no designs on his possessions or lands. The second was to Khama, at Shoshong, asking permission to pass through his country. This request caused much concern to the people of Bechuanaland. They felt that a small group of ten families was one thing, but that a much larger group of some 480 people was quite another, especially when it became clear that they were looking for a place to settle. Protracted negotiations took place but eventually Khama gave his consent and offered the same advice that he had given the earlier group.

During the last months of 1877, two years behind the leading party, Du Plessis led his group westwards, away from the Limpopo. They had 128 wagons, 480 people and 'thousands' of head of cattle. It is said that they divided into three groups and that they sent their stock on ahead. However, their total demands were too much for the ephemeral water sources of the Kalahari to bear, and they suffered most dreadfully. From this point onwards, disaster dogged their steps.

In the months that followed, dreams of an independent republic probably faded away as men, women and children fought a constant battle with the realities of an unkind Kalahari. Difficulties that others had overcome now seemed insurmountable. The sand was soft and deep. Sometimes wagons would make a mere 500 m progress in a single day. Oxen began to suffer from the heat, and thirst increasingly became a problem. Perhaps the rains failed, or were late, we do not know. The vast herds of stock drank the water at the pans, leaving little for the oxen and even less for their masters.

In a straight line, it is more than 200 km from Shoshong to the Boteti River, and their slow progress sapped the will of man and beast. The trekkers had little alternative but to go on, there remaining the hope of water ahead and the certainty of none behind. As oxen fell by the wayside the wagons' loads were lightened as trekkers were forced to discard household furniture and utensils. All manner of goods were to be found along the route for years to come. Eventually, as more oxen died, even the wagons had to be abandoned, and their owners were obliged to walk. Even to this day, apparently, wagon parts and other debris can still be found.[9]

The trekkers started in the east, from Tlhabala, and the worst of the tragedy occurred at Nkawane and Mmaletswai wells, where there simply was not enough water. It is said that the travellers would arrive at waterholes, only to find dead cattle lying in the mud. They would take the moist mud and squeeze it in a cloth, to wring out just a few drops of precious water.[10] Stock, desperate for water, could be seen licking the bright, burnished steel rims of the wagon wheels, evidently mistaking the shiny surface for water. By the time this stricken group reached Lake Ngami thirty-seven people had died and a fifth of the wagons had been abandoned. There is no record of the number of stock that were lost.

While Du Plessis's party waited on the shores of Ngami to regain its strength, the third trek joined them. A small party of eight wagons and forty people, led by Jacobus Botha, they, like the Alberts trek, had experienced no difficulties with the crossing. They were appalled at the condition of their colleagues. Indecision and uncertainty now plagued the combined groups. Some determined to return to the Transvaal, some to join Alberts at Rietfontein, while others elected to remain in the area of Ngami and the Okavango.

Those who remained near the Okavango were to suffer still more. Tsetse fly claimed almost all their cattle and malaria took its toll among the humans. Eventually the survivors were so exhausted they no longer had the strength to hunt. The situation was serious indeed. Those who could, met at a place called Debra, in Ovambo country, and here, Alberts, who had heard of their plight, found them and stayed with them. Some returned to the Transvaal, but the remainder moved on to Leeupan where, in July 1878, those of the Dorsland Trek who wished to continue were reunited and reorganised. According to W A de Klerk,[11] a total of 200 people had lost their lives in the crossing of the Kalahari and in the months spent at the Okavango. Forty-three lay buried at Olifants Pan.

Under the new leadership, and believing perhaps that things could not possibly get worse, the combined trekkers moved away from the Okavango region and arrived at Etosha Pan in northern Namibia. By this time it was generally agreed that Angola would be an attractive destination and while they rested at Etosha, scouts went ahead to find a route.

The trekkers had met up with a man named Axle Eriksson, a well-known hunter, naturalist and trader. He was horrified by their miserable condition and sent a full report to Cape Town. A copy of this report reached the hands of the newspapers and was widely publicised throughout South Africa. Great concern was expressed and the matter was debated in Parliament. An emergency committee was convened and contributions, in cash and kind, were gathered from across the country. The services of two schooners, the *Swallow* and *Christiana*, were engaged, and tonnes of supplies transported to Walvis Bay. From there, in February 1880, they were collected and taken by wagon to the near-desperate trekkers at Etosha, arriving in time to avert complete disaster in a people who were exhausted by sickness and almost overcome by the deprivations they had endured.

Records show that in November 1879 the trek party consisted of 352 whites, 70 wagons, 320 oxen and 300 or 400 cattle.[12] Revived both spiritually and physically by the emergency aid from Cape Town, the Dorsland Trekkers were ready to move on. They had decided on the Humpata Plateau in Angola, of which they had heard glowing descriptions and to which they were now determined to proceed. By the end of 1880 they were near the Kunene River on the Angolan border. Contact had been made with Major Matla, Portuguese Governor of Mossamades District, and he invited the Boers to settle in Angola, offering them farms.

In 1881 the remnants of the Dorsland Trekkers reached Humpata. There were about 55 families in all, comprised of 270 whites, together with 50 servants from the Transvaal, 61 wagons, 840 trek-oxen, 2 160 head of cattle (evidently, they had profited from some cattle-owners on their journey north!), 120 horses and 3 000 head of small stock. From the beginning of their journey, the combined treks had lost 300 whites, either through death or defection.[13] Humpata was, for them, the Promised Land. There they began to mark out farms and to plan a town. It must have been a time of great joy and happiness, after so many years of incredible hardship and tragedy. Unfortunately, their troubles were far from over.

Perhaps because of the nature of the people, or perhaps because the reasons that have been recorded were true, dissatisfaction soon set in. In the mid 1880s about half of the Hampata Boers left, claiming that disease had decimated their livestock. Some of them returned to the Transvaal, others went to take up free farms that had been provided for them in a small republic, established by W W Jordan, in Namibia. This latter group did not last long. By 1887 incessant attacks by Bushmen caused them to abandon their farms; some returned to Humpata and others to the Transvaal.

Additional Boers from the Transvaal did arrive at Humpata in 1894 to supplement the diminishing numbers there, and they helped to revive the struggling community. The Angolan Boers, some of whom may still be there today, spread throughout the country and contributed greatly to its development. They made roads, provided transport and boosted the economy through their agricultural activities. Some joined the armed forces and, it is said, provided the few reliable troops the Portuguese were to command.

Despite a promising start, events in Angola were not encouraging. Individual independence and its divisive effects, which had motivated the Dorsland episode in the first place, and possibly contributed to its tragedy, were with them still. The community dispersed and most made their living from transporting, a highly competitive pursuit. As one person who used to live there said: 'They could not live close together, lest they cut each other's throat.'[14] In the 1920s there were about 200 Afrikaans families in Angola. The hinterland, where most of them lived, was very primitive; the families were desperately poor and had no prospects. They were regarded by the Portuguese authorities as strangers and they had no rights or privileges, no title to land, despite earlier promises, and were denied the opportunity of obtaining citizenship. There were pressures upon them to give up their language, their church and their schools.

In 1928 an arrangement was made by the Portuguese Government for many of the remaining Dorsland Trekkers to leave. Not all did so: some had married into local families and others were to follow later. It seems sadly ironic that those who did take

advantage of the opportunity went south to the border by ox-wagon, the same way they had come.

The Dorsland Trekkers were remarkable people. They believed in themselves and in what they wanted to achieve, however ill-considered their objectives may seem. They were tough, resolute and independent people, with strong religious values. Above all, they epitomised conservatism and sought always to structure a world around them where things did not change. Their self-imposed isolation made them a tragic people, out of touch with the rest of their kind. The world did change, and they were left behind, and all their courage, all their heroism, in the end counted for nothing at all.

## REFERENCES

1. Silberbauer, G B. *Report to the Government of Bechuanaland on the Bushman Survey.* Bechuanaland Government, Gaborone, 1965, p 114
2. Tabler, E C. *Pioneers of South West Africa and Ngamiland, 1738 - 1880.* Cape Town: A A Balkema, 1973, pp 113-15
3. Silberbauer, G B. Op cit
4. Tabler, E C. Op cit
5. Silberbauer, G B. Op cit
6. Kayes, M T. Personal communication, December 1984
7. Eaton, R C. Personal communication, October 1984
8. Tabler, E C. Op cit, pp 31-4
9. Hitchcock, R K. *Kalahari Cattle Posts.* Government of Botswana, Ministry of Local Government and Lands, Gaborone, October 1978, pp 131-2
10. De Klerk, W A. *The Thirstland.* Harmondsworth: Penguin Books Ltd, 1977, p 29
11. De Klerk, W A. Ibid, p 42 and personal communication, February 1985
12. Tabler, E C. Op cit
13. Ibid
14. Russell, M and Russell, M. *Afrikaners of the Kalahari.* Cambridge: Cambridge University Press, 1979, p 95

# 18. A Town Like Ghanzi

THE embryonic settlement of Ghanzi struggled fitfully for life in the years that followed the death of Van Zyl. The Dorsland Trekkers had dispersed, moved on or returned to the country from which they came. A handful remained in the area and others moved further west to Rietfontein, in what was to become German South West Africa. Ghanzi, incredibly remote, would surely have returned to the dust of the desert from which it sprang were it not for one of those curious turns of history which dragged it back from the brink of oblivion and gave it renewed vitality. Ghanzi was to become, for a brief period, the focal point of the political tensions that tore apart the continent of Africa at the end of the nineteenth century. Another group of settlers was organised and sent to the western sands. This injection of vigour was not to last, but it served to keep the community alive and gave it sufficient strength to limp into the twentieth century when, eventually, it found its feet and grew to the thriving farming town it is today.

In the 1880s the great 'scramble for Africa' was at its height and the political map had changed beyond all recognition. Germany claimed a colony on the south-western side of the sub-continent, the British were installed in the Cape and in Natal, while independent Boer republics had been established in the hinterland. The British aim to bring these republics back within the fold of her administration was threatened by the evident signs of friendship between the Boers and Germany. This factor, together with Germany's well-known territorial acquisitiveness, was a cause of great concern for Britain's strategists. Much of the land between the Boer republics and Germany's South West Africa already lay under British protection but the possibility

of attack from two sides led to the realisation that ownership of empty land was not enough. Something would have to be done to fill it. In the circumstances, it was not difficult for Cecil John Rhodes, the arch-colonialist, to shape events towards his own ends and those of his British South Africa Company. He made the most of the opportunity.

The purpose of organising the settlement of a large group of white farmers in the Ghanzi region during the 1890s is difficult now to determine. The exact reasons are lost in the claim and counter-claim that obfuscates the facts of history and reflects the ever-changing priority of political motives. To some it was an attempt by the British to establish a 'buffer zone' of white presence that would serve to deter German ambitions – although how much a handful of remote and unsupported settlers were expected to achieve in the face of possible German aggression has been a much debated point. Others believe that the event is a classic illustration of Rhodes' opportunism. By sponsoring the settlement, he hoped to begin the process by which the present area of Botswana might be incorporated into his company's already extensive territorial holdings. What does seem certain, however, is that the scheme's primary purpose was not the benefit of those who took part in it. They were merely the incidental and unimportant pawns of history. In the event, the story of the Ngamiland or Rhodes Trek makes fascinating reading and provides some insight into the political expediency that directed events of that time.[1]

Having obtained the partial sanction of Whitehall for his scheme of another trek to the Kalahari, matters obligingly played right into the hands of Rhodes. A spontaneously organised trek to Ngamiland was already in the offing in the early 1890s, just when Rhodes needed it. The trek had originally been planned by Boers from the Cape, the Transvaal and the Orange Free State. It was their intention, as with the Dorsland Trekkers who had gone before them, to establish an independent republic, somewhere in the Kalahari. Rhodes succeeded in 'capturing' the trek. A series of advertisements appeared in local papers. One, in the *Patriot*, offered farms of 5 000 morgen in the Ghanzi district for the price of a £1 application fee. The free use of drilling equipment was also to be provided and free farms were promised to the eldest sons of the sixty-odd families who accepted the offer. Word about Ghanzi had spread. It was described as a plateau with an unequalled climate, in a country where no harsh or destroying winds blew, where there were no extremes of heat or cold, and no malaria. But for the fact of its inaccessibility, said one report, it might well have become the health resort of the Empire.[2] (Having spent some time in Ghanzi, in the hottest part of the year, neither its present residents nor I would be likely to agree with this description!)

With the makings of his future trek at hand, Rhodes now set about the business of obtaining the consent of the chief who was most likely to have suzerainty over the area. This step was taken in anticipation of British Government authority which had not, at that time, been granted. The way in which it was undertaken is typical of the duplicity, deceit and dishonesty which appears to have characterised many agreements of this nature at that time. Rhodes' agent was Isaac John Bosman. At the end of 1893 he went to Ngamiland, fraudulently claiming to be a representative of the Imperial Government, and obtained from Sekgoma, the Tawana chief, two written, signed concessions. They were in Dutch, a language Sekgoma neither spoke nor understood. They gave unrestricted power to the chartered company to dispose freely of all the land in Sekgoma's country, as well as complete monopoly of the mineral and prospecting rights. In return Sekgoma was given a gift of firearms. For the benefit of the chief and his councillors, a badly writ-

ten Tswana translation of the concessions was prepared. Its terms were not the same as those of the Dutch versions and spoke vaguely of a treaty of friendship between Britain and the chief!

British administration had not yet been installed in Ngamiland and Bosman left, taking his fraudulent concessions with him. However, the suspicions of the Tawana were aroused, having got wind of events in Matabeleland where, for very similar reasons, unrest was already simmering. It was not until September of the following year, 1894, that the British Government's formal representative arrived and it was to him, Lieutenant A B Walsh, that the Tawana expressed their fears. News of the fraudulent agreements eventually reached the British Government which refused to sanction them, postponed the trek and ordered the company to obtain new (and presumably honest) concessions. The British were by no means against the idea of a trek but, happily, they seemed to have had some conscience and were evidently not prepared to condone such outright and blatant dishonesty.

The Tawana, on the other hand, were extremely apprehensive about the possibility of a white settlement on the edge of their hunting lands, particularly when it was apparently to involve Boers, whom they did not care to have as neighbours. Tension in the region ran high, and distrust and suspicion of British motives grew. It was an unfortunate time for there to occur another example of Rhodes' bland assumption of authority. The event compounded the political complexity of the problem and it also established a base of misinformation about Ghanzi which did little to enhance its chances of survival as a settlement.

Early in June 1894 the trekkers had gathered, in two parties, on the south-eastern edge of the Kalahari. Half were at Pitsani and the other half at Maritsane. Despite the fact that the trek had been halted by the British Government and that permission from the Tawana chief had not been obtained, it was decided to send a reconnaissance mission to Ghanzi. A group of twenty-five trekkers, accompanied by fifteen members of the Bechuanaland Border Police, led by a Captain Fuller, set off in

February 1895. The news of their unexpected appearance in Ghanzi, when relayed to the Tawana, did absolutely nothing at all to diminish Tawana fears as to the real intentions of the British. Mistrust reached new levels of intensity and so complicated the diplomatic difficulties that it was to take a further three years before the trek finally left on its journey across the Kalahari.

Leading the reconnaissance, Fuller returned and submitted a report on the Ghanzi district. He estimated that there was land for 800 or 900 farms, each approximately 5 000 morgen. The land was well watered, the grazing was sweet and there were plenty of Bushmen available as herders of livestock. The news was well received by those who had remained behind and served to fortify them during the long wait that lay ahead. Unfortunately, little of it was true.

During that time, Rhodes was involved in the infamous Jameson Raid, an attempt to ferment rebellion in the Afrikaner Republic of the Transvaal. Dr Leander Starr Jameson led the raiding party of 600 men, which set out from Pitsani on the eastern edge of the Kalahari. Its arrival in Johannesburg was to coincide with the outbreak of an Uitlander uprising. No rising took place, however, and the raiders were ignominiously captured by Transvaal forces at Doornkop.

The effects of the Raid were far-reaching. Rhodes lost his Premiership of the Cape, the ring-leaders, including Jameson, were arrested and sentenced to varying terms of imprisonment. The British Government was highly embarrassed and the Transvaal Republic was alerted to British plans. In the incident were sown the seeds of the Boer War which was so soon to alter the history of Southern Africa. But for the Jameson Raid, Botswana might well have fallen under the rule of the British South Africa Company.[3]

Such progress as had been made towards a settlement with the Tawana, once again suffered a set-back. Following the Raid, the British South Africa Company lost all credibility and responsibility for the trek passed directly to the British Government. Sekgoma eventually placed himself under the protection of Britain and, on 6 April 1897, Chamberlain, the British Secretary of State, authorised the resumption of the trek to Ghanzi. The news was not conveyed to the trekkers until July of that year and it was not until early 1898 that the first of these patient people finally left for Ghanzi, the Promised Land. They had waited over four years.

The Ngamiland trek was supported by a contingent of Bechuanaland Border Police, and led by a remarkable man, then Major Francis W Panzera. He was responsible for the demarcation of the new Tawana Reserve, and for the settlement of the trekkers. We know little about Panzera as a person, but his accomplishments speak for him and he was clearly a precise, ordered, methodical and very efficient man. It is possible that he quickly became disillusioned when it became apparent that Fuller's reports had been hopelessly exaggerated.

Employing only a horse, compass and a stop-watch, Panzera surveyed the first farms. He gave out certificates for thirty-six, but could find in all only sixty-three of the size stipulated by the High Commissioner. The 'eight or nine hundred' seem to have been a figment of Fuller's imagination. Panzera must have been disappointed, too, by the quality of the prospective farmers. These were not red-blooded men of the soil, as he had been led to expect. Most of them, he found, were paupers, financed and given transport by the company. They were not of the pioneering farming type at all, but interested only in exploiting the area's resources and making as much money as they could with the least amount of effort. Most seemed content to exterminate the game, selling the marketable products and, having done this, were prepared to move on, abandoning or mortgaging their farms. With such material, Ghanzi, as an agricultural centre, faced a grim future.

Indeed, Ghanzi hardly survived. By 1908 almost all the settlers had left, either having returned to the Transvaal or moved to still more remote parts of the region.[4] Panzera became Resident Commissioner of the Protectorate in 1910 and he reported then that only eleven of the Ghanzi farms remained occupied. The future of Ghanzi hung precariously in the balance. However, events had already taken place which were to provide yet another injection of new and vigorous life.

The Boer War lasted from 1899 to 1902. It drew, to both sides, adventurers from all over the world. With the end of the fighting, many of these men, and many of the troops as well, seduced by the country and climate of Southern Africa, decided to make their fortunes there. They roamed the sub-continent, seeking or making opportunities for themselves. Many went into the cattle speculating business, buying and selling, hopefully at a profit. Some heard of Ghanzi and began to filter across the Kalahari to this remote outpost of the British Empire. Ghanzi farms began to change hands. The older people faded away and new blood took their place. Half of the farms were put up for auction in 1913 and it was then that many of the land barons of today made their original purchases, paid for from limited capital amassed by successful speculation.

A new breed of men emerged, who, unlike their predecessors, were committed to cattle ranching. Most were under-capitalised and development was to be painfully slow. Few had the proper skills, whilst Ghanzi's relative isolation and a poor economic climate were to nullify all their efforts. But the important thing was, they were determined to stay – and they did. Of those families who had travelled on the Rhodes Trek, only three are still in Ghanzi today. Not all of them remained there continuously either; some left and returned again. The newcomers were a mixed bag. Some were of Boer stock, others were men from the Empire, but out of the mutual exchange of skills and knowledge grew companionship and interdependence, and gradually a community spirit arose. Modern Ghanzi was born.

The spirit of independence and self-reliance that was to be such a prominent feature of the new community was quickly put to the test. The year 1914 and the outbreak of the Great War provided the opportunity and, for one brief moment in time, Ghanzi and its residents, through their heroism and courage, set an example that blazed forth like a shining light in the

Empire. The details of the incident have died with the memories of those who were involved, and I have to confess to taking a little licence in reconstructing the story.

Across the border, about 70 km to the west of Ghanzi, lay Germany's territory of South West Africa. For years the adjacent territories had lived in perfect peace and harmony. But now a state of war existed and thoughts soon turned to the possibility of a pre-emptive German strike. There was an administrative post at Rietfontein, and it was from there that an attack was thought most likely. The valiant men of Ghanzi gathered together their slender resources and prepared to defend the British Empire. The story has it that an attack *was* launched although, happily, lest the facts prove embarrassing, details have been forgotten. The attack came at night, and, although we do not know how the defenders received warning, under cover of darkness a handful of men successfully held it off. One version claims that the men kept on changing their positions, firing blindly into the dark towards the advancing enemy. The latter apparently came to the conclusion that they faced a far larger force than expected and prudently withdrew. In so far as I have been able to establish, there were no deaths and no casualties. But honour was satisfied. The Germans never again set foot upon this particular part of the Empire and the successful engagement was one of the very few ever to have taken place on British soil.[5] Ghanzi's glory was complete!

Inevitably, in an emergent community such as Ghanzi, larger than life characters stand out. Ghanzi was the ideal environment. It called to it, and fostered, tough and independent individuals who lived a life in which self-reliance was an important element. Individuality was the trade-mark of the early Ghanzi residents and many of them are remembered fondly to this day.

Tom Hardbattle is a good example.[6] Tom was an ex-policeman who had seen action in the Boer War and had speculated, successfully, in cattle. Like many bachelors in Ghanzi at the time, he experienced great difficulty in finding a wife to share with him the loneliness of the vast farmlands. In Tom's view, however, difficulties were only made to be overcome and he solved his problem in a rather unusual way. He wrote to a postal marriage bureau and in time established a correspondence with his bride-to-be. I can imagine her sitting wistfully at her far-away window, awaiting the arrival of the postman and another letter from her bronzed, handsome pioneer. The letters became more frequent and photographs were exchanged. Finally, came a proposal of marriage and, with light heart and romance shining in her eyes, our heroine set forth on the hazardous journey to meet her distant lover. A train took her to the edge of the Kalahari and from there she bounced and bumped her way across the burning, endless sands. At this stage romance may have already begun to tarnish. Ghanzi today is not an inspiring sight; one assumes that it was even less so then. The lady's resolve must have been severely tested.

At last the two lovers met, but the spark of their earlier contact ignited no raging fire of passion. It did not take Tom very long to realise that the lady was not for him – but what to do with her? Ever resourceful, a quiet conversation with his good friend Charlie Sharp solved the problem, and it was Charlie who married her, not Tom!

Tom was a hard man and some described him as mean. However, those who still remember him, or knew of him, will tell you that he was honest and true and that his word and a handshake were his bond. Some still recall Tom's first vehicle. It was a small truck and his most precious possession. Wherever he stopped he would haul out from the back of it a length of massive chain and a padlock, and would proceed to secure it to the nearest tree.

The women had to be as tough as the men, and they were. Toughness was not allowed to obscure an honest and sincere desire to live in harmony, however, to depend and to be depended upon, to help with and share the enormous burdens of their difficult and dangerous existence. Mrs Anna Christina Burger, known as 'Baby', came to Ghanzi in about 1915, when she was very young. She was married, as was then the custom among Afrikaners, when she was fourteen or fifteen. From that time on, she began to play the role of midwife. She never had any formal training beyond the guidance of her mother, and she used no instruments. At the last count, she had delivered over 500 children. She never charged a fee, neither did she discriminate as to whom should enjoy her services.

People from all walks of life came to her, from all over the region. Blacks, Bushmen, whites, Afrikaners, Hottentots, Herero and Coloureds – they all came and they all revered her. Each offered in payment what they could; some had nothing to offer, and this too was accepted. 'Baby' Burger married and had children of her own, all of whom she delivered herself. On one occasion, upon examining herself after the birth, she called back her husband, who had gone to get some hot water: 'Hold on,' she said, 'I think there's another one.' And there was!

With the coming of independence for Botswana, came a desire to improve the level of medical services. Mrs Burger's work, although appreciated, could not be allowed to continue. She was not 'qualified'. There was an immediate outcry and eventually a compromise was reached. Mrs Burger would oversee a birth under the critical and watchful eye of a doctor. He would decide her fate. Thankfully, the doctor was a man of integrity, for he had the honesty to admit that, with all his training, he could not have done the job as well himself. Mrs Burger continued to deliver babies.[7]

Not all the old characters were renowned for their honesty which, at best, was sometimes questionable and often adjusted to suit the circumstances. One such person was Andy Malone. In Ghanzi's early years, the memory of South Africa's Scotty Smith was still strong. Scotty was a rogue of the first order, who spent much more of his life outside the law than he did within it. One of his many tricks was to place a tickey (a small silver coin) in the neck of other people's horses – and then come along a year or so later and claim the animals as his own! There is no one who is prepared to say that Andy Malone did this too but their smiles and expressions leave you in no doubt as to what they think.

The Vickermans brothers are a wealthy and well-established Ghanzi family of today. One of the brothers, Theunis, is a fund of fascinating tales of the early days in

Ghanzi. He recalls one Jan Lewis, who was attacked by a leopard and, in the struggle, strangled it with his bare hands. Then there was the house of the Ramsden brothers which, after their demise, became haunted – and remains so still. The anecdotes are endless but the one I like best is the tale of his own family.[8] He and his brother started a road transport business in Ghanzi in 1953. In 1955 they married the Burton twins, Aida and Judy. Both marriages took place on the same day, at the same church, in Lobatse. The two couples have lived quite happily ever since on the same farm, in the same house. They have four children between them, two each!

Des McIntyre is a real 'man of the bush'. He is a highly regarded hunter, an outstanding shot and a 'bush' mechanic without equal. The story of his uncle, 'Little Mac', is an interesting one.[9] Andrew McIntyre, or 'Little Mac' as he was known around Ghanzi, came from an Australian family. Bitter experience there had taught him never to trust banks and it became a well-known habit of his to keep all his money at home on his farm. Legend has it that the money was kept in a milk churn but Des cannot vouch for this, except to confirm that a churn was used as a temporary store, at least. There is no certainty that it housed *all* Andrew's savings but Andrew used to tease Des, and ask him if he knew how much money, in rolled-up notes, could be fitted into a bottle. It was a common boast of Andrew's that he preferred using bottles as they did not rust.

In the 1960s Andrew died and his children inherited the cattle, goats and horses – but his money was left to Des. Unfortunately, he did not know where it was! Des is nothing if not inventive and creative. He got himself to Mafikeng and there persuaded a friend to make up a metal-detector for him. Thus armed, he returned to Ghanzi and a great and exciting search began. Metal pot-lids, old tin cans and long-forgotten lengths of chain all saw the light of day again – but no milk churn ever appeared. Sitting depressed in the house one day, with the machine by his side, Des suddenly became aware of its urgent soundings. Excited, he scanned the wall behind him, and the machine responded ever more loudly. He ripped the plaster from the wall – only to reveal a large sheet of corrugated iron, which was part of the wall's construction! Des never did find the money and has long given up the search. Of course, he admits, it may well have been hidden in bottles but where, then, he asks, does one begin to look? No one knows how much money was involved, except that, shortly before he died, Andrew made a sale for which he was paid £5 000 in cash. Where did he put it? For all we know, what was once a fortune in pound notes may still lie awaiting discovery, somewhere beneath the sands of the Kalahari.

Ghanzi seemed to dilly-dally through the thirties. Everyone was under-capitalised and few efforts at professional farming were made. There was a brief hope for development in 1934 when a distant abattoir was opened. Aimed at encouraging the cattle industry in Bechuanaland, it might have been successful had not an outbreak of foot and mouth disease forced its closure in 1937. Although there was no outbreak in the Ghanzi district, and indeed never has been, the prospects for the cattle business came to an abrupt halt. The abattoir did not reopen until the late 1950s.

Ghanzi residents turned to a number of unlikely pursuits to generate a cash income. The first was the development of the cream business. The advent of transport and a passable road from Gobabis allowed the development of this industry, which, if it achieved nothing else, at least brought some cash into the local economy. Other attempts to earn money included the domestication of several herds of eland. Cassie van Heerden and Christian Lewis were at least two of the farmers who tried experiments of this kind. Both reasoned that the animals made better use of water and grazing and were better protected against predators than were domestic stock. However, the game laws of the time were against them and eventually the successful herds had to be given up, but not before an extraordinary report appeared in the *Mafikeng Mail,* dated 15 December 1967. It declared that, on Cassie's farm, two cows had each given birth to stillborn calves that were half cow and half eland: the forequarters being completely eland

and the hindquarters totally bovine, in every respect.

Times remained difficult and development was slow. In 1936 only forty-two of the Ghanzi farms were occupied and there were approximately 200 settlers. Most of the farms were unfenced and undeveloped and still no wide-scale professional cattle ranching was underway. Many of the farmers were inexperienced and herds were allowed to roam freely and widely, cows calved unattended in the bush and the first man to get his brand on a calf became its owner.

The Bushmen had always been an integral part of the Ghanzi District. From time immemorial it had been part of their wide-ranging homeland and, as its settler population grew, so were the Bushmen drawn, more and more, away from their own traditional hunter-gatherer way of life into the permanent homesteads of the farms. Their primary contribution was labour, although many bore children to the settlers and some were married to them. Despairing of the post as a route to successful matrimony, Tom Hardbattle married a Bushman woman. Most of the settler children were brought up by Bushman servants and often spoke a local dialect before their mother-tongue.

Based as it was on close family intimacy, the relationship between Bushman and settler was an unusual one and not quite that of just master and servant. Wages were seldom paid; labour was exchanged for goods in kind and the relationship was closer to that of client and patron. In most cases, all the Bushman's needs were met and so too were those of his family and all his dependants. By some standards, the Bushmen were considered unreliable, idle and dishonest, but in fact they were seldom maliciously destructive. In a friendly atmosphere and given good supervision, they could be hard workers, working quickly and well.[10] Typically, the number of Bushmen on a farm outnumbered by three or four times those who were actually employed. The work demanded of them was menial and required no skills and, for as long as the nature of agricultural activity in Ghanzi remained unchanged, an easy-going, relaxed atmosphere prevailed. The

Bushmen became an integral part of the farming economy. Change, of course, was inevitable however.

In 1957 a surveyor was employed to help resolve the chaotic land tenure situation. The boundaries of farms demarcated by Panzera, never having been fenced, had become blurred. New farms had been added, others had changed hands, some had been incorporated into large holdings and later separated again. It took Dick Eaton five years to complete the job and in the course thereof the quality of Panzera's earlier work became apparent.[11]

On horseback, he had worked only with a compass and stop-watch. Making his way through virgin bush, he had marked out the first Ghanzi farms, and so accurate was his work that sixty years later Dick was able to find many of Panzera's original beacons.

The 1960s was a decisive decade in the development of Ghanzi. A new road had reached the town from Lobatse, across the Kalahari to the east. Opened in December 1957, it became possible for cattle to reach the abattoir in a single day. Supplies were cheaper, more regular and dependable. With the completion of the survey, farms were gradually fenced. What was once 'our' land, now became 'my' land and the nature of farming practices began to change. Title to the farms was changed by the Government from leasehold to freehold. Better quality livestock was imported and farming practices improved. Land prices slowly increased. In 1964 land was P0,75 a morgen (,85 of a hectare) but by 1972 it had risen to P3. Today the price would be in the region of P16 to P17 a morgen for poorly developed land and, for the best, anywhere from P25 to P30.

Productivity increased and cattle sales, which had remained at a steady 5 000 a year during the 1940s and 1950s, rose to 18 000 in 1972. Today Ghanzi has 2 per cent of the national herd but accounts for 12 per cent of the country's total off-take.[12] Inevitably, there are casualties of change and in Ghanzi it was probably the Bushmen who suffered most.[13] Fenced farms reduced the need for unskilled herdsmen. Deep-reaching boreholes, which proliferated now, needed skilled labour to man and maintain the pumps. No one trained the Bushmen, who were quite capable of doing the job, and so black people came to be employed in their place. Newly arrived farmers preferred to engage blacks, with whom they had worked elsewhere and whom they felt they understood better than the Bushmen. The growing practice of paying cash wages brought increasing numbers of black people into the job market, always at the expense of the Bushman.

Other changes affected the lives of the Bushmen. More farms and cattle increased the area grazed and the wild foods, traditionally part of the Bushman's diet, became harder to find. Throughout the country, owing to competition with man, the amount of game was slowly diminishing. Bushmen elsewhere, who relied upon it, now found their supplies restricted and called on their relations on the farms to help support them. The flow of squatters into the Ghanzi District became a flood. Game in the farm lands, once abundant, was now virtually extinct and the opportunity to supplement the rations given by farmers no longer existed.

All these factors contributed to what became known as the 'Bushman Problem' which, as the years passed, began to reach serious proportions. The number of Bushman squatters, dependants and unemployed on the Ghanzi farms increased and soon the farmers, tired of supporting so many people, brought pressure on the Government to do something to control the situation. In 1975 one of the more recent of many Bushman surveys reported that there were 4 000 Bushmen living on the Ghanzi farms. Of these, only 675 were actually employed, 2 050 were immediate family, and the remaining 1 275 were unwanted squatters.[14]

Numerous well-meaning attempts to resolve this problem have been made. Few of them have met with unqualified success. With all our so-called academic expertise, we still do not seem to be able to find the solutions to the human problems that change and development create and the example of the Bushman is no exception.

For a long time the Bushman problem was simply ignored. This in itself was disastrous and only served to exacerbate it. In conditions that rapidly deteriorated, their numbers, swollen by a continuous flood of refugees from the central Kalahari, grew. The burden upon land owners increased and the filial bonds of the past were stretched beyond breaking point. The relationship deteriorated. The Bushmen were now exposed to all that is bad in Western civilisation, and gained few, if any, of its benefits. Faced with increasing poverty and squalor, with overcrowding and the effects of excesses of tobacco and alcohol, they found themselves in a situation they had never had to cope with before. It led to the steady disintegration of their social and cultural systems.

Reason and logic suggested that if the Bushmen were not happy where they were, they should be moved to places of their choice where contentment might return. At every stage in the subsequent relocation project, the Bushmen were consulted – on some of the issues – and four sites were selected, with their help. In time schools were built, boreholes were put down, roads were constructed and areas for the growing of vegetables were fenced off. Tracts of surrounding land were declared for the exclusive use of the new inhabitants. The Government and international donors provided much of the finance. Eventually, the Bushmen were moved in, selected by clan so that they would be with people of their choice. They were as excited at the prospect of the scheme's success as were those in the Government and the Council who had given so much of their time and effort.

Unfortunately, the scheme does not appear to be working. Somehow it seems to have been quite overlooked that, at heart, the Bushmen are still traditional hunter-gatherers. There is little for them to hunt and they do not know how to grow vegetables – nor have they been taught. At every turn those who can, exploit them. Hawkers drive out to the villages offering basic commodities for sale – at prices 50 per cent higher than in Ghanzi. One person, elected to represent their interests and not himself a Bushman, made a fortune from illegally selling alcohol to them. The new villages were modelled on the traditional African concept of a village, but Bushmen do not have those sort of villages and they lack the social structures that are adapted to that kind of life. They are nomads and accustomed to living in small groups. They have no social mechanisms for survival in large villages. Theft and dishonesty became problems in the new settlements.

One Ghanzi farmer told me of the plight of his ex-employee, an old Bushman, who had spent his lifetime on the farm and had long since retired on it. He decided that he would like to try living in one of the new settlements. During his working years he had earned or been given a number of small stock and when he was taken to the village by the farmer his twenty-four goats went with him. Six months later, he came back to the farm with only two of them left. The wealth of a lifetime was gone. His stock had been stolen and eaten by villagers who had not been able to find wild meat for themselves.

What were the people in these villages expected to do for a living? This does not seem to have been thought about in any great detail. Some stock was provided, but Bushmen are not pastoralists and no one showed them how to manage them. The cattle were eaten. Leather-work and craft production were considered but there were problems here too. Firstly, there was no outlet for the products and secondly, Bushmen were not accustomed to organised production of this sort. There were, and remain, great difficulties with quality control.

All efforts should not be condemned out of hand, however. Much good has come from the scheme. The Bushmen do have schools to send their children to, water supplies are assured and there is a free health service. However bad it is, the quality of life must surely have improved when compared with the worst levels on the farms at Ghanzi. Above all the authorities concerned have shown the most important ingredient – a genuine willingness to help.

A number of individuals and organisations, apart from those which the Ghanzi Council had set up, had on their own initiative established similar experimental villages. Some came into being quite spontaneously when small, semi-permanent Bushman communities, seeing the benefits that the Government gave to other citizens,

demanded for themselves, and sometimes received, the same advantages. Altogether there are probably about twenty of these establishments today, spread widely throughout the central Kalahari. How successful they will be in the long term remains to be seen.

To me, the saddest thing of all is that success must mean the end of the Bushman as we know him today. It is a great tragedy that there is no room in the modern world for the Stone Age hunter-gatherer. He himself does not desire to remain as he is. Blinded by the material culture of Western civilisation, he seeks only to join it, and to emulate it. In doing so, his traditional way of life will become obsolete. For our part, one could say that we are supervising its death, and the tragedy lies in that we do not know how to make the transition comfortable. The Bushmen are a people in transition and for them it is a painful and unhappy experience.

Dr H J Heinz is one of those gentle and dedicated people who, no more successfully than anyone else, tried to establish a small village in which to help the Bushman leap from the Stone Age to the twentieth century. He had a warm, understanding and loving relationship with the Bushmen but events turned against him and, for other reasons, he left the project. Many years later, he returned. Always, in any Bushman community, the little dwelling places are situated close to one another. With their thin grass walls there are no secrets. The community is one, and everything is shared. For there to be distance between the huts would be almost incomprehensible and, if it happened, would speak of great unhappiness, unrest and dissension. I asked Dr Heinz to describe the village of Bere as it was when he saw it again. His words seemed to sum up the whole sad situation. 'I could see at a glance it wasn't working,' he said. 'The huts were all too far apart.'[15]

While it is true to say that the Bushmen are looked down upon by Batswana (citizens of Botswana), who consider them to be of the lowest social level, they are at the same time feared by the local people. This is partly because of their widely believed ability to turn themselves into lions. Not all the Bushman groups in the area, of which there are four, are credited with this ability but the Makaukau, who are, create a kind of halo effect that includes all of their race.

Ed Flattery, a level-headed, responsible Ghanzi farmer, told me the following tale, which happened to him in 1982.[16] On his farm, he'd lost two cattle, killed by lions on separate occasions a few days apart. At the second killing he and two of his Bushman employees found spoor that they could follow. Ed was brought up with Bushman playmates. He knows them and their language as well as he knows himself. The three of them followed the spoor of two lions. It passed through several fences and eventually left the vicinity of the farming area and headed out into the open Kalahari.

After some time they saw a spiral of smoke rising ahead of them – in the direction towards which the spoor was heading. Ed's Bushmen now refused to go on, saying that it was not lion they were following but Makaukau who had changed themselves into lions and had been hunting. Shaking his head at this nonsense, Ed persuaded them to follow him and, being a good tracker himself, continued on the spoor. It led towards the fire where he could see two small grass huts and between them the usual open space. Outside one of the huts a fire was burning. In the centre of the cleared area was a large pile of discarded ash. The lions' spoor led directly towards it, passed across it – and disappeared! Ed is not a fool. He knew that this could not happen, but nor could he pick up the spoor again. His companions pointed out to him the occupants of the huts. There were two males, two females and some children. Both males had been injured. One wore a bandage around his head, the other round his chest. To the Bushmen, this was convincing evidence of what the two had been up to, proving how they had been injured by the horns of the cattle. Ed has no explanation.

Thus Ghanzi continues into the future, a fascinating and quixotic blend of old and new, a strange but powerful and vibrant mix of people and cultures. It has a professional and organised cattle industry on cattle ranges which even Texans envy. Rapidly, the town is becoming more modern, yet people who can turn themselves into lions may still exist there and if you ask for a toothpick in the hotel, you get a matchstick with the head broken off!

## REFERENCES

1. **Truschel, L W.** 'The Tswana and the Ngamiland Trek'. In *Botswana Notes and Records,* Vol 6, 1974, pp 47-54
2. **Author unknown.** *The Great Ngami Trek.* 1925, pp 81-102
3. **Pakenham, T.** *The Boer War.* London: Weidenfeld and Nicolson, 1980, pp 1-24
4. **Gillett, S.** 'Notes on the Settlement in the Ghanzi District'. In *Botswana Notes and Records,* Vol 2, 1969, pp 52-5
5. **Silberbauer, G.** *Report to the Government of Bechuanaland on the Bushman Survey.* Bechuanaland Government, Gaborone, 1965, p 116
6. **Hardbattle, J.** Personal communication, October 1984
7. **Drotsky, A C.** Personal communication, December 1984
8. **Vickerman, T.** Personal communication, October 1984
9. **McIntyre, D.** Personal communication, December 1984
10. **Silberbauer, G.** Op cit, p 120
11. **Eaton, R C.** Personal communication, October 1984
12. **Ibid**
13. **Barnard, A.** 'Basarwa Settlement Patterns in the Ghanzi Ranching Area'. In *Botswana Notes and Records,* Vol 12, 1980, pp 137-9
14. **Russell, M and Russell, M.** *Afrikaners of the Kalahari.* London: Cambridge University Press, 1979, pp 1-161
15. **Heinz, H J.** Personal communication, December 1984
16. **Flattery, E.** Personal communication, October 1984

# Part 6
# The Threatened Sands

# 19. The Tamed Killers

FOR much of recorded history Africa has been known as the Dark Continent. To Europeans and visitors from afar it has always been regarded as a place of mystery and strange phenomena. Early attempts to explore it were not always successful and often a high and tragic fee was paid in human lives. The continent's reputation as a place beset with dangers and difficulties was thus enhanced. In retrospect we can see that it was not so much Africa itself that was more dangerous than any other country, but the lack of knowledge and understanding on the part of those who came to probe its secrets. After all, Africa was inhabited and the people who lived there did so in complete harmony with their environment. They accepted the realities and adjusted to them, even if they did not always understand them.

In some respects there have been deliberate and sustained attempts to protect Africa's secrets and to keep the foreigner out. E W Bovill, in his book *The Golden Trade of the Moors*,[1] describes the ways in which for hundreds of years, the source of West Africa's gold was kept secret from Europe. Attempts by individuals and by governments to locate it were frustrated at every turn, a situation aided by the ignorance of the seekers. Thus is a reputation like Africa's created and developed.

For the most part, however, it has been a lack of knowledge and understanding that has preserved Africa's air of mystery for so long. One area in which this lack has exacted a colossal price is disease. Many thousands of lives were lost through malaria, for example, before the advent of quinine and the relative protection it conferred upon those who had not already acquired a low level of immunity to the dreaded disease.

There were, and remain, many other debilitating illnesses. Trypanosomiasis, or sleeping sickness, is one of them.

Like malaria, sleeping sickness has played a significant role in the development and exploration of Africa. It has been a bar to local mass movements of population and a deterrent to external invasion. Immunity is not acquired by exposure, and where the fly flourished, man did not venture. If he did, he went at his peril, even though it was more commonly his transport animals that suffered.

The tsetse fly, although not as old, perhaps, as Africa, can still claim a respectable ancestry in antiquity. Fossil flies have been found in South America, suggesting a pre-Gondwanaland existence, and also in the Oligocene shales of Colorado. For at least 35 million years, therefore, this creature has been with us. Its earlier distribution may have been very widespread, but today it is found only in sub-Saharan Africa. The fly has almost certainly been in Africa as long as man and there are a number of early references to it.

Dr J N P Davies, in a fascinating paper delivered as the Fourteenth Raymond Dart Memorial Lecture, in 1976, gave an account of the tsetse's role in African history.[2] There are some grounds for believing that the Fourth Plague, which afflicted the land of Egypt at the time of the Israelites, may well have been tsetse fly. Certainly Isaiah, writing in about 750 BC, seemed to have a very good idea of them. In 150 BC Argatarchides complained of the difficulties in raising cattle in Africa, because of the seasonal presence of the flies that killed them. There is a delightful story from the southern Sudan which tells how the local inhabitants of the Koalit hills used the tsetse fly as a weapon of war to protect their country and their cattle from Arab invaders. It is said that they used a pot of fresh blood to trap a number of tsetse flies. When sufficient had been caught, the pot was sealed, transported and opened again among the cattle of the invading Arabs. In time the cattle caught the dreaded *nagana* disease and died. The invaders, left without cattle, departed!

Dr F L Lambrecht explains that tsetse flies belong to the genus *Glossina*, of which there are twenty-three species.[3] They occupy large areas of Africa between 15° and 29 °S but are seldom found at altitudes above 1 800 m and all need tree-cover for shelter. The disease they transmit, called sleeping sickness in humans and *nagana* in animals, is caused by a microscopic trypanosome, a slender flagellate, about three or four times the length of a red blood cell. These are carried by the blood-sucking flies from one animal to another. Five of the numerous types of trypanosomes are of interest to us here, two of which affect humans and three, domestic stock.

The two human trypanosomes have quite different distributions and share a common area only in the vicinity of Lake Victoria in East Africa. The species which occurs in the Kalahari and Southern Africa is, unfortunately, the more virulent of the two. It is carried by the fly *Glossina morsitans* and is known as *Trypanosomiasis rhodesiense*. This type of sleeping sickness is acute and affects the central nervous system at an early stage. If untreated, death can result in a few months. There is, however, no need to be unduly concerned. Not every bite results in the disease, and indeed, very few do. A routine check within 10 days of leaving a tsetse area can identify an infection, and it responds quickly to modern drugs. Our ability to control the progress of sleeping sickness in humans tends to blind us to the seriousness of this disease and the devastation it has caused in the past. In the Congo basin, for example, between 1896 and 1906, it is estimated that in excess of 500 000 people died from it, and in an area north of Lake Victoria, between 1902 and 1905, two-thirds of the population of 300 000 were carried away by the disease.

*Nagana* is transmitted by a number of trypanosomes of which, in the Kalahari,

three are most common: *T. vivax, T. congolense* and *T. brucei*. The reservoir for these trypanosomes, as with the human types, is in game animals, which themselves are not generally affected by the parasite, having acquired in past millenia a tolerance denied the more recently domesticated animals and human newcomers. Interestingly, game animals translocated from a non-tsetse area to one in which these flies occur, sometimes succumb to the disease. There is a case of this happening when springbok were moved from the southern Kalahari to the Okavango.[4]

Our ability to understand and control the disease has taken time and effort. A description of the lethargy found among slaves taken from the Guinea Coast comes to us from 1742, but the existence of trypanosomes was not discovered until 1846, and their presence in man not until 1890. However, the significance of this discovery was not fully appreciated at the time. During the early 1900s great strides in gaining knowledge of trypanosomes were made but, surprisingly, it was not until 1958 that *T. rhodesiense* was isolated from a wild animal.

Dependent as it is upon the existence of a large game population to serve as a reservoir, the survival of both human and domestic animal trypanosomes is entirely related to the continued availability of game. For this reason, when vast numbers of both game and stock were annihilated during the great rinderpest epizootic at the end of the nineteenth century, the prevalence of sleeping sickness and the tsetse fly was greatly reduced. Not all game species were equally affected by rinderpest, but among those that were the warthog, kudu, buffalo and reedbuck were favoured hosts of the tsetse fly. In some places the lost ground has never been recovered. In others, reinfection has been rapid and extensive. In the Kalahari, at the turn of the century, the disease was said to be reduced to three small foci in the wetlands of north-western Botswana, but as game populations expanded, so did the area occupied by the fly.

Sleeping sickness was not clinically identified in the southern continent until 1908, but clearly it was by no means unknown in

▲Grazing is scarce at Tsabong ▼Daniel January's farm at Bokspits

▲Sand dunes at Bokspits are constantly on the move ▼Black-maned Kalahari lion, Nossob River, Kalahari Gemsbok National Park

the Kalahari before that time. Gordon Cumming, writing in 1846, popularised the Setswana word, *tsetse*, for the fly. The Batswana had a name, current before the end of last century, for a disease of drowsiness, which they called *kotsela*. As early as 1909 a Dr Moffat was asked to investigate its occurrence in Ngamiland. However, it was not until 1934 that the first definite case of sleeping sickness in humans was recorded from Chobe and 1938 from the Okavango. *Nagana,* of course, was not new and the tribesmen constantly moved to avoid the ever-expanding areas affected.

Despite a slowly growing understanding of the enemy, there was little consensus on how to combat the disease, a situation which can be appreciated when so little was known about the biology and ecology of the tsetse fly itself. However, it resulted in the waste of a great deal of time, effort and money, not to mention trees and wildlife. In parts of the Kalahari, the rate of the fly's recovery was rapid. In Botswana, from 1922 to 1942, it regained some 8 000 km², and by 1962 it occupied approximately 16 000 km², existing in almost as wide an area as it had done before the rinderpest. In 1943 a Tsetse Fly Control unit was established to combat the further advance of the fly, which was now spreading outwards from the Okavango Delta and the Chobe River. The need was growing ever more desperate. Of the 11 000 cattle in Ngamiland in 1942, more than 2 000 died of *nagana* and 320 people had been treated in the Maun hospital for sleeping sickness.

There was much speculation in those early days on how best to curtail its spread. Ideas were plentiful but, in the light of today's experience, some seemed excessive. Suggestions emanating from various parts of Africa at that time included the erection of fences, organised destruction of game, the discouragement of game reserves, the poisoning of pans where water collected, bush clearing and even the reintroduction of rinderpest.[5] Other suggestions were the movement of human populations, destruction of forests, handcatching of flies, large-scale burning, ground spraying with DDT and the releasing of sterile male flies.[6] (Methods of sterilising included radiation and exposure to a high musical note of a particular frequency. Unfortunately, this second and intriguing method does not lend itself to practical applications!) In the event, a combination of some of these ideas was adopted in Ngamiland. Fences, bush clearing and hunting were all tried, with differing degrees of enthusiasm and success, at various times. The attempt at game elimination provides some interesting facts.

In Botswana's north-western regions, in the vicinity of Maun, organised hunting continued for twenty-seven years without a break. On average, between forty and fifty hunters were employed and their daily task was to work through appointed areas, find game and shoot it. It was slaughter. However unpleasant the idea may sound to us, it is not an activity for which the governments and individuals of the time should be criticised. People believed it to be effective if it was efficiently done and it was not an uncommon practice in many parts of Africa.

Between 1940 and 1967, in an area to the south-east of the Okavango Delta, in excess of 63 000 animals were killed.[7] Horrific as this figure may seem, it conceals a point of major significance. In that time there was a remarkable change in the composition of species shot. Whilst it was true that the numbers of animals such as tsessebe and wildebeest declined quite dramatically, others actually increased and no species of game was eliminated. Thus, despite the combined efforts of hunters for a total of twenty-seven years, the numbers of duiker, steenbok, impala, warthog, reedbuck and buffalo actually climbed. Furthermore, the total annual off-take of meat for the whole period remained, albeit unintentionally, remarkably constant. Without realising it, a sustained yield programme had been achieved! This underlines the irony of the fact that, within ten years of the end of organised game destruction, most large game species had disappeared from the area. This, it has been suggested, is probably due to more efficient tribal hunting which was not strictly controlled.

Fences remained, throughout the first thirty years of the control effort in Botswana, a major offensive weapon and many hundreds of kilometres were erected. They demarcated the cattle-free zone, areas in which it was hoped that the fly would be held at bay, and the hunting areas. Fences were expensive to build, though, and cost even more to maintain. There is no ready record of the many thousands of hectares of trees that were destroyed. Some were felled by hand, others with mechanical saws, more were treated with dieseline and still more were ring-barked. Indeed, even to the present day, it is possible to drive, in areas south of Moremi for example, through great standing forests of dead trees. Ring-barked, they stand like hard grey gravestones, baked to iron in the African sun, mute testimony to man's ignorance and capacity for destruction.

The progress of battle against the Okavango's tsetse fly ebbed and flowed in tides that closely reflected the amount of money available to pay and the interest of those who led the effort.

In 1972 the first aerial spraying experiments with the chemical Endosulfan took place, and by 1974 aerial application was occurring on a large scale. Spraying was not new. Its technology and methods had been developing throughout Africa. In 1961 the World Health Organisation assisted with the first spraying programme. A 3 per cent Dieldrin solution was used on primary fly habitat up to 5 ft above ground level. At Maun, on the Okavango, experiments with Dieldrex were attempted again in 1963. In both cases, the ecological cost was high but, from 1967 onwards, the use of this chemical, together with DDT, increased and continued until 1973. As aircraft became more involved, it was evident that there was much to learn: how to create a mist of spray with the right droplet size, what height to fly and what were the best spraying times. Much work was needed to determine the correct swathe widths and application rates.

Night applications seemed to be the most effective and this alone created new problems. The Delta is flat and is a complex of waterways, lagoons, rivers, channels, reedbanks and islands, the last mentioned often being mantled with dense vegetation and tall trees. There are no roads and few obvious landmarks, and none at all at night. The logistical problems were enormous, but they were overcome. Large areas were de-

marcated with powerful searchlights at critical points; sophisticated electronic equipment assisted. And the aircraft flew.

I was in the Delta one night when they sprayed with Endosulfan, harmless in those concentrations to humans. It must have been a moonless evening, because I particularly remember the stars. The black blanket of night, fathomless, intense, was pierced by a million pinpricks of light that shone through with a clarity not found in other, polluted, light-reflecting skies. A massed amphibious choir serenaded the warmth and stillness with an anthem of joy. At first, from the distance, we heard nothing more than a low droning sound. It was faint, but enough to stop conversation. We looked in the direction from which it came. Nothing but that sound disturbed the night. Then, suddenly, the night exploded. Three aircraft appeared. Flying parallel courses they were just above tree height. Each carried a single, Cyclopean light that seemed to banish the dark and trailed behind it a veil of white mist. The nocturnal serenade was replaced by a howling cacophony of sound. In a second they were gone, passing over our heads. The shattered silence returned as slowly as the white mist settled gently about us. I thought of gas warfare, of Gallipoli and Flanders, and realised how helpless those soldiers must have felt.

Extensive use of insecticides against tsetse gave rise to much controversy, especially in the early years when the practice was in its infancy, and the full ecological implications of long-life poisons and their impact upon food chains were little understood. With the advent of new chemicals, many of these fears were removed. Successive tests claimed to show that the organochlorine insecticide known as Endosulfan 35%, administered in ultra low volume aerial applications, had little adverse effect on any but the target species. Although demonstrably less lethal than DDT and Dieldrin, doubt persisted. Many called for more research. Accidental oversprays would occur and mixture errors were possible – what would happen then?

By the end of 1974 most of the technical problems were understood, if not actually solved, and for the first time in the history of the fight against tsetse fly in Botswana's Okavango region, the possibility of complete eradication, of total victory, lay within reach. Increasingly, as time passed, confidence in the ability to eliminate the fly grew.

By 1977 a plan aiming at this objective was ordered. In the meantime, Sir Seretse Khama, President of the Republic of Botswana, went on record promising the people of Ngamiland that the fly would be eliminated. In late 1979 Botswana's Cabinet approved the plan, then estimated to cost P5,5 million. However, the plan has not yet been implemented and the reasons lie in still unresolved controversy. There are doubts as to whether 100 per cent eradication is in fact possible, the use of insecticides is questioned and strong reservations are voiced by powerful local and overseas conservationists – all of which have made those responsible hesitant to finance the scheme.

Since the Tawana people moved to Ngamiland, many years ago, cattle have been of overriding importance to that district's economy. The Okavango Delta has held the key to the success of this traditional ranching industry. Where the absence of tsetse fly permitted, the peripheries of the Delta afforded lush grazing and ample water. As human and cattle populations expanded, the demand for more land increased, as did the pressure of exploitation upon the Delta itself. More and more of it was exposed to the depredations of man and his cattle. Conservationists began to fear for its survival. They saw the tsetse as a critical factor in preserving the future of the Okavango. As long as it held sway, it was said, there would be natural limits imposed upon the areas to which cattle could have access. Remove the fly and the Okavango, pristine wilderness that it is, would be destroyed.

In the earlier days of this controversial debate there was little commercial exploitation of the Delta by tourism, hunters or any other activity. When this did develop little of the benefit accrued to local tribesmen, who therefore to this day remain unconvinced that they and their cattle should be denied access to these lush grazing lands simply so that foreigners should have un-

impaired enjoyment of the area. There are also political overtones to this complex question. Botswana is an outstanding example of democracy in Africa. There is universal suffrage and every person in Ngamiland has a vote.

Dr Jeffrey Bowles, the Chief Tsetse Fly Control Officer in Ngamiland, explains the other side of the coin by pointing out that the fight against the fly has been waged for over forty years, and that this has been done to contain, if not reduce the fly-infested areas, so as to remove the risks of both human and cattle trypanosomiasis.[8] It has consumed vast sums of money. In simple terms, he says, it is cost effective to control the fly on the shortest possible front. The cheapest way to keep those areas free of tsetse fly which are currently occupied by cattle and people is to eliminate it completely. His department has within its means the techniques to do this, to drive the fly right back to Botswana's borders and, in co-operation with Namibia, hold or eliminate it there.

It will cost far less to hold the fly on 50 km of the Chobe River than to maintain constant surveillance over the vast Okavango. The P6 million needed to do this will be a sound investment. Dr Bowles agrees that it is difficult to convince people that the Department's plan is not to clear the Delta, just to let the cattle in. Although tsetse is now down to less than 1 per cent of its former levels, the Department has not embarked upon a campaign aimed at total eradication. Control is taking place in peripheral areas and is becoming steadily more difficult as pedestrian, aircraft and vehicle movements increase, reflecting expanding commercial activity in and around the Delta. In time, the cost of holding the fly down to present levels will rise and so eradication will always remain a possibility. Dr Bowles believes that the answer to the complex conservation issues at stake lie in proper land use planning and strictly enforced legislation.

In 1982, 242 km of what is called the 'Buffalo Fence' was built, at a cost of P1,5 million, around part of the south and south-eastern Delta. Its purpose was to provide a line demarcating the point beyond which cattle may not go. It is of sturdy construction and has twelve manned gates. People may pass through, and indeed small communities, and some goats, do live on the Delta side. Cattle, however, may not pass through to graze. Much faith is placed in this structure as a source of protection for the Okavango, but its presence underlines what may prove to be a more reliable long-term deterrent.

Botswana's cattle industry is the country's third largest earner of foreign exchange. Much of the meat goes to the EEC, which imposes exceptionally strict measures to avoid, in Europe, outbreaks of foot and mouth disease (FMD). It is known that buffalo are in some way connected with the transmission of FMD and many of the strict controls demanded by the EEC are aimed at ensuring the absence of contact between these animals and cattle. It happens that there are, seasonally, numerous buffalo in the Okavango Delta and another function of the Buffalo Fence is to keep these two populations separate. Supporters of tsetse eradication point to the presence of buffalo as the long-term guarantee of the Okavango's integrity as a wilderness area. They say that the cattle lobby is too powerful to allow a challenge to the continuation of its markets by a FMD outbreak caused from buffalo-cattle contact. There is a deeply vested interest in protecting Botswana's meat markets, and therefore in keeping cattle and buffalo apart. The presence of buffalo may yet be the saving of the Delta.

Thus the problem remains for the moment unresolved. The tsetse fly could possibly be eliminated, though some question this. If it is, the cost of control will be reduced. There are fears that removal of the fly will expose the Okavango Delta to widespread and destructive exploitation by Ngamiland cattle ranchers. This is countered with the fact that a fence has been built that will prevent this from happening and by reliance on a cattle-owning political group who know where their interests best lie. Who is right or which view is correct is hard to tell, but one is left with the feeling that the most important faction of all, the local tribesman, has not been sufficiently considered. He sees desirable grazing of which he cannot take advantage. He experiences no direct benefits from alternative uses of the Delta –

and he has a vote. When, in time of drought, his few poor cattle are starving, will he be interested in the broader problems or will he be tempted to think first of himself and his family? People who overfly the Delta regularly claim to have seen cattle on the 'wrong' side of the fence and I have heard that this is not uncommon.[9] Sadly, only time will tell. And then it may be too late.

Rinderpest is another of the great scourges of Africa. It is a virus disease that affects cattle, the symptoms being fever, restlessness and loss of appetite. The animal weakens rapidly and dies. It is highy contagious and spreads from direct contact with an infected animal or by oral contact with contaminated grazing or water. The virus is not persistent outside the body and is killed within a few hours by sunlight. In the last decade of the nineteenth century, rinderpest swept through Africa, killing tens of millions of animals, devastating economies and drawing in its wake untold suffering, tragedy and death. Almost overnight the wealth of tropical Africa was swept away.

The disease originates from the steppes of Russia and prior to 1864 seems never to have occurred in sub-Saharan Africa, although it was well known in Egypt, to which it was repeatedly introduced from Turkey, Russia, the Balkans and Asia Minor. Its history is known to go back much further than this, however.[10] Rinderpest may well have made its presence felt among the Greek cattle during the siege of Troy and it might have been responsible for the plague that ravaged Egyptian cattle prior to the Exodus. It was certainly known in Europe at the time of the Goths and there was a serious outbreak during the reign of Charlemagne in AD 810, which spread as far as Britain. Since then, outbreaks in Europe have not been infrequent, especially where there was close contact with Russia, or following wars with that country.

Britain has experienced rinderpest at least as recently as 1865 when 500 000 cattle, valued at £4 million, died from the disease. There were great epizootics of rinderpest in Europe after Napoleon's Russian adventures and the Crimean War in 1865. In that same year, after yet another outbreak in Egypt, the disease spread to

French Sudan and across to West Africa, inflicting unimaginable devastation, eventually to die out for lack of further victims.

We are ignorant of the precise circumstances which gave rise to the fearful events of the 1890s in Africa. We do know that British troops, on their way to relieve Gordon at Khartoum in 1884, took with them cattle from South Russia. The expedition failed and Britain virtually sealed off the Sudan where famine, locusts and disease greatly reduced the population. It was the time when European powers were busily engaged in dividing Africa among themselves and, faced with the situation in Sudan, as well as German and French expansionism, Britain, with her hands temporarily full, encouraged Italian aspirations in the Horn of Africa. This resulted in Italian occupation of Massawa and Kassala. Cattle, to supply meat for the troops, were imported from India, Aden and South Russia.

In 1889 rinderpest broke out in Somaliland and soon extended into Ethiopia, Sudan and East Africa. It has been obliquely suggested that this outbreak may not have been entirely accidental, since the purchase of meat was handled by Russian agents, friendly with French adventurers in Ethiopia.[11] Both may have had more sympathy with the objectives of their countrymen elsewhere in Africa, than they did with the Italians. Whatever the politics and facts, the disease was there. A holocaust of hitherto unimagined proportions had been unleashed and Africa was about to receive a blow that would send her reeling.

The virus seemed much more virulent than in any previous outbreak and few animals survived. Mortality was as high as 95 per cent and it affected not only cattle but sheep, goats and wild animals, including buffalo, eland, bushbuck and most small antelope. Giraffe, bush-pig and warthog also succumbed. Like the malignant, raging beast it was, rinderpest spread at breakneck speed. It leapt mountains, rivers, desert barriers and international boundaries with equal ease. Nothing seemed capable of checking its flight. By 1890 it was well established in Uganda and reached Lake Tanganyika the same year.

In July 1892 it was at the north end of Lake Malawi. Zambia and Mozambique fell next before the onslaught and by February 1896 it was on both sides of the Zambezi. In this fertile area where, even then, cattle densities were high, rinderpest appeared to acquire new vigour and, thus rejuvenated, sped on at an ever more rapid and terrifying rate. Within a month it reached Bulawayo; in weeks, it had infected Mafikeng, spreading from there and Zimbabwe to the Kalahari, moving through the eastern side of Botswana and far out across the sands, wherever cattle and game would take it. It was in the Transvaal by early April, where it paused briefly before the final assault on the vast remaining cattle wealth of South Africa.

The devastation of rinderpest can hardly be described. It is not possible to reckon the numbers of animals that died, but some understanding of the human consequences can be imagined. Throughout Africa there existed both pastoralists, whose economy was based entirely upon their stock, and agriculturists who depended, mostly, upon what they could grow. Being more mobile and having a means of more readily moving and displaying their wealth, the pastoralists generally considered themselves superior. It was, of course, they who were hardest hit by the rinderpest. In a few short weeks they were transformed from a proud, arrogant and independent people to poor begging shadows of their former selves. The cattle aristocracies faced complete ruin.

The Fulani, for example, an East African tribe, lost everything. It is said that many committed suicide or wandered the bush, broken people, calling the names of imaginary cattle. Many Masai, likewise, committed suicide. Indigenous people, once part of stable social groups, found themselves without the support of their society – it had ceased to exist as the attentions of its members were focused on individual survival. Children were sold into slavery and tribes which had earlier been regarded with disdain were now turned to for help. Former pastoralists had not only looked down upon those who grew food but were quite without the skills to grow it for themselves. What they begged and later came to grow did not always suit them and they starved. People who had lived on a diet of milk and blood and meat could not adjust to the new foods. Milk, a staple of many, ceased to be available as cows fell in untold numbers to this ravaging disease. Where some cattle still remained, they became objects of renewed and fierce inter-tribal warfare which contributed further to the chronic mayhem which settled upon the continent.

Those who lived by the plough did not escape unscathed. Most relied upon oxen as draught animals and, with their demise, the plough lay idle. At a time when the need for agricultural produce was greater than ever before in history, there was not enough to meet the needs of starving inhabitants. The unploughed fields lay fallow and barren. The gaunt spectre of starvation was everywhere at hand. Human mortality was astronomical, vast stretches of land lay unoccupied, while on the surface were countless animal corpses. The whole countryside reeked of death and was scarred with heaps of bones and the horns of dead animals. All about, scavengers prospered, satiated by newly fallen victims. Sudan, Ethiopia, Somaliland, Kenya, Tanzania, Uganda, Malawi, Mozambique, Zambia and Zimbabwe, Angola, Namibia and Botswana, not to mention the whole of West Africa – none escaped the dreadful pestilence.[12]

In the Union of South Africa, the horrors of rinderpest and its ghastly consequences were, thanks to experience from other parts of Africa, anticipated in something approaching their reality. The resolution to halt its progress was strong and no cost was considered too high. Infected herds were shot; fences were erected and guarded throughout the day and night; cattle movements were strictly controlled. But still the rinderpest spread. By April of 1896 it had reached Kimberley. In the whole of Africa, only the last bastion of the Cape Colony remained. Here efforts to halt the disease were most strenuous of all. Nearly 1 600 km of fencing were strung between the Indian Ocean and the southern Kalahari. This was patrolled by police and anyone wishing to cross this line had to have their clothes completely disinfected. But it was all for nothing, for despite holding back the onslaught for a year, in March 1897 rinderpest broke through and ranged unchecked

among the cattle and sheep that had so far escaped it. An entire continent had been laid waste.

Quite how, despite the intense precautions, the breach occurred, is not known for certain. A tale is told, however, of the leader of an ox-span who found, some distance south of the fence, a sack containing dried meat and a pair of bloodstained trousers. He donned the trousers and kept the meat. Within days, his animals were infected and it was too late to stop the damage. In total, it is estimated that in excess of 5,5 million cattle died south of the Zambezi, 1,5 million of them in Zimbabwe – and these figures exclude small stock such as sheep and goats as well as innumerable game animals. Lord Lugard chose this period to lead an expedition through the Kalahari. He had the greatest difficulty in organising transport and there were reports of 64 000 trek oxen, dead from rinderpest, between Gaborone and Bulawayo alone, leaving stranded 4 000 wagons.[13]

There was an overwhelming response from the scientific world to the needs of various African countries in fighting the rinderpest epizootic. A galaxy of talent offered its services. There were many outstanding individual scientists but one seems to stand above them all. He was Dr Robert Koch and he pioneered immunisation techniques so that, by the end of 1898, the disease was eliminated south of the Limpopo. It was reintroduced in 1901, but soon after 1903 it disappeared from Southern Africa. Today, rinderpest does not exist south of Tanzania's central railway line, although it has become enzootic in most of East Africa where it flares up from time to time.

Europe may not have seen the last of rinderpest. It was widespread in Eastern Europe as late as the First World War and there was a serious outbreak, starting from Antwerp, in 1920, which was, however, quickly contained. Strict veterinary controls, universally applied, do much today to see that it remains that way. Whilst those concerned should not relax their vigilance, it seems that we may hope never again to be faced with a killer of such terrifying efficiency. We can only reflect sadly upon those men and animals who fell victim to it in such bewildering millions and pray that we will be spared another visitation.

Yet another of Africa's diseases is one which, like rinderpest, does not affect man directly, yet it has enormous economic impact and is probably regarded, certainly in the Kalahari, as the most serious 'commercial' disease. The words 'foot and mouth', uttered in the hearing of cattlemen anywhere in the world, will earn the speaker immediate attention, as it is universally feared.

Foot and mouth disease (FMD) in Southern Africa is first recorded as far back as 1795 and there are references which may refer to it occurring in 1850 and 1858. It appeared, briefly, in Zimbabwe in 1892, but not again until an outbreak on a ranch at Mwenezi, in 1931. The first known occurrence in the Kalahari took place in 1933. FMD is a virus disease for which there is no known cure, although in Southern Africa spontaneous recovery almost always occurs. It is remarkable, despite the great strides in our knowledge of the disease since 1931, that there are still gaps. The most critical of these is that the circumstances under which it is communicated from animal hosts to victim cattle, are still not fully understood. Once cattle are infected, however, the disease passes easily among them.

The 1931 outbreak in Zimbabwe did not occur on a fenced farm.[14] Had it done so, the history of the disease and the growth in our knowledge about it might have been very different. As it was, before the authorities knew where they were, ox-drawn transport had spread it over a large portion of the country. A major outbreak was on hand. The effect on trade was staggering. There was an immediate cessation of all agricultural imports from Zimbabwe to both Britain and South Africa. This, for a young nation dependent almost wholly on agriculture for its foreign earnings, was catastrophic. Little was known about FMD and reactions may have been somewhat excessive, but being aware of the awful consequences experienced by Britain, for example, one can understand her concern. Even so, it is a little difficult to see how halting the import of grapes from South Africa to Zimbabwe might have helped stop the spread of FMD!

Denied the chance of isolating the original outbreak by destroying the cattle involved, the Zimbabwean authorities of the time were faced with a difficult problem. At a conference in December of that year it was decided to embark upon a programme of deliberately infecting all animals in a herd at the same time. Strange though it may sound, this decision made good sense. There was no way of curing the disease; it was not as virulent as elsewhere so the herd would not die, but left to itself the disease would linger on and control would be almost impossible. It was far better to have all the animals infected at the same time so that recovery would be simultaneous and quarantine restrictions could be lifted. This method was to be followed throughout Southern Africa, for the next thirty years.

FMD is a viral disease and it occurs throughout the cattle raising areas of the world, although it is not established in Australia, New Zealand or North America. The virus, which is smaller than the wavelength of light, attacks both cattle and small stock, although in the latter the symptoms are less severe. An infected animal will develop severe lesions on the mouth and feet and, in European breeds, on the teats as well. Excessive salivation and lameness are both features of the disease and the latter is often associated with a frightful condition known as 'slipper formation'. The name, all too graphically, accurately describes the condition which is caused by the hoof separating from the heel, giving rise to a characteristic clicking sound as the animal walks. Generally speaking, in Southern Africa animals recover without difficulty and, having done so, retain a lifetime immunity from further infection.

While the disease runs its course loss in productivity and in exports is a serious factor. The fear of infection being taken to other parts of the world is so great that trade in meat commodities and products from the afflicted country stops immediately, and lengthy quarantine periods must pass before it can be resumed. The economic consequences of this can be serious. For example, in Lobatse, on the eastern edge of the Kalahari, a modern and expensive abattoir was built in 1934 to process the country's growing cattle production. Poor prices and FMD restrictions on meat exports, among other factors, forced it to close down, at great financial cost. Continuing problems with FMD almost resulted in the total breakdown of Botswana's livestock industry. In 1957 FMD again put a halt to all Botswana's meat exports for a year.

As we have seen, the first line of attack on FMD was to restrict cattle movement and infect the entire herd. This technique, called 'apthisation', involved using fluid from the blisters of infected animals and was widely adopted. In Botswana's Kalahari, the difficulties in offering to the cattle industry any kind of veterinary service, however limited, were great. The country was vast, there were very few gravel roads (no tar roads at all), there were no fences and there were hundreds of thousands of cattle needing attention, all in isolated, mobile herds. Attempting to treat an outbreak of FMD was an almost impossible task, the more so when the herds themselves could not easily be located.

John Hobday who, in the early 1940s was Director of Veterinary Services, had a rather interesting way of approaching the problems.[15] He had field staff widely dispersed among the hundreds of nomadic herds in northern Botswana. His problem was twofold: to find the herds in the first place and to get infected fluid out to them so that the cattle could be treated. His staff were well briefed. As soon as they heard the sound of an aircraft, knowing that the director flew his own, each would rush to the nearest tree and climb it. Taking from his pocket a large square of material, this would be shaken out and used as a flag in an attempt to catch the pilot's attention. One can imagine the barren Kalahari suddenly and unaccountably bursting into a blaze of colour as groups of large flowers sprang suddenly to life from the tops of trees! From the open window of his aircraft, Dr Hobday would throw out containers of infected fluid, securely fastened to homemade parachutes, which would float gently down to earth to be collected and used by the men on the ground.

In 1931, as today, the cattle industry was of vital importance to social, cultural and economic life, especially in developing African nations. The threat of such massive disruption to trade could not be tolerated and the race was on to learn more about FMD. The first critical step was to learn where the disease came from; wild animals were very soon suspected as the source but it was some time before attention was focused on the buffalo. In the meantime it was learnt that FMD in Southern Africa is quite different, and much less severe in its effects, than its European counterpart.

There are seven known types of virus – three European (A, O and C), one Asian and three that were to be called Southern African Territories (SAT) 1, 2 and 3. The European types do not generally occur in Southern Africa, although there have been isolated outbreaks on the northern border of Malawi and in Ovamboland in Namibia. Southern African types have never been found in Europe. By the late 1950s evidence pointing to the buffalo as the carrier was mounting and the focus was narrowed to this animal. One of the most eminent figures in the decades of research that followed was Dr John Condy, of the Zimbabwe Veterinary Service. Working with colleagues and the Animal Virus Research Institute at Pirbright in England, more facts slowly emerged. The buffalo was indeed a carrier and, although it does not show symptoms of the disease itself, it harbours live FMD virus. That it could do so for at least five years was proved experimentally. (On an island in Lake Kariba, where a herd had been isolated for fourteen years, between 70 and 80 per cent still carried the virus.)

The first evidence for carrier status raised many scientific eyebrows, as the original blood samples were found to contain live virus for one SAT type and an antibody for another. As is so often the case, learning some of the answers served only to raise more questions. Later it was discovered that, remarkably, buffalo, unlike any other species, were capable of simultaneously carrying virus for all three Southern African types, one predominating at any particular time. Research elsewhere showed that in every African country where buffalo had been sampled, FMD virus was found and these animals have since proved to be the only known reservoir for the disease.

A check on buffalo in the northern Kala-hari showed that between 55 and 65 per cent were active carriers of live virus. In 1970-71, in Botswana's Chobe National Park, 62 buffalo were sampled, from just over half of which live virus was isolated. Seven of the animals carried more than one type of virus. Some of the virus was of a type that had not been seen in any outbreak since 1966. Further research revealed that not only cattle, but kudu and wart-hog also showed symptoms of the disease, while wildebeest and elephant were not affected by it at all and are in fact thought to be highly resistant to it. Carrier status was shown to exist among kudu and cattle but not at sufficient levels to infect other animals, or to harm the carriers. Among cattle the carrier status does not persist for more than two years and, if stressed, they lose it.

The search was closing in but there remained a great many unanswered questions. The most important of these was how the disease was transmitted from buffalo to cattle. Dr Condy initiated a series of experiments aimed at answering this question.[16] For two and a half years he kept susceptible cattle in close association with disease-carrying buffalo in order to find out how the transfer of FMD took place. The animals herded together, grazed together and shared the same water. Remarkably, nothing happened. The cattle did not acquire FMD despite the disease being passed from one buffalo to another twice during the experiment. Clearly, he concluded, there is an unknown link or set of circumstances necessary before infection passes from buffalo to cattle. To this day we do not know what this is.

In later experiments Dr Condy was able to infect cattle from buffalo but how exactly it happened, remains a mystery. Buffalo are proven carriers of FMD, there is no other significant reservoir, yet they do not always infect cattle and we do not know what the precipitating factor is. There are other unsolved questions. For example, how is it that in the north of Zimbabwe buffalo are frequently found to be carrying SAT 1, yet there has never been an outbreak of this type in that part of the country? Similarly, in Uganda SAT types have been found in buffalo but there has never been an outbreak of those types in cattle.[17]

Since the early days of apthisation, vaccines to innoculate against FMD have been developed and are now used extensively. Botswana, whose economy depends so heavily upon the cattle industry, makes extensive use of this development, and has done so since 1964 when vaccines first became available. So much has Botswana been involved, that the country now has its own vaccine factory which produces more than 21 million doses a year and provides, through exports, a valuable source of foreign currency as well as a service to neighbouring countries. Present-day vaccines, developed in Botswana, simultaneously treat all three SAT types but the immunity lasts only for 6 months, after which re-vaccination in susceptible areas is necessary.

Botswana's dependence on cattle and her meat exports to the EEC demanded that means to control FMD outbreaks had to be found. It was for this reason that fencing was used to divide the Kalahari into vast paddocks in an effort to control the movement of cattle. The fencing and its effect on game populations raised controversial questions (see Chapter 20) but they certainly gave the required degree of control. Although primarily for the control of cattle, when first constructed the fences were aimed at excluding all game, as it was not known at the time that the buffalo alone was the responsible carrier. Today, some people agree that there may be a case for reconsidering the location of some of these fences, especially in areas where buffalo are known not to occur and where those game species that do exist are not carriers.[18] With the help of fences, by strict movement control of all animals and animal products, and by constant re-vaccination of every herd where there is a risk of contact with buffalo, Botswana has succeeded in controlling outbreaks of FMD in the Kalahari, the last of which took place in 1980.

In the fifty-five years since Southern Africa's first serious outbreak of FMD, much has been learnt about the disease and how to control it. The unfortunate buffalo, upon whom the blame is heaped, has become something of an outcast, receiving little sympathy. When the buffalo's role became clear, there were insistent calls for its eradication and governments responded. 'Destruction of Buffalo Orders' were promulgated in some countries, notably Zimbabwe, only to be met with a storm of protest, mainly from people such as hunters whose livelihood depended upon them. As a result, since 1978, in Zimbabwe, herds of FMD-free buffalo have been built up, in the hope that they can be used to re-stock ranches and game parks where the species has been eliminated as a result of disease control.

One does not usually link the Kalahari with bubonic plague yet it has occurred there and, like plague elsewhere, has exacted its toll of human lives. It is no longer a danger, though, thanks to the efficacy of modern drugs, and there has been no outbreak of plague for over twenty-five years.

Plague is a disease caused by bacteria. It was once common in Europe but is now restricted largely to Asia. It caused millions of deaths in Europe during the years 1348-9 and again in 1665, when it was known as the 'Black Death'. It is transmitted through the bite of a flea, which acquires the infection from a number of sources or vectors. In Europe the rat acted as carrier and when the disease first invaded Southern Africa, the same creature brought it ashore from ships.[19] Once people are infected, it is spread by coughing and sneezing. In bubonic plague, after incubation a fever develops, accompanied by swelling of glands in the groin and elsewhere. The mortality can be as high as 80 per cent.

The coastal towns of South Africa were the first victims of the plague after it arrived in 1894 from Hong Kong. For a decade the outbreaks were confined to ports and urban areas. The last outbreak was in Durban in 1912. During those years, however, over 1 700 cases had been reported, with 986 deaths. From about 1914 onwards the plague appears to have transferred to wild rats and it spread progressively, until about 1940, in South Africa, and until 1961 in the Kalahari, when the last outbreaks were recorded.

The first occurrence of bubonic plague outside South Africa was in Ovamboland,

in the far north of Namibia, in 1932. It was soon discovered that the disease had transferred from wild rats to gerbils (a type of rodent), and by this means had silently spread through 1 300 kilometres of Kalahari, from one gerbil population to another. More outbreaks followed in succession and between 1920 and 1961 there were a total of ninety-three in various places within the Kalahari.[20] At the height of an outbreak of plague gerbil populations die out and other rodents, ones that associate with man, occupy the empty burrows. In this way they acquire the infected fleas and pass them on in due course to humans.

Plague in the Kalahari tends to be seasonal. For example, in Ngamiland it is always between September and February, although in the southern parts outbreaks occur in April and even July. The worst year for Ngamiland was the season 1944-5. There were 304 cases reported and the mortality rate ran at 50 per cent. Generally, it was not as serious and, in the fifteen years from 1935 to 1949, the seven outbreaks in Botswana resulted in a total of only 404 cases.[21] What is of particular interest is that outbreaks are often associated with a population explosion of rodents.

Dr Reay Smithers, one of the foremost authorities on mammals in Southern Africa, tells of a collecting trip during the 1960s, near Maun in Ngamiland, when one of these explosions in a species of mice was taking place.[22] A serious drought had ended in 1965 and was followed by a good year, during which the population increased considerably. By September of 1966, owing to the extremely rapid breeding rates of the mice, the population had reached extraordinarily high levels and began to exceed the supply of food available. A 'population crash' followed, during the course of which hundreds of thousands of starving animals searched frantically for food.

Dr Smithers was setting trap lines, usually of one hundred traps, to catch specimens for the museum. He found that the mice were so desperately driven by hunger, that he seldom had time to set more than ten or fifteen traps before the first ones would go off, signalling a capture. Indeed, unless he was quick and returned hurriedly to the beginning of his line, he found that other mice would have set upon and devoured their captured companions.

The threat of bubonic plague is no longer a major one in the Kalahari. In Central and East Africa, however, its hold is strong and its occurrence in those parts dates back for more than 300 years. Plague can lie dormant, and is known to have reappeared after a dormancy period of thirty years.

Although the four diseases discussed in this chapter have largely been brought under control, all of them in some degree remain a threat. There are many other diseases, malaria for example, that are as dramatic and horrifying in their effect. There is never room for complacency in dealing with disease anywhere in the world, and especially in Africa. Diseases have a habit of mutating and new forms frequently evolve that circumvent the barriers we have erected against them, often striking back in a more virulent form. Fighting disease is a never-ending battle.

## REFERENCES

1. Bovill, E W. *The Golden Trade of the Moors.* 2nd ed. London: Oxford University Press, 1970
2. Davies, J N P. *Pestilence and Disease in the History of Africa.* Fourteenth Raymond Dart Lecture, 23 June 1976. Johannesburg: Witwatersrand University Press, 1979, pp 1-20
3. Lambrecht, F L. 'Notes on the History of Sleeping Sickness'. In *Botswana Notes and Records*, Vol 1, 1968, pp 41-9
4. Campbell, A C. Personal communication, March 1986
5. Davies, J E. *The History of Tsetse Fly Control in Botswana.* Government of Botswana, Gaborone, Department of Tsetse Fly Control, c 1981, pp 38
6. Potten, D H. 'Aspects of the Recent History of Ngamiland'. In *Botswana Notes and Records*, Vol 8, 1976, p 69
7. Davies, J E. Op cit, Appendix vii
8. Bowles J. Personal communication, December 1984
9. Tshweneagae, M. Personal communication, December 1984
10. Mettam, R W M. 'A Short History of Rinderpest with Special Reference to Africa'. In *Uganda Journal*, No 5, 1937, pp 22-6
11. Mettam, R W M. Op cit
12. Ibid
13. Potten, D H. Op cit, p 65
14. Condy, J B. 'A History of Foot and Mouth Disease in Rhodesia'. In *Rhodesian Veterinary Journal*, Vol 10, No 1, March 1979, pp 2-10
15. Windsor, R. Personal communication, February 1985
16. Condy, J B and Hedger, R S. 'The Survival of Foot and Mouth Disease Virus in African Buffalo with Non-Transference of Infection to Domestic Cattle', In *Research and Veterinary Science.* 1974, No 16, pp 182-5
17. Condy, J B. 'Foot and Mouth Disease'. In *Zimbabwe-Rhodesia Science News*, Vol 13, No 8, August 1979, pp 175-6
18. Condy, J B. Personal communication, April 1985
19. Davis, D H S. 'Ecology of Wild Rodent Plague'. In *Ecological Studies in Southern Africa.* The Hague: Dr W Junk, 1964, p 301-14
20. Ibid
21. Davis, D H S. 'Plague in Africa from 1935 – 1949'. In *Bulletin, World Health Organisation*, 9. 665-700, 1953, p 689
22. Smithers, R N H. Personal communication, May 1984

# 20. Farming the Desert

WE have already learnt that the area of Kalahari sands encompasses some 2 million km$^2$ and that the range in rainfall throughout this area is considerable. It varies from the scanty, erratic rain of the extreme south to the more tropical conditions in the north. As the quantity and reliability of the rainfall vary, so too does the vegetation. Given these facts, what then is the agricultural potential of the Kalahari?

I am not a farmer and, although I love the land and the things that live in and on it, I do not have the farmer's feel for it, that sometimes intuitive sense that tells him what best to do with it and how to do it. Having travelled widely across the Kalahari, one cannot but be impressed by its infinite spaces and apparent potential for food production in a world where the demand grows ever more urgent.

As elsewhere, the choice in the Kalahari is between growing things in it or feeding animals on the plants that are already there. In fact, little is grown there and livestock raising is by far the dominant form of agricultural activity.

Certain cereal crops form the staple diet of the majority of Africa's peoples. Maize (corn), sorghum and millet are examples, of which, in Southern Africa, maize is the most widely consumed and cultivated. To a limited extent maize is grown in the Kalahari but it is not generally suited to the arid conditions and poor soils. Where it does occur, yields are low or considerable technology must be employed to bring a crop to harvest. This is very much to the disadvantage of a country like Botswana, for example, 70 per cent of which lies under Kalahari sands. Twenty per cent of that country's population live out on the sands and struggle against great odds to produce crops of any kind. They are hampered not only by the vagaries of the climate but also through lack of skills and knowledge which would allow them to produce the best with the limited resources at their disposal.

If irrigation is not a possibility, owing to insufficient water, the unsuitable nature of the soil and the high cost of irrigation schemes, what is called 'dryland' farming is the only alternative. This simply means that the farmer leaves himself totally to the mercy of the rains. With one or two exceptions, this is the type of farming generally practised in the Kalahari and its results have not been impressive. The average maize yield for the traditional farm in 1983 was 257 kg per hectare. For commercial farms in the same year, it was 1 123, bringing the national yield to a meagre 433 kg per hectare.[1] These figures are for the whole country, including all the officially recognised arable lands of the east, which are not in the Kalahari, where the majority of the population live. Actual yields for the Kalahari itself would be much lower. For example, in Ngamiland 100 kg per hectare is the figure given.[2] One wonders if the effort is worth it and it comes as no surprise to learn that the country annually expends some P50 million importing grain foods. In 1984 P24 million was spent on importing 92 000 tonnes of milled and rough maize.[3]

The situation is not without hope, however. Dr Gus Nilsson is a Swede who went to Botswana in 1967, under the auspices of the United Nations Food and Agricultural Organisation, to conduct agricultural research on dryland farming techniques.[4] He now has his own farms where he grows flowers and vegetables. His ideas may be fairly controversial but he appears to have proved them in practice. Recently the Government of Botswana, anxious to attain self-sufficiency in food production, has been showing interest in his techniques.

Transvaal farms in close proximity to the Kalahari receive between 300 and 500 mm of rain a year, and obtain a yield of between 2 and 5 tonnes per hectare. The soil, of course, is not Kalahari sand, but the point Dr Nilsson makes is that a similar rainfall in the Kalahari ought to produce more than 257 kg a hectare. Kalahari sands, as a medium for growing anything, are, he admits, a poor choice. The sands are 'burnt out', by which is meant that most of the organic matter has been broken down by micro-organisms and gone off as $CO_2$. The replacement of this organic matter is a long-term programme, but it is within the means of the rural farmer who, with his cattle enclosures, has large quantities of a suitable material for the job. Despite the poor quality of the sands, Gus, using techniques of his own devising, went out to Hukuntse, an exceedingly remote part of the central Kalahari and there, restricting himself to the cash and equipment that would be available to the traditional farmer, tested his theory. The results were quite startling.

For two successive years he ran experimental plots. In the first year he spent approximately P50 on trace elements and fertiliser. The distance between his rows of plants was 1,5 m, twice the usual distance. In that time 198 mm of rain fell but his yield was an astonishing 2 000 kg per hectare! In the following year over 270 mm of rain fell, the same amount of fertiliser was added but the distance between rows of plants was halved. Despite the extra rain, the yield was but a quarter of its previous level at 500 kg per hectare.

The critical variable, Gus maintains, is the distance between plants. The sand has great water-holding properties and significant quantities remain trapped in it between successive wet seasons. Plants have the ability to reach down to this moisture but they must be compensated for the poor quality of the soils – hence the extra space between them. Space is something that is expensive on the conventional farm but, as Gus is quick to point out, in the traditional lands of the Kalahari it is not a critical factor. Trace elements are important and in the Kalahari sands these are in short supply, particularly zinc, boron and molibdynon. All, however, are inexpensively and easily added.

Gus has many ideas for improving the agricultural potential of the Kalahari. Another he would like to see introduced is strip farming. With limited ploughing power available, this would involve planting in narrow, parallel strips, thus avoiding the necessity of preparing ground which is never to be productive. He also advocates the planting of seed on low ridges. The sand quickly becomes saturated, depriving the plants of oxygen and retarding growth. By keeping at least part of the root system clear of too much water, oxygen supply is assured and higher yields result.

Gus's interesting work and experiments have yet to be tried on a commercial scale, but he is confident that they will work. He boldly claims that, at a rate of one plant per square metre, 100 000 ha of the Kalahari could make Botswana self-sufficient in maize. It is an exciting thought, not only because of the obvious benefits to Botswana, but because developing nations throughout the continent could likewise benefit.

There is one part of the Kalahari sands where quite amazing yields are obtained and, although at the moment the benefits accrue to only a small group of people, the results underlie the bright-eyed optimism which is expressed whenever the Okavango, as an agricultural resource, is discussed.

All around the Okavango there are features which are locally known as 'molapo', and the cultivation of grain crops on them has come to be called molapo farming. Typically, a molapo is a long, shallow depression, left from earlier times when rivers or streams flowed through it. Today they are the winding swathes of grass and sedge between the rich riverine tree growth so common on the edges of the Delta. There are two critical factors which give special properties to some molapos. They often have a deep, black, heavy soil, and every year they are inundated by the rising waters of the Okavango's annual flood. It is when the floods recede that the land is tilled and planted. The heavy soil holds the water well, providing moisture, with help from erratic rains, for the entire growth cycle of the plant. Traditional practices give yields of 2 000 kg per hectare and researchers, using more advanced methods, have obtained yields of 6 000 kg per hectare![5] It is for this reason that the flow of the old Thaoge River is being restored and it is hoped that the project may allow for the exploitation of the molapo's remarkable fertility.

For all the dreams of the crop farmers and those inspired to help them, it is cattle which represent the agricultural wealth of the Kalahari. Almost all the indigenous people who live in or near it are pastoralists. Being so close to the hearts and pockets of its people, the cattle issue is fraught with misinformation, misunderstanding and emotion. This is particularly so when many experts believe that cattle and associated problems represent the greatest single ecological threat facing Botswana and the Kalahari.

The origins of this problem are not difficult to appreciate. Traditional pastoralists throughout Africa have, in times past, grazed their herds and moved on when pastures failed. The freedom to do so did not necessitate understanding such concepts as range management or carrying capacities. The limits to herd size were not ecological constraints but logistical ones – how frequently and how far did one have to move as the herd grew larger and consumed grazing more rapidly? In a society where cattle mean wealth, quantity is more important than quality and, in this respect, logistical constraints are far more generous than ecological ones. When such things as international boundaries, population pressures and legally specified land use areas begin to restrict these practices, change becomes necessary. However, the attitudes and beliefs of any people are not easily altered, especially those of pastoralists whose bovine possessions are not just a source of economic wealth, but also of social status, and lie at the very centre of their cultural existence. It takes time. Although realisation of the need for change is emerging, no dramatic, short-term results can be expected, and in the meantime the ecological risk is one of potentially severe proportions.

Accurate estimates of Botswana's cattle population are hard to come by. The official count in 1983 was 2,8 million cattle – roughly three animals to each head of the population – plus 1 million goats and sheep.[6] During the same year the United Nations, however, estimated that the actual figure was closer to 4 million cattle and 1,5 million goats and sheep.[7]

In the early days of Botswana's history, possibly the majority of the population and its cattle lived closer to the eastern side of the country. Because of its inaccessibility and lack of water, only a small proportion of its people lived and kept cattle in the Kalahari. Since then, a number of factors have changed. Populations of both humans and their stock have increased dramatically, and at the same time the quality of the now overcrowded and overgrazed eastern lands has deteriorated steadily. These factors alone gave doubly good reasons for finding a way to ranch cattle in the Kalahari.

Boreholes and water-drilling technology made this possible. Almost daily new boreholes are being drilled, the distribution and location of which is not always carefully ordered so that expansion is not completely under control. Another factor which has powered and motivated rapid expansion has been the support of Botswana's beef industry by the European Economic Community. As a result of negotiations, the price of Botswana's beef rose to a level 60 per cent above world prices from 1971 onwards. As a consequence, revenue to producers rose from P8,2 million in 1970 to P30,8 million in 1977, with only a 50 per cent increase in the number of cattle slaughtered. A potential ecological problem lies in the fact that this massive boost to the cattle industry came during a wet decade when abundant grazing was available everywhere.[8] There are real fears as to the consequences if Botswana's quasi-twenty-year cycle of wet and dry decades holds true.

In the last thirty years there has been an escalating invasion of the Kalahari. This in itself is not necessarily a bad thing. The Kalahari does have good grazing and it is excellent cattle country. The problem is that it is also a fragile environment.

Delicately adjusted to its heat, its soils and its peculiar rainfall, the vegetation of the Kalahari survives with little margin for error. It is therefore particularly susceptible to misuse and abuse and, unlike more moist and fertile lands, it takes longer to recover. Properly managed, there is ample evidence that it can sustain a vast and highly productive beef industry; badly used, it could become an arid dustbowl, in danger of turning again into a true desert. Access to underground water has made possible the maintenance of permanent cattle stations in the Kalahari where good management practices are not used. As a result, the grazing is quickly exhausted as the most palatable grasses are consumed. Destructive as well as irreversible damage to the climax vegetation takes place. Many expert conservationists, who fear for the future of the Kalahari, maintain that the only way to prevent this is through proper management.

A very large portion of the Kalahari's cattle herds are managed in the traditional way upon what are known as communal lands. These lands, as the name suggests, are owned by the people at large. There are no fenced-off areas and all cattle may roam freely anywhere upon it. Of the 75 per cent of Botswana which comprises her range-lands, only 5 per cent is fenced.[9] Whilst this system has advantages, it also has some disadvantages. There is little control of the carrying capacity, i.e. the number of hectares per head of cattle. Selective breeding to improve the stock is not possible and control of disease and the maintenance of health and hygiene among the herds is made more difficult. There is no incentive to any individual to care for and maintain the grazing and no means by which responsibility for misuse can be apportioned. As a result, unintentional abuse of the land is widespread. An example from Ngamiland illustrates this point.[10]

It has been estimated that the total cattle carrying capacity for the entire area of the Nokaneng flats, on the southern edge of the Okavango Delta, was approximately 21 800 animals. In the 1970s the cattle population doubled every five years. In 1971 it was estimated that there were 9 300, which rose to 19 000 in 1975. By 1980 there were 37 335 cattle on the flats although, in 1981, the figure had dropped to 34 568, well over 50 per cent above the recommended stocking rate. These figures do not include an allowance of 20 per cent for calves. As one of the researchers so succinctly put it, cattle owners 'question the environmental dogma that grazing is a limited resource. Most herdsmen believe that herbage is an infinitely renewable resource.'[11]

According to David Field, who was then employed by the Ministry of Agriculture, the carrying capacity of Botswana as a whole is 2,7 million head.[12] He would, I am sure, be the first to admit that this is at best a rough guide and may well be an underestimation. At the same time, however, a situation where the present stocking rate is approaching a figure which is 50 per cent greater than the recommended level, is surely grounds for concern.

This problem situation led to the Livestock Development Programmes (LDPs) and Tribal Grazing Land Policy (TGLP) being evolved. The schemes were to be a repetition of the 'enclosure' movement in England which took place during the eighteenth century, and they encountered the same resistance, for the same reasons, and created the same problems. Despite experience gained from that and many similar, later schemes, the Botswana programmes were just as badly implemented. It is always easy to sit on the sidelines and criticise, but many of those who were intimately involved in the various projects were critical too. An examination of both TGLP and LDP will show why.

TGLP[13] sought, through the means of fencing, to divide the tribal grazing lands into three types of area: commercial lands, where individuals would pay rent for exclusive rights; communal lands, where the system of land use would not change but efforts would be made to improve management; and reserved lands, where no development would take place and which would be held for future use. The idea was that the owners of the larger herds would move out of the communal and into the commercial lands and that some of the smaller operators would be encouraged to join together and, as a group, occupy a commercial farm. In this way it was hoped that stock densities would be reduced in the communal lands, and that those which remained there would benefit from demonstrations of better management techniques. The scheme also envisaged that stock numbers in both types of land would be carefully controlled.[14]

The scheme faltered because of a number of basic assumptions which were not in fact valid at all. One was that there was sufficient additional land available for the scheme to operate, whereas investigation showed that there was not. Quite sizeable and numerous communities were found to be living in what was intended to be commercial land. Many were displaced, while others, together with their own small herds, were incorporated within the commercial land, thereby defeating the object of its creation. An integral part of the TGLP was to reserve areas as safeguards for the poorer members of the population, but this was not done and, in view of the now apparent shortage of land, the provision was dispensed with. Contrary to what had been originally intended, rents for the commercial farms were set at so low a level that they provided no significant income and no source for payment of compensation to those whom the scheme had deprived of their land. Finally, there was widespread apathy towards the idea of strict controls on the number of livestock in the commercial and communal areas.

The people to whom the new lands were allocated were often those who were already in occupation and who, by virtue of their ownership of the water there, believed they had a prior claim. Thus the new farms were not always allocated to people with the capital base and requisite skills to manage them as viable commercial concerns. Most of them quickly degenerated to the same level as the over-used, abused communal lands. In one area only two of the first twelve new ranches allocated were taken up by people who had been keeping their stock in the communal lands.[15] The scheme's objective in reducing over-stocking in the communal lands was not achieved. The 'good-husbandry' clause that was part of the commercial ranch conditions, was not enforced and scant attention was given to fire-break regulations, herd size or range management. Some believe that TGLP has contributed to, rather than reduced, the destruction of the national rangeland resource.

There have been a number of Livestock Development Projects, many far-reaching and ambitious in their scope. An account of the scheme at the Ncojane ranches illustrates their fate. Ncojane is in the far west of Botswana, on deep Kalahari sands. It was proposed that a total of thirty ranches should be created and that, as a turnkey operation, they should be offered as commercial enterprises, already equipped with boreholes and fully fenced.

The reasons for the scheme's partial failure are legion, but among them were the remoteness of the area, the time it took to develop the ranches, the difficulty in finding water, the long period of time which was taken to get the leases signed and the fact that, despite warnings by ecologists, the farms were located across a traditional wildebeest migration route.

In the event, only twenty-three of the ranches were built and allocation methods did not ensure that qualified farmers, with capital, appropriate skills and determination, were chosen. The results were predictable. Today no farm is being properly managed and all are being used as traditional cattle-posts. Fences have been destroyed by game and not repaired. There is a high level of absentee landlords and a low investment of time and effort. Recommended carrying rates are totally disregarded, despite the fact that they are monitored and reported upon by competent staff from the Ministry of Agriculture. Apparently, it is impossible to enforce them, as the following figures show. The average carrying capacity of each of the farms has been calculated at between 400 and 460 livestock units. In 1982 the farms were, on average, 50 per cent overstocked and, although this figure fell as the drought claimed its toll, in 1984 the rate still stood at 36 per cent above the recommended level. These figures are only average statements and at least one farm carried over three times the number of cattle authorised for it.[16]

Efforts to improve the problems being

caused by overgrazing in Botswana generally, and in the Kalahari in particular, have not so far been noticeably successful, but often, in critical appraisals of such schemes, sufficient credit is not given where it is due. That attempts have been made to tackle the problem is very much to the credit of the Government of Botswana. Their job has not been an easy one and several factors other than the monumental task of changing the attitudes of peasant pastoralists make it even more difficult.

In the first place it is widely known that a very high percentage of the national herd is owned by a very small number of people. Estimates range from 5 per cent owning 70 per cent of the herd to 10 per cent owning 60 per cent of it. Whatever the true figures, they show that there exists a small but very powerful group whose wealth gives them great economic, social and political strength. Often these people are in senior positions in both Government and commerce. Their cattle interests are managed by subordinates as they do not have the time to devote themselves exclusively to ranching. They possess neither a great interest in increasing productivity nor a concern of ecological considerations. Such a powerful lobby complicates the Government's exercise of control. In addition, the cost of providing new ranches with borehole water can be extremely high. Sometimes two or three attempts must be made and a rancher can expect to invest as much as P70 000 or more before he has a sufficiently productive hole. In the circumstances, his outlay is high and this tends to lead to his exploitation of the rangelands.

In the second place, the Government, in the absence of local expertise and technical skill, is, like the governments of many developing nations, compelled to call in foreign consultants. Experience shows, with distressing frequency, that these people, experts as they might well be in the lands where they come from, are often ignorant of local conditions. They do not understand, nor do they seem to make the effort to try to understand, the problems. As John Cooke, Professor of Environmental Sciences at Botswana's University, has said: 'The "expert" advice received in good faith by the policy makers has at times

been wrong, ill-advised and sometimes downright bad.'[17]

It is as well, however, not to minimise the seriousness of the problem a large, poorly managed, national herd creates, nor to make excuses for it. Dr Graham Child, then UN (FAO) ecologist, working with the Botswana Government, has pointed out the rather frightening fact that significant numbers of people did not settle or make use of the Kalahari until about 150 years ago. Because of the rinderpest, cattle numbers were exceptionally low at the turn of the century and, therefore, only in the last eighty-five years have Botswana's enormous herds been built up.[18]

Universally, both inside and outside Botswana, there is condemnation of the present abuse of the rangelands. The United Nations, reporting in 1984, called for urgent attention to be given to the situation.[19] A series of environmental symposia in recent years has done likewise.[20] Another FAO ecologist in 1971 described Botswana's rangelands as 'sick from neglect and exploitation'.[21] That there is a solution to the problem is clear from the work carried out at a Kalahari Pasture Research Station. There they have been able to show that at reasonable stocking rates there is no deterioration or any change in the density or floristic composition of the rangeland, after twenty-nine years' continuous use.[22]

One of the difficulties in combating the creeping cancer of environmental degradation caused by overgrazing, is its slow and insidious nature. It is not easy to convince humans of their responsibility for its spread when they cannot see any changes. Evidence from an Australian source in the person of Dr Newsome is very interesting in this regard.[23] He recounts how Australians failed to recognise the inevitable changes to the pastures and soils caused by the ever-growing number of sheep that were being raised. 'The drought' received the blame, and the occasional lush years were considered normal. More watering points allowed for an increase in stock numbers, which effectively masked the declining carrying capacity of the land.

The land's productivity declined steadily over several human generations. The long-term changes were subtle and man's short memory allowed him to adapt to those changes, slipping easily into the belief that there was no change at all – and this belief was perpetuated. Inevitably the disaster, when it came, was of the first magnitude. In New South Wales, a major drought reduced sheep numbers from 17 million to only 4 million, and in the years that followed their numbers never again exceeded 6 or 7 million. In places the vegetation and soil simply never recovered; it was worthless and men walked off the land, penniless.

In north-west Australia soil erosion, caused by the denudation of vegetation through overgrazing, was threatening the future of a large dam. Eventually the Government had to accept responsibility for regenerating approximately 400 000 ha of totally degraded rangeland. To do this, the land had to be fenced and sub-divided, the cattle were removed and nearly 80 000 km of furrows were ploughed, to help retain rainwater and to provide seed-beds for new grass. The cost was horrific.

Whilst the Botswana Government deserves every encouragement for the courageous efforts that it has made, the battle will be a long, slow one. In my travels across the Kalahari I have met many people working for change and improvement. From their comments and from my own observations, it occurs to me that one of the most serious underestimations made in programmes of this nature is the amount of time it takes to implement change. Again and again 'It shouldn't take more than a few years' turns out to be ten or fifteen years. The magnitude of the task in encouraging people to move from traditional to commercial production is seldom fully appreciated. I suppose it is rather like teaching someone to swim or ride a bicycle. When you can do it yourself it is hard to remember how difficult it was to learn.

There is a small but growing karakul industry, ideally suited to the more arid parts of the southern Kalahari, that is well established in the region of Bokspits, in the south of Botswana, and also in the northern Cape's Gordonia District, south of the Molopo River. In Southern Africa the karakul sheep is the source of a very fine, tightly curled wool, which elsewhere is known as

astrakhan. Lambs are killed when very young and the pelts are used to make fashion garments, usually coats. Ideally, the lambs should be less than twenty-four hours old when they are killed.

The karakul industry has long been established in Southern Africa and began, many years ago, in Namibia. At that time there were very strong protectionist laws aimed at nurturing the infant industry but the wily residents of neighbouring countries soon invented a great many methods of smuggling out live stock. In this way the karakul arrived in the Kalahari. The Livestock Development Programme in Botswana has gone some way towards providing a boost for this small industry, but an equally important one came from a rather exceptional and charming Norwegian named Ingebjorj Vaagen, who at the time was working in Lobatse.

As part of an international aid programme, Ingebjorj had helped establish a carpet-weaving business, run by and employing local Motswana. In the course of her work, she found out about the karakul farmers in the southern Kalahari and also discovered that all the wool clippings were thrown away. (Like many sheep, the animals need to be clipped every six to nine months.) At a pitiful ten thebe (100 t = 1 Pula) a kilogram, it was not worth the farmer's labour to collect and sell it.

The mixture obtained from karakul is half wool, half hair. Ingebjorj was aware that in Europe similar types of material were used to make a number of products, ranging from carpets to fine clothes. Karakul wool is also one of the main components of Persian carpets. Her investigations led to the acquisition of suitable machinery and today, after much experimentation, Lobatse's little cottage industry is one of the few places in the world using a woollen spinning process to produce spun yarn from karakul sheep. The new wool has a number of advantages over the more usual varieties: it has much more spring to it and there is a wider range of natural colours. Two grades are produced, one a coarser variety, used for tapestries and floor carpets, and another, lighter and softer, as a knitting yarn. The production of yarn has soared from 12 000 kg in 1983 to

32 000 kg in 1985. Not only has this increased turnover in the business but the Kalahari's karakul farmers have also benefited. From a mere 10 t a kilogram, the price for clipped karakul wool has risen to an average of P1,05, with a range, depending on quality, from 75 t to as much as P2,40.[24]

The discussion of any form of stock-raising in the Kalahari, but particularly cattle-ranching, inevitably raises the question of Botswana's controversial fences. As we saw in Chapter 18, the fences were erected by the Veterinary Department in order to afford them control over the movement of cattle, so that they could prevent and control outbreaks of foot and mouth disease. In this, they have been very successful. The controversy concerns a conservation issue and arises over the claim that the fences are causing a massive reduction in game numbers. Others argue that this is not the case and hold that it is the general encroachment by man into the Kalahari, and his expanding use of that resource, that is denying the game its traditional home.

About twenty-five years ago it was estimated that there were 2 to 3 million animals, mostly game, in the Kalahari. Today it is estimated that this has dropped to possibly below 1 million, whilst the number of cattle has increased. Overall, the number of animals may not have changed – cattle have simply taken the place of game. The gross number of animals in the Kalahari is a function of its average carrying capacity. If the size of one group increases, it must be at the expense of the other.[25] Before returning to this question in some detail, it is as well to review, briefly, the history of Botswana's fences.

The first fences were erected in 1954 and 1955 (see map). The construction of fences has continued since then and new ones are still being built today. At the moment there are 2 569 km of fencing, varying in size and strength according to the threat of game that is considered likely. For example, the 'buffalo fence', which demarcates the south and south-eastern side of the Okavango Delta, is a sturdy affair approximately 3 m high and is designed to keep out buffalo and at least discourage elephant. On the other hand, some of the fences that cross the Kalahari are three or four strands of wire on ordinary metal droppers, not more than 3,5 m high. In some cases, there is a double fence with a track between the two sections.

Have these fences really affected the game populations? The most outspoken opponents of the fences are probably Mark and Delia Owens, who lived in the Kalahari for seven years, working on a quite unconnected research project.[26] However, their work and their obvious love of the wild brought them into close contact with all the animal species of the Kalahari, particularly those affected by the fences. They were also intimately involved with what has subsequently proved to be one of the most infamous stretches of fence – known to all as the Khukhe fence. This fence begins on Botswana's western border, itself fenced completely from north to south, and extends due east for 286 km, separating the Ghanzi farms from Ngamiland. At that point it turns due north, passing just to the east of the Okavango Delta. In this way it serves to separate the game of the central Kalahari from the Okavango itself. Any game that is in Botswana's Kalahari south of the Khukhe fence, no longer has access to the Okavango.

About 50 km east of the point where the Khukhe fence turns north lies the Boteti River, which always has pools of water in it, even if it is not flowing. Eighty km downstream, and in a south-easterly direction from that point, is Lake Xau (pronounced 'Dow') and, a few kilometres beyond it, Mopipi reservoir, which supplies Orapa diamond mine with water. Lake Xau sometimes has water, but not always. At the end of the dry season Lake Xau and Mopipi are the only two areas of potential standing water to which migrating game from the central or southern Kalahari have access.

The areas of the Boteti, Lake Xau and Mopipi are all heavily populated and, with surface water throughout most of the year, are the centres of intensive tribal grazing. Usually, at the time when game most need the water and the grass in this area, so too do the numerous herds of cattle. The consumption of water is not so much the critical factor as is the elimination of the grazing within walking distance of it.

Another factor of importance is the location of one particular, fairly short, length of fencing. At the point where the Khukhe fence turns through right angles from east to north, there was located what was known at the time as 'the tail'. This was 38 km of fencing that headed off in a south-easterly direction and then abruptly stopped. This meant that an animal wishing to head in a north-easterly direction, for example, would

first strike the Khukhe fence and be turned east. It would then strike 'the tail' and be obliged to walk south-east for perhaps 40 km before being able to go round the end of the fence and resume its chosen route. The tail apparently no longer exists, having fallen into disrepair and not been maintained. It is no longer a barrier but it was a barrier in the past.

In August 1979 the Owens reported that

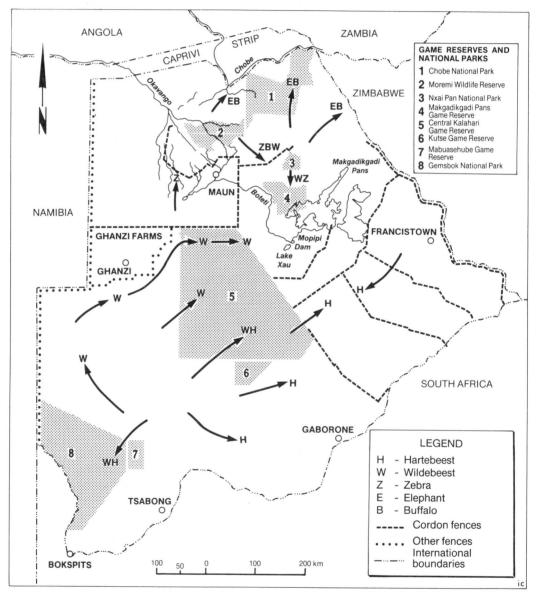

**DRY SEASON WILDLIFE MOVEMENT AND MAJOR FENCES**

**Sources:** *Ngwamatsoko*, K.T. "Lessons for future livestock development projects in Botswana: wildlife resources considerations," *Botswana's First Livestock Development Project and its Future Implications*, National Institute of Research, Gaborone, June 1982, p. 147.
Department of Surveys and Lands, *Botswana: Foot and Mouth Veterinary Control Fences*, Gaborone, January 1985.

the Khukhe fence had channeled over 80 000 wildebeest eastwards to the grass plains of Lake Xau. On their way north the animals had piled up against the fence where many had died. More died on the journey to Lake Xau and, at the lake itself, the plains of which had been overgrazed by cattle, large numbers began to die off. In the same year the Owens reported that wildebeest and hartebeest were unable to reach the Limpopo River, in the east, from the south-east Kalahari. The barriers included not only a veterinary fence, but the main north-south road, the railway line and, of course, dense inhabitation.[27] The assertion, in both of these reports, is that the fences deflected or denied migratory animals access to water and grazing, as a result of which they died.

Fencing has been criticised for other reasons too, and these are perhaps best summarised by Mr K T Ngwamatsoko, of Botswana's Department of Wildlife and National Parks.[28] The fences, he states, have trapped and killed animals such as giraffe, hartebeest, ostriches and other species – although he does not estimate numbers. The Veterinary Department has issued permits to local residents to shoot animals causing damage to fences. When one of the north-eastern fences outside the Kalahari was being damaged by elephants, permits were again issued, illegally authorising the elephants' destruction. It was necessary for the Attorney General to intervene to stop this practice. However, it is claimed that permits for the 'control' of game are still given out and, up to 1982 at least, there seems to have been some substance in the accusations that the Veterinary Department may have been abusing its authority. This is reinforced by the statement that 'permitted' animals included kudu and springbok, both of which easily jump the fences.

It is also claimed that there is little or no liaison between Veterinary and Game Departments over the siting of new fences, which often cut through game migration routes. There is, perhaps, a need for better communication between the Veterinary Department, responsible for the fences, and other sections of the Government and the public. Not understanding the situation, the public cannot be blamed for asking questions. Why, for example, are there fences where there are no cattle on either side? Why, when an excellent vaccine has been produced, which can prevent outbreaks of foot and mouth disease, are new fences being constructed at an ever faster rate? Why, when it is thought that buffalo are the only carriers of foot and mouth who can pass it to cattle, are fences constructed where there are no buffalo? The Veterinary Department no doubt has rational explanations for these questions, but their continued silence does nothing to quieten fears about the fences and their long-term effects.

The European Economic Community heavily subsidises Botswana's beef industry and has also sponsored extensive wildlife research in Botswana. Mr Ngwamatsoko finds this a contradictory situation, in that the cordon fences they insist upon are contributing to the demise of the wildlife. There may be sound reasons for the EEC's position and here again lack of information and communication aggravate the situation. It has been pointed out that the position of the EEC is that they do not, and never have, insisted upon the erection of cordon fences. They only require that Botswana must have FMD under control and make no stipulations as to how this should be done. Whilst this may be perfectly true it seems a little sanctimonious. There are indeed many other ways in which FMD could be controlled without resorting to wire barriers. However, all of them are likely to be prohibitively expensive and so, for economic reasons alone, Botswana is left no alternative but to build the controversial fences.[29]

Writing in 1981, Hobbs and Yaxley[30] made an unsubstantiated claim that the fences had been directly responsible for the death of about a quarter of a million animals in 1970/80. The Department of Wildlife and National Parks estimates the worth of these animals as being in the region of P30 million. In addition a considerable amount of the taxpayer's money is being spent on fence erection and maintenance.

Doug and June Williamson, two biologists engaged in research on ungulates in the central Kalahari, worked at Deception

Valley after the Owens left.[31] Anxious to throw some light on the controversial question of Botswana's fences, Doug sought to establish a comparison between the actual and theoretical carrying capacity of the Kalahari. By this means he hoped to arrive at some estimate of the animal losses attributable to the fences. His conclusions showed that the actual biomass of large herbivores in the Kalahari is but 24 per cent of what predictions say. He concluded that the fences have caused a severe reduction in the number of game animals. He points out that the existing fences have effectively cut off the Kalahari from nearly all the perennial surface water at its perimeter and claims that this must reduce the carrying capacity for the more water-dependent species. On the nearby, unfenced, Makgadikgadi plains the average biomass is 6 000 kg per km². In the fenced Kalahari, the figure is 439 kg per km². An independent survey arrived at a mass of 400 kg for the same area.

There is no disputing Doug's data and he is firmly of the opinion that fences around the Kalahari have caused a severe decline in the large herbivore biomass of the region. Whether his conclusion is valid, however, is an entirely different matter. There are, as we shall see, others who reject it.

It is perhaps appropriate at this point to add an observation from personal experience. In his comparison between the central Kalahari and Makgadikgadi, Doug states that, although the latter has a marginally higher rainfall, the two areas are similar, and therefore comparable, but for the fact that the Kalahari does not afford access to open water, whilst the latter does. I am not convinced that the areas are comparable, however. To the untrained eye, they appear to be very different, and small differences can often mean a great deal. However, the Makgadikgadi, much of which is a game reserve, does offer access to water.

The area is immediately to the north-east of the Boteti, Lake Xau and Mopipi and there are no fences to prevent the animals reaching them. In January 1985 I spent some time in that area, and while I was there I counted a total of thirty-seven dead zebra. All of them were within a day's walk of the Boteti, which was flowing and had abundant water. I cannot guess at how many more I would have seen if I had been conducting a proper survey. It was the end of another drought year and the local people's cattle, which illegally use the area in which I found the zebra, were also dying. Their owners said there was no grazing for them. Even my inexpert eyes could agree with this.

In condemning the fences, the greatest publicity has been focused on the deaths of large numbers of wildebeest. Alec Campbell, who spent some of his career in charge of Botswana's National Parks, explains that there is good evidence to suggest that there have been large fluctuations in herbivore populations in the twentieth century in the Kalahari.[32] In 1910 the wildebeest populations were apparently very low. They built up to high levels and, in the 1930s, following a severe drought, crashed dramatically when large numbers died on the eastern side of the country. There they experienced difficulty in penetrating the densely populated region to gain access to the Limpopo and its perennial water. Following this collapse, the herd sizes built up again and another population collapse was recorded in 1963. Several more followed in quick succession.

There are two large populations of wildebeest in Botswana (see map on p. 238), one in the north and one in the south. Both range extremely widely and migrate over considerable distances from one end of their territory to the other. Both approach the area of Makgadikgadi towards the end of the dry season because that is the only area where perennial water is then available. One comes down from the north, the other from the south. As they arrive at different parts of the same area, they do not mix. It is generally believed, in Botswana for example, that wildebeest are a naturally adapted, Kalahari dwelling species, hence the theory that they only leave this natural habitat in times when grazing and water are scarce. Proponents of this theory argue that providing reserved areas in the arid Kalahari is enough to ensure the survival of the species. There is an opposing view, however.

Alec Campbell suggests that wildebeest are *not* adapted to the harsh Kalahari environment and that their natural habitat is on the periphery of that great wasteland. In times of plenty these animals will venture into the Kalahari but, in times of scarcity, need to be able to return to more bountiful areas. It is these latter areas that are now completely dominated by man, thus depriving the wildebeest of access to them and, effectively, ensuring their ultimate fate. Not being suited to the Kalahari yet having no choice but to live there, they must, ultimately, die out completely.[33]

The largest wildebeest die-off, in 1963, occurred among the northern population, in the Nata area, at the northern end of Sowa Pan. Alec drove through this herd in May 1963, and estimated that there may have been in excess of 250 000 animals. They were so weak that they were unable to move. At the time, there was a commercial demand for the tails of wildebeest, and the animals were also considered a threat to grazing. The local people were able to move among the animals, quite openly, spearing them and cutting off their tails, for which they received 15t a tail at the local store.

During this time, from 1962 to 1963, Alec was stationed at Ghanzi and several times had occasion to drive along the Khukhe fence, and once flew its length. He saw large herds of wildebeest east of the Ghanzi farms but they never seemed to reach the fence. Once, in 1963, flying along the fence-line, he counted about 500 dead wildebeest and only 200 alive. However, he never saw as many dying animals along the Khukhe fence as he was later to see at Lake Xau or Nata. When he did visit the lake later that year, he found animals from the southern group were congregating and dying there, but not in such large numbers as at Nata, although the following year approximately 15 000 wildebeest died at the lake. Examination of the corpses showed that the animals had died of starvation, and perhaps exhaustion, owing to the fact that they had to walk 20 km from the nearest grazing to water. The 1960s was a decade of severe drought in Botswana.

In 1965 George Silberbauer, who was then working in the Ghanzi District, reported considerable numbers of wildebeest near the Khukhe fence. He gave no actual figures but estimated that 10 per cent of them were dying every week. He claimed the animals were dying of starvation as there was no grazing after three years of drought.[34]

In 1970 there was yet another die-off of wildebeest in the vicinity of Lake Xau. This was investigated by Dr Graham Child who reported that about 15 000 animals died.[35] The die-off took place over a period of three months and he was struck by the significant absence of a build-up of predators in the area On investigation, he observed that this was because the carcasses were so emaciated that there was nothing for predators to eat. By November of that year the wildebeest were in such an advanced state of starvation that they were entering the native villages and eating the dry thatch off the hut roofs. He was convinced that the main cause of mortality among these animals was starvation, aggravated by the fact that because of local grazing pressure the wildebeest had to walk long distances, perhaps 20 or 40 km, between food and water.

We have now seen abundant evidence that animals of the Kalahari have died in great numbers, but the question remains: are the fences responsible and, if so, are they solely responsible or are there other contributing factors? Alec Campbell strongly advocates a fair assessment, free of the emotionalism so clearly associated with this issue.[36]

The game species of the Kalahari are highly adapted to their environment. Some, like the eland, gemsbok and springbok, can manage without surface water altogether. Others, like the wildebeest, have a higher water requirement, which in good years may be met by the moisture content of their grazing and from rain pools. In bad years they have to find water. Wildebeest compensate for this greater dependence upon water by being highly mobile. This mobility demands space as well as grazing, and access to water somewhere within their range.

Records show that there have been no significant changes in the rainfall pattern in the Kalahari for the last 100 years. There are no reasons, therefore, to suppose that the natural vegetation is very much altered. What has changed significantly, though, is the human occupation of the Kalahari and the demands that people and livestock make upon its resources. Between 1960 and today the population of Botswana has doubled and the number of cattle has trebled. The simple fact is that there is much less space available to wildlife than was formerly the case. Naturally, features that attract game will also attract man and his cattle. Thus, all the areas where open water is available have now been settled by man and his domestic stock. Game and cattle are in competition for the same resources and the cattle, who are always where the water is, are winning.

In every reported incident where die-offs have occurred, the animals have been seeking either water or grazing or both. However, the important point is that it does not seem always to have been fences that were responsible for denying them access. In the east of the Kalahari, where some migrating species have attempted to reach the Limpopo, they have been forestalled not only by cordon fences but by the fact that that is the most densely populated part of Botswana. At least 60 per cent of the country's people live there in the cities, towns and villages. The main north-south road passes through there, as does the railway line. The whole countryside in that vicinity is divided by fences into plots, smallholdings and farms. This, too, is cattle country, and you may be sure that, if grazing is in short supply in the Kalahari, it will be even less so in the east. Thus, when the animals attempt an eastern migration its failure cannot be attributed solely to the presence of veterinary fences.

The same seems true of both migrations that centre on the Makgadikgadi region. In the light of massive mortality rates at Lake Xau, it cannot be argued that the Khukhe fence prevented all the wildebeest from finding their way there. Some, admittedly, may have died on the way, but the vast majority seemed to have survived the journey. They died of starvation because there was no grazing anywhere along their route nor at the end of their travels. This

seems to be an unfortunate fact of the Kalahari and its periodic droughts. It does not seem fair to lay the blame on the fences alone.

One wonders what would happen if the Khukhe fence did not exist. Would the wildebeest then migrate due north to the Okavango? Did they ever do so in the past? I have not found any suggestion that they did. The distance is certainly shorter, by about a third, but would they be any better off on the edges of the Okavango than they were at Lake Xau? Distance, to the wide-ranging wildebeest, does not seem to be a critical variable in the circumstances; it is grazing and water that are the key factors. As at Lake Xau, water would certainly be found but I suspect that grazing would be no more abundant. The people who live on the southern edges of the Okavango are also cattle-keepers and overgrazing problems exist there too. They are no less acute than at Lake Xau and along the banks of the Boteti River. I do not see that the removal of the fence would make a great deal of difference. More animals might well survive but, because of the absence of grazing, the massive die-offs would not be avoided.

The same is true of those wildebeest that migrate south from Botswana's northern regions towards the Makgadikgadi. It was here, in 1963, that Alec Campbell reported the emaciated herds of 250 000 animals. No fences had prevented or obstructed their movement. They were following a traditional migration route which passed through an area of dense cattle populations. Consequently, there was no grazing. Graham Child has made the interesting observation that this northern wildebeest population may have been artificially encouraged to increase in numbers and extend their range because of the provision of wells in the nearby Hwange Game Reserve, in neighbouring Zimbabwe, to which they have access through the border between that game reserve and Botswana.[37] Once again, it is difficult to see how the fences are responsible, when the needs of man appear to have superseded those of the wild animals with whom he shares the land.

Consider the following scenario: the

Kalahari's large ungulate population can, in good seasons and when their overall numbers are low, survive quite satisfactorily within their present range, modified and dictated as it may be to a certain extent by the fences. When the herd numbers begin to exceed the available resources, either because of the sheer volume of grazing required or because the grazing no longer exists, due to drought, large numbers move to the extremes of their range where, historically, that grazing has been available. Now, because of the presence of man and the requirements of his domestic stock, it is no longer available. The 'bank' upon which the wild animals have traditionally relied is empty, and they die, by the thousand, of starvation.

It seems more than coincidental that the horrifying die-offs that have been reported seem always to be associated with periods of prolonged drought, suggesting that it is only then that the game has to fall back on its emergency grazing reserves. This suggestion is only a hypothesis but it would seem to confirm some of the basic premises that Alec Campbell has made. Not enough research has been done into patterns in the past and not enough is being done right at this moment. No global approach has been adopted, and thus, while we know a great deal about small incidents, we do not have the information with which to fit it all together into a large and comprehensive picture.

There can be little doubt that there must have taken place a significant decrease in the number of animals in the Kalahari in past decades. Doug Williamson's biomass findings tend to confirm this. Such high mortality rates as we have seen cannot be sustained indefinitely and an overall decline seems inescapable. That the cordon fences have taken some toll is also undeniable. That they are solely responsible, or even responsible for the majority of deaths, I find difficult to accept. The principal factor is that man is using resources that once the wildlife relied upon and which he is now denying them. Remove the fences and very little would change. The animals would still continue to die. Certainly, the fences may serve to concentrate animals into smaller areas as Doug

Williamson has suggested[38] but I cannot be certain that the grazing would be any better elsewhere, where there is also surface water. All those places are now occupied by man and his cattle.

That the issue has raised such controversy is easy to comprehend. It appears to have been dogged by misunderstanding and a lack of information, and its complexities have been compounded by a number of factors. Some authorities, through an excess of enthusiasm, may have rendered themselves vulnerable to a charge of abusing their powers. In other instances, authorities, both directly and peripherally concerned, have tended to neglect the public relations aspects of their work, leaving a responsible, concerned sector of the public without important facts. Uncertain of what was going on, they reacted predictably to strongly emotive appeals in the popular press, and it is hardly surprising that a ferment of controversy arose. The fences were an obvious scapegoat.

Perhaps His Excellency, President Masire, Head of State of the Republic of Botswana, should have the last word on the issue.[39] Speaking publicly in Botswana in March 1984, and referring to the so-called 'fences of death', he said: 'We can pride ourselves as one of the few leading nations of the world in the conservation of our wildlife heritage ... Thus the unbridled and uninformed criticism we received from mainly overseas wildlife enthusiasts, is largely unhelpful because it is unbalanced. Indeed some of the fences not only protect livestock against diseases, such as foot and mouth, but also serve as barriers against human settlement and livestock encroachment into some of our major wildlife areas. In their uninformed criticism, they often fail to recognise the disastrous coincidence of the years of drought ... and the consequent high mortality on both wildlife and livestock alike ... We in Botswana have set aside seventeen per cent of our land mass for national parks and game reserves.'

### REFERENCES

1. **Botswana Govt.** 1983 Botswana Agricultural Statistics, Ministry of Finance & Development Planning, Gaborone, Botswana, p 87

2.  **Kraatz, D B.** *Restoration of the Flow in Thaoge River.* Technical Note 18. United Nations, FAO, Republic of Botswana, November 1976

3.  **Botswana Govt.** Department of Customs and Excise, External Trade Statistics, 1983/4, Government Printer, Gaborone

4.  **Nilsson, G.** Personal communication, November 1984

5.  **Kraatz, D B.** Op cit

6.  **Botswana Govt.** 1983 Botswana Agricultural Statistics, Op cit **p 23**

7.  **United Nations.** Report of the UNEP Clearing-House Technical Mission to Botswana, UNEP/Nairobi, 1983

8.  **Cooke, H J.** 'The Struggle against Environmental Degradation – Botswana's Experience'. *In Desertification Control,* UNEP, No 8, 1983, **pp 9–15**

9.  **Field, D I.** *A Handbook of Basic Ecology for Range Management in Botswana.* Ministry of Agriculture, Government of Botswana, Gaborone, 1978, **p 67**

10. **Bendsen, H and Gelmroth, H.** *Land Use Planning, Ngamiland, CDFA.* Ministry of Local Government and Lands, Government of Botswana, Gaborone, August 1983

11. **Ibid, p 87**

12. **Field, D I.** Op cit, **p 88**

13. **Hitchcock, R K.** *Kalahari Cattle Posts, Vol 1.* Ministry of Local Government and Lands, Government of Botswana, Gaborone, October 1978, **p 4**

14. **Carl Bro International.** *An Evaluation of Livestock Production in Botswana, Vol 1.* Ministry of Agriculture, Government of Botswana, January 1982, **p 205**

15. **Ibid, p 2–06**

16. **Botswana Govt.** District Offices, Ghanzi. Personal communication, October 1984

17. **Cooke, H J.** Op cit, **p 15**

18. **Child, G.** *The Future of Wildlife and Rural Land Use in Botswana.* Proceedings, SARCCUS Symposium on Nature Conservation as a Form of Land Use. Gorongosa National Park, Mozambique, Sept 1971, **p 78**

19. **United Nations.** Op cit

20. **Campbell, A C and Cooke, H J** (eds). *The Management of Botswana's Environment.* Botswana Society, Gaborone, Botswana, 1984

21. **Van Rensburg, H J.** 'Range Management in Botswana'. *In Botswana Notes and Records,* Vol 3, 1971, **p 113**

22. **Butler, K E.** 'Environmental Constraints to Livestock Production'. *In Botswana Notes and Records,* Vol 3, 1971, **p 170**

23. **Newsome, A E.** 'The research and practical experience gained in the development of semi-arid areas in Australia and the possible role of the endemic fauna in raising the productivity of those areas'. In *Botswana Notes and Records, Special Edition No 1.* Proceedings of the Conference on Sustained Production from Semi-arid Areas. October 1971, Gaborone, **pp 204–06**

24. **Vaagen, I.** Personal communication, July 1984

25. **Campbell, A C.** Personal communication, March 1986

26. **Owens, M J and Owens, D.** *Cry of the Kalahari.* London: Collins, 1985

27. **Owens, M J and Owens, D.** *Preliminary Final Report on the Central Kalahari Predators Research Project.* Report to the Department of Wildlife and National Parks, Government of Botswana, Gaborone, 1981

28. **Ngwamatsoko, K T.** *Lessons for Future Livestock Development Projects in Botswana: Wildlife Resources Considerations.* Proceedings of the symposium on Botswana's First Livestock Development Project and its Future Implications. National Institute of Research, Gaborone, Botswana, June 1982, **pp 143–63**

29. **Campbell, A C.** Personal communication, March 1986

30. **Hobbs, J C A and Yaxley, E L.** *The Environmental Consequences of Veterinary Cordon Fences.* Report to the Central District LUPAG, Serowe, Botswana, 1981

31. **Williamson, D T and Williamson, J E.** 'An Assessment of the Impact of Fences on Large Herbivore Biomass in the Kalahari'. In *Botswana Notes and Records,* Vol 13, 1981, **pp 107–10**

32. **Campbell, A C.** 'A Comment on Kalahari Wildlife and the Khukhe Fence'. In *Botswana Notes and Records,* Vol 13, 1981, **pp 111–18**

33. **Campbell, A C.** Personal communication, March 1986

34. **Silberbauer, G B.** The Bushman Survey Report to the Government of Botswana, Gaborone, Botswana, 1965

35. **Child, G.** 'Observations of a Wildebeest Die-off in Botswana'. In *Arnoldia,* No 31, Vol 5, July 1972, **pp 1–13**

36. **Campbell, A C.** 'A Comment on Kalahari Wildlife and the Khukhe Fence'. In *Botswana Notes and Records,* Vol 13, 1981, **pp 111–18**

37. **Child, G.** Personal communication, September 1984

38. **Williamson, D T.** Personal communication, June 1984

39. **Masire, Q K J.** Public speech at the opening of Chobe Game Lodge, Botswana, 15 March 1984, **p 2**

# 21. The Fragile Wilderness

IN all its sprawling vastness and for all the millenia that it has withstood the ravages of time, today the Kalahari and its wildlife face a greater threat to their continued existence than ever before. Least attractive to man and most inhospitable of the remaining unoccupied land in the vast Southern African continent, it has been populated last of all and is the region most recently subjected to the depredations of man. It is also, ecologically speaking, one of the most fragile and delicately balanced ecosystems and, as such, it is quick to succumb to mismanagement and abuse.

At the present time, the population living in the Kalahari is extremely sparse. For example, Botswana, with a surface area of 581 730 km², is slightly smaller than the state of Texas or the Cape Province and a little larger than France.[1] Seventy per cent of the country is Kalahari and so most of Botswana's million people live on the eastern side, away from the sands. Despite this, the population density is claimed to be the second lowest in the world, after Mongolia.[2] Other parts of the Kalahari, beyond Botswana's borders, are not likely to be any more densely populated and so its human carrying capacity is currently low. It has, therefore, been largely spared human occupation and its plant and animal resources, until the last 200 years, have been relatively little used. It is not true, however, to say that they have not been used at all and it is the increasing level of this usage which is currently cause for great concern.

Traditionally, those who have lived in or close to the Kalahari have relied heavily on its wildlife to sustain them. We have seen that whilst there is agricultural potential in the Kalahari, the technology has yet to be perfected and, for the moment, the tribesman regards it as being only marginally attractive for any agricultural acti-

vity. The abundant wildlife is what makes life possible for him and there is therefore a high dependence on renewable natural resources.

Figures from 1967, somewhat dated now, give an indication of the importance of these resources. In that year, it was calculated, 60 per cent of all the protein consumed in Botswana came from wildlife, which provided not only an essential source of supply but, through the sale of various trophies, some cash income to meet tax and schooling obligations. A more detailed study by the same researcher in the southern part of Botswana's Kalahari showed that 60 per cent of the population there were almost entirely dependent upon hunting and wildlife for their livelihood. The remaining 40 per cent were pastoralists but even they supplemented their diet by hunting and, to a lesser extent, gathering. The report concluded that, in the ten years prior to its being written, there had been a definite decline in wildlife populations which, it was felt, was linked to habitat deterioration and over-exploitation associated with ever-expanding human activities.[3]

Since the 1967 report cattle populations have increased at least threefold and the human population has very nearly doubled. Among a people who have a tradition of regarding the wildlife as a resource available for their use, it is inconceivable that they would, abruptly, have ceased to rely upon it. Indeed they have not and the demands upon the Kalahari's wildlife since then have not diminished. The demand is not restricted only to wildlife. In 1984 it was calculated that half of the energy used in Botswana is provided by wood fuels that cater for 75 per cent of the population.[4] The trees, as well as the wildlife, are being heavily exploited.

Recognising the heavy dependence upon

the country's wildlife, particularly by its rural population, but at the same time seeing the need to control its use for fear that there would soon be none left at all, the Botswana Government was quick to declare Controlled Hunting Areas (CHAs), of which over forty exist, covering between them all state land. Hunting within these areas is controlled by permit, for which a series of different prices are charged.

Citizens of Botswana get more favourable rates than non-citizens and, to the local people, permits were not expensive. In this way it was hoped that the off-take from wild game would be controlled.

Quotas were established for each area but demands for permits always far exceeded the number allowed. In the absence of any other method, lottery allocation was sometimes resorted to. Whilst the idea was essentially sound, it suffered from some severe drawbacks. Chief among these was the fact that there was no way of enforcing control as some people did not endorse kills upon their permit until they were actually accosted by the relevant authority. The system is now being changed, which will hopefully put an end to this abuse; while it remains unchanged, however, it exacts a high cost in wildlife stocks.

There is a striking diversity of game in the Kalahari and much of it is highly adapted to survive without surface water for most if not all of the year. In order to do this, it must cover large distances. Kalahari game is thus characteristically highly mobile and, for proper conservation, requires large reserves. Regrettably, many of the Kalahari reserves are not the result of careful ecological planning, nor are they necessarily complete ecological units. Often they were mere accidents of history and circumstances at the time of their creation.

In Botswana there was no Game Department until 1956 and a proper conservation policy was not introduced until 1966.[5] However, that the Botswana Government is serious in its efforts to protect its floral and faunal resources is shown by the fact that over 17 per cent of the country is now set aside as game parks and reserves. There are other Kalahari reserves as well. South Africa has set aside the Kalahari Gemsbok Park which, on its own, is just over 9 000

km$^2$ in extent and, when added to Botswana's adjacent Gemsbok National Park, provides a total sanctuary of some 34 390 km$^2$. Etosha National Park in Namibia is also located on Kalahari sands and covers 22 270 km$^2$.[6] There are a number of national parks in Angola, some of which are on Kalahari sands. Their present status and fate, in view of the civil war that rages there, is unknown. However, there seem grounds for fearing the worst and Angola's reserves may be a tragic illustration of the fact that setting aside such areas is not sufficient to ensure protection of valuable plant and animal resources.

Angola's conservation history has been characterised by an absence of continued application and dedication since the first parks and reserves were created in the 1930s. As elsewhere in Africa, conservation areas were declared without proper consideration of ecological constraints, adjustments have never been made and boundaries were designated more out of convenience than planning. On more than one occasion, existing permanent populations were incorporated in newly declared reserves and no efforts were made to move the people or to provide for them elsewhere. An example is the Giant Sable Reserve which contained over 90 per cent of the world's population of these rare and beautiful animals, which numbered then between 2 000 and 3 000. In 1974 there were 18 000 people living in this nature reserve. The problem of human occupation was compounded by the presence of fourteen trading stores, extensive rice fields and intensive diamond prospecting activities.

Prospects for the protection of Angola's animals were not enhanced by such activities as 'glorious hunts', organised for the benefit of visiting officials. Such occasions resulted in something akin to wholesale slaughter. In one hunt in the 1960s over 300 head of game were killed in a single day in one of the western reserves. In the same period there is a report of twelve giant sable being killed during a similar hunt.[7] The record of the former colonial regime is not impressive. In order to open the Huila District for cattle ranching, the notorious Diploma Legislativo Number 2242 of 1950 declared the area a free hunting zone. As a result, a mass slaughter of game took place that has been unequalled in Angola's history. Virtually every large mammal was eliminated. It has been estimated that the slaughter included 1 000 black rhino, several thousand giraffe, and tens of thousands of wildebeest, zebra and buffalo. The Diploma was not repealed for nearly two and a half years, by which time the damage was done, and there were no animals left.[8]

In 1974, the latest date for which I have been able to find any reliable information, there were ten conservation areas in Angola, including between them some 50 000 km². Six of these were national parks, three were designated 'reserves' and one was a Controlled Hunting Area. Of these, the last mentioned and three national parks are located in the west or south of the country, on Kalahari sands. Bicuar National Park contained a number of large mammals whose populations were slowly recovering from the slaughter of the 1950s. Its fate today, ten years later, is highly uncertain. Much the same can be said for its near neighbour, Mupa National Park, which, like Bicuar, is in southern Angola on the western extremity of the Kalahari sands. Even then, in 1974, there were no resident game rangers and the park contained a large human population. Cameia National Park in the east, on the Zambezi flood-plains, was severely affected by poaching and its present status, at the centre of a strife-torn area, can only be guessed at.

In the south, sharing a common border with western Zambia and with the Caprivi Strip, is the Controlled Hunting Area of Cuando-Cubango Coutadas. This large area of 91 500 km² is also the centre of a disputed war-zone and the fate of its elephant, giraffe, sable and wildebeest is best left to the imagination.[9] Today in Angola there is not a single national park that meets the minimum requirements as laid down by the IUCN. It has been suggested that the major reason for the shocking misuse of Angola's wildlife can be blamed on the failure of the administration to enforce the conservation legislation they had provided, and which itself was adequate. At the same time insufficient manpower was allocated to the job and it was not given the official backing and support it needed.

The wildlife resources of the Kalahari are under severe stress. There are numerous authorities who will agree that the number of wild animals has steadily diminished over the last fifty or more years. There has been a tendency to blame veterinary fences for this but, as we have seen, it seems far more likely that other of man's activities are at least equally responsible. Indiscriminate hunting may be one of them. In 1974, 90 per cent of all the game animals shot were taken by traditional hunters and, whilst the permit system represents a laudable attempt to control the size of this off-take, the knowledge that it may be at least two or three times greater than official figures estimate is disturbing.

It raises the question of how much longer an expanding population can continue to take an ever-increasing share of a diminishing resource, before the resource itself is finally exhausted.

Fears for the Kalahari come not only from the consumption of its game or its trees: it comes from increasing human occupation and the consequent destruction of the habitat, which renders it unsuitable not only for game but, ultimately, for man himself. Cattle-ranching is an enormous threat on its own. We have seen how cattle numbers in Botswana have escalated from about 1,2 million in 1966 to between 3,5 and 4 million in 1984/85. Cattle-ranching as an industry has burgeoned in the last twenty years, spurred to even greater vigour in the 1970s by the incentives of higher EEC prices. The pressure for new grazing lands that this has created, supported by increasing general wealth and the availability of improved water-drilling technology, has exacerbated the rate of man's expansion into the Kalahari.

This is not, in itself, an unwanted situation. The Kalahari is there to be used and it should be used. The problem is caused by the lack of understanding, the lack of range management skills and the lack of any awareness of the need to avoid short-term exploitation at the expense of long-term, sustained use. A high proportion of the Kalahari's cattle industry is owned and run by individuals whose hazy grasp of ecological limitations is blurred by attractive financial considerations. Overgrazing is the almost inevitable result. As we saw in the last chapter, the problem is compounded by the fact that most of Botswana's Kalahari is communally owned. Recognition of this has not so far led to any solutions, as the Livestock Development Programme and the Tribal Land Grazing Policy have amply shown.

Professor John Cooke, a leading conservationist at the University of Botswana, points to the need for optimal utilisation, based on realistic planning and careful management. Conservationist Alec Campbell explains that, in the short-term, the Kalahari's climate fluctuates through a series of wet and dry periods in a regular and predictable pattern. Currently, Government planning is based on the expectation of the mean between the two extremes. Alec suggests that it should be based always on the expectation of the worst situation. In that way, he claims, Botswana would not enjoy the maximum utilisation of the Kalahari, but it would benefit from the optimum use, ensuring that, under any conditions, the region would not deteriorate.[10]

Professor Cooke points out that our ability to tap underground water has made it possible to establish permanent cattle posts deep within the Kalahari and that their spread is neither planned nor subject to proper management or control. Cattle quickly consume the better and more nutritious grasses and, because the environment is so fragile, this causes irreversible damage and destructive changes to the climax vegetation. The Kalahari must be managed as a renewable resource and, if it is not properly used, we shall lose it.[11] Numerous range studies have shown unequivocally that over-stocking leads to rapidly spreading conditions of rangeland degradation. Areas of bare ground, without vegetation cover, increase in size, top-soil is removed by the wind and by water erosion, the palatable grasses disappear and there is an increase in thorn scrub and woody shrubs. In places, evidence of man's former occupation of the Kalahari is still clear after forty and sometimes up to seventy years.[12]

As is often the case, all the consequences of rangeland abuse are not necessarily obvious. Sometimes the long-term, less visible effects are the more serious but, because they are more difficult to determine, are often overlooked. Two studies in the Kalahari have recently shown the frightening prospects for climatic change than can follow large-scale rangeland abuse. In 1971 R J F Andersson,[13] who was then a meteorological officer with the Bureau in Botswana, completed a comparative study of mean annual temperature changes in two places, one at Mahalapye on the extreme eastern edge of the Kalahari and another at Ghanzi, towards its western side. Both of these areas have been subjected to intense grazing pressure which has increased steadily during the last fifty years. Andersson believes that overgrazing and the consequent extension of bare ground, is the direct cause of adverse temperature change. He found that at Mahalapye the mean maximum temperature in the three months preceding the rainy season had increased in the twenty-five years between 1921 and 1946 by .3 °C.

In Ghanzi the temperature increase for the period 1933 to 1946 had been .2 °C. In the period from 1951 to 1970, however, when cattle numbers had increased more rapidly, the rise was much more dramatic. In the east it was an additional .7 °C and in Ghanzi, 1.0 °C. These figures sound small but, as Andersson points out, they are sufficient to create a heat inversion over the country which could absorb, at all levels, what little moist air penetrates the arid centre of the sub-continent. Only strong, moist air masses would be able to break it down. The heat inversion could, therefore, result in a reduction in rainfall.

Andersson's research went further, however. He found that the mean minimum temperatures had also risen by significant amounts, a factor which gives cause for concern as it can adversely affect plant growth, since plants then tend to have a reduced opportunity to cool during the night and recover from the wilting effects of hot days. Using identical thermometers on grassed and on eroded, bare areas of sand, Andersson found differences in temperature between the two areas, immediately above the ground, that ranged between 3 °C and 7 °C. The presence or absence of grass cover makes a great deal of difference to ground temperatures.

A researcher in the western Kalahari[14] was able to show that bare ground increased the chances of air temperatures at a height of 45 cm being lower by a significant amount than over partially or fully covered ground. This creates what is known as a temperature inversion, where a slightly cooler layer of air lies on top of a warmer layer. The warmer air is prevented from rising by the 'weight' of the cooler air on top of it. The implications of this thermal depression effect are well known. One effect is that ground temperatures are increased. Also, it results in a decrease of the lifting of air necessary for the rain-forming mechanisms to operate and can actually lead to a deterioration in local climatic conditions. Elsewhere it has been shown that the clearing of sandy soils can result in a sharp reduction in local rainfall.

We have considered some of the environmental hazards that threaten the Kalahari. Its wildlife, although protected in many areas, is increasingly being denied the enormous ranges that it needs and the number of animals is being steadily reduced for this reason. Many humans depend upon the wild game to supplement their diet and, as the number of those humans increases, so does the hunting burden on the natural herds, already significantly affected by restrictions in their range. At an accelerating rate, cattle-ranching is moving into the Kalahari with serious consequences to the ecology of the region. Overgrazing is leading to critical changes in the vegetation and may be having an effect on the overall climate. The future for the preservation of this unique and fascinating region is gloomy.

However, the area of the Kalahari is vast and the future is not entirely without hope. There are many caring and responsible people, concerned about and concerned with the Kalahari. There is an understanding of the problems. The solutions are extraordinarily complex and will take much time to effect. During that period, the environmental situation in the Kalahari will certainly deteriorate further. However, because

of its size and the relatively early realisation of our responsibilities towards future as well as present generations, there is a possibility that it will not all progress to hopeless ruin. The Kalahari is almost too big to destroy and we can only trust that its breathtaking spaces and its endless, fascinating interest will remain for the future.

## REFERENCES

1. Campbell, A C. *The Guide to Botswana*. 3rd edn. Gaborone: Winchester Press, 1980, p 15
2. Campbell, A C and Cooke, J. (eds). *The Management of Botswana's Environment*. Gaborone: Botswana Society, 1984, p 11
3. Von Richter, W. 'Wildlife, and Rural Economy in S.W. Botswana'. In *Botswana Notes and Records*, Vol 2, 1969, pp 85-94
4. Campbell, A C and Cooke, J (eds), Op cit, p 17
5. Campbell, A C. 'The National Park and Reserve System in Botswana'. In *Biological Conservation*, Vol 5, No 1, January 1973, pp 7-14
6. Huntley, B J. 'Ecosystem Conservation in Southern Africa'. In *Biogeography and Ecology of Southern Africa*. Edited by Werger, M J A. The Hague: Dr W Junk, 1978, pp 134-8
7. Huntley, B J. 'Angola, a Situation Report'. In *African Wildlife*, Vol 30, No 1, pp 10-14
8. Huntley, B J. 'Outlines of Wildlife Conservation in Angola'. In *Journal of the Southern African Wildlife Management Association*, Vol 4, No 3, 1974, p 162
9. Ibid, pp 164-5
10. Campbell, A C. Personal communication, March 1986
11. Cooke, H J. 'On the Conservation of Natural Resources, with Special Reference to the Kalahari in Botswana'. In *Botswana Notes and Records*, Vol 13, 1981, pp 141-3
12. Child, G. 'Ecological Constraints on Rural Development in Botswana'. In *Botswana Notes and Records'*. Vol 3, 1971, pp 157-64
13. Andersson, R J F. 'Insolation as a Factor in Rainfall Distribution and Retardation'. In *Botswana Notes and Records, Special Edition No 1*. Proceedings of the Conference on Sustained Production from Semi-Arid Areas. October 1971, Gaborone, Botswana, pp 315-16
14. Cooke, H J. 'The Struggle against Environmental Degradation — Botswana's Experience'. In *Desertification Control*, UNEP, No 8, June 1983, p 12

# Index